Prince of Spies

Alex Gerlis is the author of the acclaimed Spies series of four Second World War espionage thrillers which are noted for their detailed research and intricate plots and feature two great adversaries: the British spymaster Edgar and his Soviet counterpart Viktor. The television/film rights for *The Best of Our Spies* have been bought by a major production company.

Born in Lincolnshire, Alex was a BBC journalist for nearly 30 years. He lives in west London with his wife and family and three black cats, a breed which makes cameo appearances in his books. He's a lifelong supporter of Grimsby Town, which has provided some preparation for the highs and lows of writing novels. When asked if he has worked in the field of espionage he declines to answer in the hope some people may think he has.

Also by Alex Gerlis

Spy Masters

The Best of Our Spies
The Swiss Spy
Vienna Spies
The Berlin Spies

The Richard Prince Thrillers

Prince of Spies
Sea of Spies
Ring of Spies
End of Spies

ALEX GERLIS

PRINCE OF SPIES

1ᴺCANELO

First published in the the United Kingdom in 2020 by Canelo

This edition published in the United Kingdom in 2021 by Canelo

Canelo Digital Publishing Limited
31 Helen Road
Oxford OX2 0DF
United Kingdom

A CIP catalogue record for this book is available from the British Library.

Print ISBN 978 1 80032 037 6
Ebook ISBN 978 1 78863 872 2

Look for more great books at www.canelo.co

Printed and bound in Great Britain by Clays Ltd, Elcograf S.p.A.

Principal Characters

Richard Prince: Lincolnshire detective superintendent recruited to MI6, code name *Agent Laertes*

Aliases in Denmark:

Hans Olsen (from Esbjerg)

Jesper Holm (first ID in Copenhagen)

Peter Rasmussen (second ID in Copenhagen)

Ulrich Leuschner (German identity)

Pierre Breton (French slave labourer at Peenemünde)

Hanne Jakobsen: *Agent Osric*

Otto Knudsen: Danish businessman, code name *Agent Horatio*

Sophia von Naundorf: British agent in Berlin, code name *Agent Blackbird*

England

Tom Gilbey: Senior MI6 officer, recruits and runs Prince

Hendrie/Douglas: British intelligence officer, introduces Prince to Gilbey

Roland Bentley: MI6, Hendrie's boss

Sir Roland Pearson: Downing Street intelligence chief

Lord Swalcliffe: Government scientific adviser

Frank Hamilton: Air vice marshal, head of RAF intelligence branch

Tim Carter: Wing commander, RAF intelligence branch

Long: From the Ministry

Wolfgang Scholz: 'Andrew Martin', German spy, code name *Poacher*

Lillian Abbott: Fascist in Peascombe St Mary

Oberleutnant Hofmann: U-boat officer

Llewellyn Tindall: SOE Danish section

Robert Webster: Lieutenant colonel, head of SOE Danish section

Greta Poulsen: Secretary to Tindall at SOE Danish section

Martin: MI6 trainer

Lieutenant Jack Shaw: Royal Navy escort

Bert Trent: Skipper, *Northern Hawk*

Sid Oliver: First mate, *Northern Hawk*

Jane Prince: Richard Prince's late wife (d.1940)

Grace Prince: Richard Prince's late daughter (d.1940)

Henry Prince: Richard Prince's son

Evelyn: Richard Prince's sister-in-law

Treslake: MI5/6 watcher

Group Captain Hanson: Commanding officer at RAF Tempsford

Flight Lieutenant Green: Halifax pilot

Prudence: Woman at safe house

Denmark

Niels: Danish resistance, Esbjerg

Marius: Danish resistance, Odense

Egon: Danish resistance on ferry

Jensen: Cycle shop owner

Browning: Ferdinand Rudolf von Buhler, German diplomat

Margrethe: Danish police officer at Kastrup airport

Jens: Danish police officer at Polititorvet HQ

Peder: Sailor on ferry to Rostock

Julius Oppenheim: Doctor in Copenhagen

George Weston: MI6 Stockholm (Sweden)

Germany

Bruno Bergmann: Horatio's contact in Berlin

Albert Kampmann: Luftwaffe *Oberst* in Berlin, alias: *Kurt*

Frau Henlein: Old lady on train

Hans Hinkler: Waiter at Das Bayerischer Haus

Rudolf Hoffmann: Owner of Das Bayerischer Haus

Gruppenführer von Helldorf: President of the police in Berlin

Manfred Lange: Gestapo officer

Gunther Frank: Kriminaldirektor, Berlin Kripo

August: German communist at Neuengamme and Peenemünde

Émile: French slave labourer at Peenemünde

Alain: French slave labourer at Peenemünde

Karl-Heinrich von Naundorf: SS *Brigadeführer*, husband of Sophia

Konrad: SS *Brigadeführer*, friend of Karl-Heinrich von Naundorf

Chapter 1

Lincolnshire, September 1942

'Come up now, get a move on… we can't hang around here forever!'

It was Hofmann, the young Oberleutnant who'd been in charge of him with ill-disguised resentment ever since they'd left Kiel three long days before. For most of that time he'd been confined to a cramped bunk area next to the captain's tiny cabin, not allowed any contact with the rest of the crew. When he was half asleep the previous night, he'd overheard a half-whispered conversation between the Oberleutnant and his captain.

'We should be hunting Allied ships, Kapitänleutnant, not acting like a taxi service.'

'Stop complaining, Hofmann. We have our orders.'

'I know, Kapitänleutnant, but this is a waste of our time. How long do these people last in England before they're caught? One day… two? That's assuming he even makes it ashore.'

When he finally reached the top of the conning tower, he was surprised how near to the coast the U-boat had surfaced. Dawn was still a good hour away and there wasn't much moonlight, but nor was it cloudy, so he had a reasonable view of the land, his first ever sight of England: the blurred silhouette of a cluster of buildings behind what looked like sand dunes and the very faint outline of what he took to be a church spire beyond them. He was relieved he wouldn't have to paddle the dinghy as far as he'd feared, but he was concerned the U-boat could have been spotted from this distance and they'd be waiting for him.

I

He was helped – more like pushed and hauled – out of the conning tower and onto the deck. The dinghy had already been launched and was held tight by a rope, his rucksack and suitcase strapped to the little wooden bench. Hofmann took him by the elbow, his tone now less hostile. Perhaps he was relieved the mission he so clearly resented was over. Or maybe he was just feeling sorry for him. *How long do these people last in England… one day… two?*

'You'll climb down this rope ladder and start paddling straight away. We can only stay on the surface for another minute or two, and you want to be well away from us when we submerge.'

He nodded, well aware of his instructions.

'And remember, there's a strong north-to-south current here. Concentrate on rowing hard to the shore, and let the current take you south. That's the village called Saltfleet over there: you remember it from your map?'

He nodded again. He was beginning to feel quite sick, between the nerves and the swell.

'You'll need to get a move on. With some luck you should land where you're meant to, just north of Mablethorpe, seven miles due south of here. The cutters for the barbed wire are in the box at the front of the dinghy. Remember, as soon as you land, release the air valves on the dinghy and push it out to sea. It should go out with the tide and sink. Good luck.'

Hofmann hurriedly shook his hand and guided him to the rope ladder. He hesitated, but he wasn't sure why. In his training they impressed on him how important it was to get away from the U-boat quickly. *You don't want to be dragged down by it, do you?*

–

The village of Peascombe St Mary was arranged around a series of narrow lanes winding through the fields between the Lincolnshire Wolds and the North Sea coast. It was adjacent to its smaller neighbour, Peascombe St Thomas, a hotchpotch of ploughed fields separating the two. Between them, the villages mustered barely five hundred souls, though they did have the comfort of two churches and the convenience of a railway station at which the occasional train stopped en route to either Mablethorpe or Louth. Although smaller, Peascombe St Thomas did have a pub, the Ship Inn, whose improbably low ceilings, protruding beams and dimly lit interior were proof, as far as the landlord was concerned, of its origins in the fourteenth century.

Peascombe St Mary was just a few miles north of Mablethorpe and a mile inland from the sea, which lay to the east. Apart from the blackout, barbed wire on the beach and a few troops billeted in the village, the war had not made too much of an intrusion. True, a dozen or so villagers had been conscripted, but many more were exempt, as farming was a protected occupation. The nation, after all, did need to eat and the two villages adequately met their obligations in that regard.

Peascombe St Mary was a place where people minded their own business: for reasons locals didn't bother to dwell on, it was not one of those villages that thrived on gossip. That was regarded as the preserve of folk who lived in Mablethorpe and other metropolitan centres.

That preference for privacy could well have been one of the attractions Peascombe St Mary held for Lillian Abbott, a lady perhaps in her early fifties who'd moved to the village in the early 1930s when she found employment as a schoolteacher in Mablethorpe.

Having lived in the village for just a dozen years, she was still regarded as a newcomer, but she was a newcomer who understood the unspoken rules: she kept to herself, she minded her own business and she never indulged in gossip.

Villagers were aware that she'd been widowed after her husband was killed at Passchendaele in 1917 and had no children. Before moving to the area she'd lived in London for a while, and possibly Birmingham, though people couldn't be sure, and of course it was not something they'd discuss.

Lillian Abbott lived in a small cottage on Pasture Lane on the eastern edge of the village, close to the coast and with the sound of the sea ever present. To one side of her was an outbuilding belonging to a neighbouring farm, and she was separated from the house on the other side by an unused paddock where six-foot-high weeds shot up through the cinder and provided a welcome curtain to add to her privacy. Behind her cottage were fields, through which a narrow track led to the beach.

In the early hours of the previous Saturday morning, she had left her cottage before dawn. She had received the message four days before: *Not before Saturday, not after Wednesday. Wait there from three to six every morning until he arrives.*

That message had terrified her out of her wits. She couldn't sleep, lying motionless in bed, too frightened to move, bitterly regretting having been persuaded to do something against her better judgement years previously. She'd spent the years since first hoping and then assuming it had all been forgotten, leading as inconspicuous a life as possible: moving to a part of the country that felt close to the end of the earth, visiting the village church often enough for any absences not to be remarked upon.

He'd not turned up on the Saturday morning, nor on Sunday, and when it passed five o'clock on the Monday and she'd only have to wait another hour, she even allowed herself to think it was possible he might not arrive at all. If that was the case, she'd leave the area. She'd find another job easily enough and move somewhere they wouldn't find her. One of those cities that had been bombed. There were plenty of them.

She was crouched behind a shrub just below the beach in the area where she'd been instructed to wait. Just in case anyone questioned her, she'd laid a trap to catch rabbits. It wasn't much of a trap, and predictably no rabbits had been tempted by it, but with some luck it would allow her to explain her unlikely presence there in the early hours of the morning.

4

He appeared in front of her like an apparition. She'd assumed she'd hear him approaching – footsteps, perhaps, or breathing. But one moment she was crouched behind the shrub wondering what she would change her name to, and the next a wet and exhausted man was standing in front of her, a rucksack on his back and a dripping suitcase in his hand. Her first thought was how ridiculous the suitcase looked and how it would be impossible to explain away trudging across the fields with a man carrying one.

'Could you tell me how to get to Lincoln?' He had a strong German accent. She hadn't expected it to be quite so marked.

'Go to the village and by the church you can catch a bus.' She couldn't believe how farcical this exchange sounded, but she understood they needed to identify each other correctly. One more question from him, one more reply from her.

'My name is Andrew Martin. I am from Liver Pool.' Liverpool as if it were two words, with a long gap in between.

'I haven't visited Liverpool since I was a child.' They nodded at each other and he smiled. She realised she was trembling. 'We'd better hurry. Follow me – the path is narrow. Is that case absolutely necessary?'

–

'Four days ago, you say?'

The man with the hint of a Scottish accent nodded. He'd deftly ignored more than one invitation to give his full name and say exactly who he worked for, and was now clearly irritated at having to answer the same question yet again.

From the top pocket of his dinner jacket, the Chief Constable, the man who'd asked the question, removed a handkerchief so long he gave the impression of a magician performing a trick. He wiped his face and then ran the handkerchief under his collar, causing his bow tie to become crooked.

'Well I'd have thought that if he came ashore four days ago, he'd be in your neck of the woods by now.' He leaned back in his chair and folded his hands on his large stomach, his smug look indicating the answer was an obvious one.

'And where would that be?' The Scottish accent was a bit more pronounced now.

'Where would what be?'

'My neck of the woods, as you put it. You seem to know where it is.'

The Chief Constable hesitated. It was apparent the other man outranked him in more ways than one, even though he knew next to nothing about him. It was Scotland Yard's fault: they'd insisted he meet him, even ordering him to interrupt an important Masonic Lodge dinner to do so. *You need to see him as a matter of urgency. Just don't pry too much. Answer his questions rather than ask too many of your own. That's how they work.*

'A figure of speech, that's all. Obviously, we'll do all we can to help, but in my experience – going back very many years, I can assure you – criminals do not hang around the scene of their crimes.'

'That may well be the case with house burglars and the like, Chief Constable. In this case, no crime has been committed per se – at least not in the sense you deal with on a day-to-day basis.'

'Even so, I doubt he'd have stayed in the area for long. I'd be most surprised if he was even still in Lincolnshire. Assuming he actually came ashore, of course; we can't even be certain of that. There are no witnesses, after all, and the shore patrol saw nothing—'

'No, Chief Constable. The shore patrol saw no one, but they didn't see nothing, as you put it. They found the barbed wire had been cut on the Town Beach, just north of Mablethorpe. Plus the contact in London received the correct coded message to say he'd arrived.'

The door opened and a man hurried into the room, muttering what could possibly have been an apology had it been at all clear before taking a seat alongside the Chief Constable, opposite the Scotsman.

'Ah… at last. This is Detective Superintendent Prince. Richard Prince. I was telling you about him. Perhaps, for his benefit, you could tell us again about the purpose of your visit?'

The man caught the gaze of Detective Superintendent Prince. He was notably younger than he'd expected, probably no more than his mid-thirties, and with what his wife would insist on describing as matinee idol looks. He certainly had a presence about him, and a purposeful stare. He sat quite still, with a very slight air of superiority about him. The Chief Constable had already told him Richard Prince was the best detective on his force – indeed, by far the best one he had ever worked with.

'Very well then, Prince: you will of course respect the very confidential nature of what I am about to say.'

The Scotsman leaned forward in his chair, and as he did so, his face caught the light above him, showing the ruddy, lined appearance of someone who'd spent a considerable time out of doors.

'Some eight months ago, we arrested a Dutch national in south London. Let's call him Laurens. We'd been on his track and knew he'd been sent over as a Nazi spy, specifically to be a point of contact between other Nazi agents in this country and their controllers back in Germany: a radioman. It has been our policy – where appropriate – to turn such spies to our advantage. Where we think it is feasible, we offer them a choice: they can stand trial for espionage and if found guilty expect the inevitable death sentence. Or they can allow themselves to become double agents, to work for us. We don't offer this to every Nazi spy, and it's not without its risks. But in the case of Laurens, it made sense.

'In the early part of the war, the Germans did send over quite a number of agents, but they were a pretty second-rate bunch and we're confident we captured all of them. Since late 1940, early 1941, the number being sent over has dropped off noticeably, and in the eight months that Laurens has been with us, no agents have been in contact with him.

'We were beginning to think that maybe he'd pulled a fast one on us – by which I mean that despite our best endeavours he'd somehow managed to slip a warning signal in one of his messages to the Germans. In fact, we were considering giving up on him and handing him over for trial. Then one week ago, he was contacted by Berlin. An agent called Poacher would be arriving in England in the next few days. A U-boat would drop him off the Lincolnshire coast, and once safely ashore, Laurens would receive a telephone call with an agreed code word. He was then to let Berlin know Poacher had landed safely and wait for him to arrive in London.

'Laurens was told Poacher would reach London within forty-eight hours of his initial telephone call, at which point he'd contact him and they'd meet at a pub called the Thornhill Arms. It's on the Caledonian Road, only a few minutes' walk from King's Cross, which is the mainline station you'd arrive at from Lincolnshire, so that all fits. Laurens was then to bring Poacher back to his house in Clapham, keep him there for a few days, make sure he had enough money and the right documentation – ration cards and the like – and drive him down to Portsmouth. We think he may have a contact there, so it was essential for us to let him get there. If there is indeed a Nazi cell operating in our largest naval port, we'd rather like Poacher to introduce us to it.'

The man with the Scottish accent paused and looked at Prince, who'd clearly absorbed the information in a way the Chief Constable hadn't. He smiled, indicating he was finding the story interesting rather than one he felt he had to pick holes in.

'And Poacher has disappeared?' He was well-spoken, his voice strong.

'Why that presumption, Prince?'

'Otherwise you wouldn't be visiting us, would you?'

'We know Poacher must have arrived in the early hours of Monday morning because Laurens received a telephone call that lunchtime with the correct code word to indicate his safe arrival. And at low tide that evening the shore patrol spotted a section of barbed wire that had been cut on the beach just north of Mablethorpe. Do you know the place?'

'I do, actually.'

'The actual point was at the northern end of what I understand is called the Town Beach. On the other side of the beach are sand hills and then open fields. The assumption has to be that Poacher landed on the early-morning low tide; the subsequent high tide then washed away his footprints and whatever he landed in. Since then – nothing. Not a whisper.'

'He's probably miles away by now. I told our—'

Prince interrupted his Chief Constable. 'There's not much around there apart from fields and sand dunes – and it's very open, nowhere for him to hide. But I don't think he'd have got far. He must have had some help; he's most likely to be in a safe house.'

'We need to find him. Can't have a German spy wandering around, can we? Until now we've been reluctant to do anything that would attract attention. We gave him the benefit of the doubt: perhaps he was exhausted after coming ashore, maybe he needed to keep his head down for longer than planned, possibly his journey to London was not as straightforward as he'd hoped. It's even possible he was injured, who knows? But it's Thursday now, he's been in this country for the best part of four days and we want to know where the hell he is, not to put too fine a point on it. My sense is that for whatever reason, he has not got very far. He may well be too frightened to move from his safe house. But we need to be careful; we don't want word getting out that a Nazi spy is on the loose, do we?'

There was a long silence. From somewhere in the room a clock ticked noisily; the only other sound was the Chief Constable clearing his throat. Richard Prince stood up and walked over to a large framed map slightly askew on the oak panelled wall. The man with the Scottish accent joined him, the Chief Constable eventually moving in behind them. Prince studied the map carefully before speaking.

'There are two obvious ways out of the Mablethorpe area: by road or by rail. Even by road it's a long way to anywhere and I'd have thought it risky. The area's teeming with army camps and RAF stations; there are roadblocks and patrols everywhere. He'd be exposing himself for far too long going that way. You say you think the plan was to arrive in London by train?'

'Only because it makes sense with the pub on the Caledonian Road being the rendezvous point.'

'It would certainly be wise for him to use the rail network. There's a station at Mablethorpe, on what they call the Mablethorpe Loop. There are four or five trains a day in either direction. He could either have gone north to Louth and from there connected to a mainline station such as Lincoln, or – which I think more likely – gone south to Willoughby, where at least one train a day connects with the Cleethorpes to King's Cross service.'

'How long's the journey?'

'From Mablethorpe to Willoughby? A quarter of an hour.'

'And what would security be like?'

'Assuming his papers are in order and he didn't attempt to purchase his ticket with Reichsmarks, he oughtn't to have had any problem. I presume they've sent over someone who speaks decent English. Likewise on the King's Cross train. We rely on the railway staff to be alert. I assume there's no description of him, nothing like that?'

'Of course not. You'd better get to Mablethorpe tonight, Prince. Be ready to start looking for this chap first thing in the morning.'

Prince looked at the Chief Constable, hoping he'd say something. The Chief Constable glanced away.

'I'd prefer to go first thing in the morning, sir. One or two things I need to sort out first. How will I contact you?'

'You don't need to worry about that. I'll be joining you.'

'I need to have a word with you.'

Prince had left, and the Chief Constable followed the Scotsman into the corridor outside his office. The windows were draped in blackout material and the only lighting came from a couple of weak bulbs high above, casting a yellow gloom over them.

'It's about Prince. I hope you don't think he was being rude just now. You know... telling you he's not going to Mablethorpe tonight.'

'I did wonder.'

'There are... reasons.' The Chief Constable sounded awkward. 'Two years ago, his wife and daughter were killed in a motor accident, just outside Lincoln. She was turning out of a minor road onto the main road and they went smack into an army lorry – didn't stand a chance. His daughter was only eight. Tragic, of course, and for reasons I've not quite fathomed, Prince blames himself. I suppose that's what you do... blame yourself.'

'How dreadful.'

'Indeed. His son, Henry, was supposed to have been on the outing with his mother and sister but stayed at home with a nanny as he was unwell. He's a smart little chap; Prince brings him in here every so often. He was just a year old when the accident happened. Prince is absolutely devoted to him. They have a nanny and a housekeeper, but Prince is wonderful, doing the kind of things for the boy you wouldn't imagine a father doing: he takes him for walks and even gives him baths, I'm told. He likes, if at all possible, to be there when Henry goes to bed and when he wakes up in the morning. He's such a smart detective I'm happy to cut him a bit of slack. I simply thought you ought to be aware, though he wouldn't expect any special treatment. If this German chappie is in that area, Prince is by far your best chance of finding him.'

The North Sea wind was throwing everything it could muster at the coast road and Prince was drenched by the time he returned to the police station on Victoria Road. He'd gone for a walk to clear his head and the storm had certainly done that. Now he had an idea.

Before leaving Lincoln, the Chief Constable had taken Prince into his confidence, reaching up to lean unnecessarily close to him, his bad breath causing Prince to pull away.

'*Entre nous*, I'm pretty sure that chap is MI5 – or MI6, one of the two.' He'd coughed as he said 'MI5' and mispronounced *entre* as *entray*, and he'd clearly hoped Prince would be more impressed than he evidently was.

'I know, sir. Of course he is.'

'You knew?'

'I knew he couldn't be anything else.'

The Scotsman told Prince he could call him Douglas, though it was unclear whether this was an assumed first name or an assumed surname. They'd been in Mablethorpe for three days and were no nearer to finding the German agent, and they were close to admitting that the German must have left the area. He'd disappeared.

Their one last shot was a plan to draft in officers from across the county and visit every house in the area on the pretext of searching for a missing soldier. They'd come up with a story that the soldier was Norwegian, which they hoped would alert people to and account for a foreign accent. Though Prince thought if the agent had managed to stay in hiding for a week, a knock at the door and a few questions about a missing Norwegian soldier would be unlikely to flush him out.

But as he was sprayed with half of the North Sea and much of the sand from the beach, he had another idea. In 1938, he'd been asked to compile a list of political extremists in the county. The communists were easy enough because someone had already helpfully provided them with a list. The fascists were a bit harder, even once he'd managed to persuade some sceptical senior officers that they were indeed a threat. Then he'd had a brainwave: the British Union of Fascists had a newspaper called *Action*, which was posted to members every week. Prince had alerted the postal sorting offices and within a fortnight had a detailed list of all recipients in the county.

Once back in the police station he made a call, and an hour later Inspector Lord arrived from the divisional headquarters in Skegness.

'You've brought the files?'

Lord placed a manila file bound with white string on the desk, the words *Fascists 1938/9* typed on a peeling label on the front.

'And this is up to date?'

'It's up to date to the start of the war, sir. As you know, we started playing a different game after that, taking them more seriously. There were thirty-three members of the British Union of Fascists in this division by the summer of 1939. I've checked the file and just over half of these would be what I'd describe as nominal members, people who weren't active and who just received that newspaper – many of them had probably ceased being members years previously. Probably a dozen of them were what we'd describe as active members. Two of those have since died, four no longer live in the area and four of the remaining six have been interned on the Isle of Man.'

'And the other two?'

'We keep an eye on them: they're a married couple in Skegness, but the husband had a stroke last year and the wife looks after him.'

'So the twenty or so what you describe as inactive members – let me see their files.'

'The inactive members? Surely—'

'They're the ones I'm interested in. Let me have a proper look.'

By Tuesday morning, Prince was confident his hunch was right. He'd been through Inspector Lord's list and narrowed it down to three former members of the British Union of Fascists who lived in the Mablethorpe area. Two of them were visited that morning and were ruled out, but a schoolteacher called Lillian Abbott was more interesting. Lord had found another file on her that showed that in the early 1930s she'd been a much more active fascist than had originally been realised. Prince sent two officers to her isolated cottage that morning with a brief to have a discreet look. When they returned, they reported that they were sure they'd spotted some movement inside, even though they knew the owner was at work.

They followed Lillian Abbott as she cycled home later that afternoon and watched as she stopped at two farms. Both of the farms later confirmed she had started buying food from them in the past week. *She told us she's got two soldiers billeted with her.*

Richard Prince decided to keep a watch on the house that night and raid it first thing in the morning. That evening he went for another walk along the seafront, a sentry allowing him through the barrier to the sea wall. It was completely deserted and he soon found the spot they'd come to on their last family outing two years before.

It was meant to be a pleasant day out after he'd worked for two weeks without a break. Grace was running in every direction chasing seagulls and Henry wasn't letting his father hold him. He only wanted his mother. His wife was on the verge of tears.

'I simply can't cope with looking after them on my own all the time.'

'But you have help, we—'

'It's not the same, Richard, and you know that. I can't remember the last time you had a day off. Surely—'

'But if I'd been conscripted, I wouldn't be here at all, would I? I could be on the other side of the world.'

He'd moved to put his arm around her, but instead she passed Henry to him, her arms now crossed tightly as they walked along the front, a gap between them.

'You know I've been feeling so miserable ever since Henry was born. You keep telling me to snap out of it, but it's really not that easy. If only you were around more. Will you at least promise me you'll try?'

He was walking in the same spot now: the sudden dip in the pavement and the boarded-up café with a rusted ice cream sign swaying noisily in the breeze. They'd seemed to move further away from each other and he'd failed to answer. Jane had looked across at him, angry, tears welling in her eyes.

'Are you listening? I asked whether you could be around more. Surely that's not too much to ask, is it?'

He could feel the tears filling his own eyes now. Why on earth had he not answered and told her he was sorry and of course he'd do his best to be around more? He could even have told her he loved her and that he understood how she felt. Maybe he should have said he'd try and take a week's leave, though he had no idea as to how he could have managed that. But at least it would have cheered her up. Instead he said nothing for quite a while, until the silence became too awkward.

'You know I can't say that, darling. I can't possibly promise something I may not be able to do.'

She shrugged and said nothing. They walked on a bit further, gathered up the children and drove home. Try as he might, he couldn't remember whether they'd said anything to each other that evening. What he could remember was spotting her in the gloom of the front room. She was unaware of him watching her as she poured a very large measure of whisky, quickly followed by another. The following morning he'd left for work even before the children woke up, and it was that afternoon when one of his colleagues had appeared alongside his desk and told him about the accident that had killed Jane and Grace.

Since that day he'd avoided Mablethorpe. He had hoped that being back there might at last give him some peace of mind. But instead it had made him feel worse. The place was haunted with ghosts who would never go away.

—

They'd made it back to her cottage safely enough, and Lillian had sorted him out as best she could. He'd removed his wet clothes and had a bath and she'd showed him where he was to stay when she was out. 'Don't flush the toilet until I return, and under no circumstances are you to go anywhere near the windows or the door: you understand?'

She made him a cup of tea and a sandwich before cycling to work. She hurried out of school during her lunch break – something she rarely did – and walked briskly to the nearby small parade of shops. From a telephone box, she called a London number. *Uncle Andrew is much better. He arrived home from hospital early this morning. He'll be visiting you as planned, hopefully very soon.*

On her journey home after school, she stopped at a farm she only rarely visited and bought some eggs, vegetables and a rabbit. She resented paying black market prices and wasn't convinced the rabbit was as fresh as they said it was.

Back at the cottage, she prepared supper for them both. 'I made the call. They know you're here.'

'Good.'

'How do you feel?'

'I am fine, thank you. I managed to sleep. I have barely slept for many days.' His accent was appalling.

'You don't need to give me any details, but what identity do you have?'

'I don't understand…'

'Your papers – what nationality are you supposed to be? I hope to goodness you're not pretending to be English?'

'My papers show I am a Dutch refugee. I am an engineer, travelling to London to work. I specialise in electic, is that how you say it?'

'You mean electric – electricity. I'd better write it down for you. Do you speak any Dutch?'

'No. Do many people in this country speak Dutch?'

She assured them they didn't, but she couldn't help thinking it was obvious he sounded decidedly German rather than Dutch. 'And you will leave tomorrow?'

He shrugged, as if he hadn't got round to thinking about it. Without being invited, he poured the rest of the stew she'd made onto his plate, some of the sauce dripping onto the white tablecloth. She had hoped it would last another meal.

'I understood you have to be in London within forty-eight hours of arriving here?'

He shrugged again as he reached across the table and helped himself to bread, which he then dipped into the stew. She tried hard not to show her disapproval.

'There is a station in the village: a train leaves tomorrow morning at eight o'clock. Maybe twenty minutes later it arrives at Willoughby. From there you can catch another train to London, to King's Cross.'

'Maybe I go Wednesday.' He shrugged again, drinking from his glass of water while still chewing, wiping his mouth with an already heavily stained sleeve.

But Wednesday came and went and he still showed no signs of leaving. He told her he'd hurt his ankle coming ashore and wanted to wait until it healed. *It will draw attention to me.* She hadn't spotted even a hint of a limp, but she thought better than to question him.

'You'll have to leave by Friday; there're no trains over the weekend on that route.'

He told her he'd need to see how his ankle was. And maybe she could buy some beer? He liked strong beer, he told her. He'd heard most English beer could be very weak and he really didn't want that.

He'd stayed the weekend, and on Sunday night told her Tuesday would be safer than Monday. He didn't admit it to her, of course, but after all he'd been through, he was rather enjoying the rest, and also the opportunity it gave him to make his own arrangements. The past couple of months had been so hectic and stressful: he'd had no intention whatsoever of being conscripted, and believed he'd got away with it. He'd managed to assume a false identity in what even the Gestapo acknowledged was an expert manner and had started a new life in Leipzig, managing to convincingly add ten years to his age, which ought to have prevented him from being conscripted. But then a night of madness: too much to drink, a woman who was difficult but who he still shouldn't have beaten up, and then arrest, a night in the police cells and his whole story began to unravel. Within days he was presented with a choice that wasn't much of a choice: a punishment battalion on the Eastern Front or working for the Reich.

He'd chosen the latter, and by the time he discovered to his horror what this entailed, it was too late. *You'll make a good agent. You've already demonstrated you have many of the skills we require. And you speak good English. Some of the agents we've sent over there have been less than reliable and also unlucky. We hope you'll be neither. It shouldn't be too difficult, not once you get to Portsmouth…*

He couldn't help thinking they were mad: why on earth would anyone think he'd make a good spy? It was like he was reading a bad book, but he had no alternative but to go along with it. The training was exhausting, and he began to be quite fearful, regretting choosing this over the Eastern Front. By the time he boarded the U-boat – that voyage was a nightmare in itself – he'd determined that given half a chance, he'd avoid the journey to London and Portsmouth and instead find a quiet life for himself in England. It couldn't be that hard.

When he discovered that the German agent who'd be looking after him when he landed would be a woman, he'd hoped she'd be the kind who'd fall for his charms, but the moment he saw her that plan went out of the window. Now he was just delaying the journey to London while he thought of something. He was even beginning to wonder what the consequences would be if something happened to the woman: would anyone miss her?

–

By Tuesday, Lillian Abbott couldn't ignore an unmistakable menace about the German. Despite his frequent smiles and apparently relaxed manner, she felt thoroughly intimidated. Even aside from harbouring a German spy, there was also the fact of having a stranger in her house. Apart from his bath on the first morning, he never seemed to wash, so had a foul odour, and he was eating so much she was buying more than was wise on the black market. She was concerned she could be drawing attention to herself, even in an area where people apparently didn't indulge in gossip.

As she was about to leave on Tuesday morning, he announced that he'd need another day at least before he could consider moving on, and as she cycled to work, the realisation that he might have no intention of ever going to London began to dawn on her.

That afternoon, on the way back, she stopped at Peascombe cricket club. It was situated between the two villages, and when she'd moved to the area, she'd attended their matches, partly because it seemed to be the right thing to do and also because she enjoyed cricket, certainly more than attending church. Now the ground was abandoned. The low metal railings that had skirted the boundary had been uprooted and sent to aid the war effort, probably now being turned into tanks. The outfield was also serving the war effort, having become a series of vegetable patches, though inevitably there'd been bitter disputes between the two villages as to who was responsible for maintaining them, and as a result most had gone to seed. The clubhouse was boarded up and the large roller, which required two men to pull it, lay rusting on what had been the batting strip.

She propped her bicycle against a tree and sat on the one bench remaining on the boundary, its paint peeling. Leaning back against a barely legible plaque commemorating a member who'd once scored a century, she lit a cigarette and in the silence tried to gather her thoughts. What would be the worst that could happen if she cycled back to Mablethorpe, to the police station on Victoria Road, and told them there was a German spy staying at her house? She'd tell them she'd found him in her cottage when she'd returned home that afternoon, and of how he'd threatened her, but she'd managed to escape. Of course, they might believe her story – who would trust a German spy posing as a Dutchman rather than a respectable English schoolteacher? But then they might delve into her past, which was the last thing she wanted. Maybe he was telling the truth; maybe he would leave the following day after all, or the one after that.

That night he told her his ankle was still stiff but assured her he'd go by the end of the week. He told her that she needed to buy some more beer, and that he preferred meat to vegetables. He didn't like rabbit, he told her: beef was his favourite meat. As she'd washed up their meal, she noticed her large carving knife was missing from the drawer by the sink. She had very little in the way of jewellery, but that morning she'd discovered that a brooch that had belonged to her mother wasn't in the metal box in her bedside table.

She would, she resolved, definitely go to the police the next morning.

She never had the chance.

Early the following morning, she was woken by the sound of cars stopping outside her cottage, followed by footsteps on the path. The German hammered on her door and asked what was going on, panic in his voice.

She told him to hide in the hall cupboard as she'd shown him and to remember to cover himself with the coats. By then there was loud knocking on the front door and the German looked terrified – the first time she'd seen him like that since he'd arrived. He pushed past her and opened the back door. As he did so, he found himself face to face with two large policemen.

The police officer who arrested them both introduced himself as Superintendent Prince. He was somewhat younger than she'd imagined someone of that rank to be, but he was very civil towards her – even quite pleasant, if the truth be told. In the few hours she had to herself in the cell at the main police station in Lincoln, she had plenty of time to reflect on her predicament and refine her story. She knew she had to ensure it was consistent, and by the time she was escorted into the interview room, she felt she was prepared. She was going to tell how the man had broken into her cottage; how he'd threatened her and prevented her from leaving. She would tell them she couldn't describe how relieved and grateful she was that they'd come to rescue her. She would also address the inevitable question before it was asked: of course she had never been involved in politics. She was not a Nazi sympathiser. She was a British patriot. Her husband had been killed at Passchendaele, after all. She had no idea whatsoever why her cottage had been targeted; perhaps because of its proximity to the beach.

Before she could speak, however, the polite young superintendent calmly set out the evidence against her. He told her how they knew the German had landed by U-boat the previous Monday morning. They knew a call had been made to a contact in London later that day to signify his arrival; that call had been traced to a telephone box very close to the school where she worked, and the caller had been a woman. He believed that woman to be her. The phone call, he said, checking his notes, had been made at a time when the headmistress of her school confirmed she'd left the premises. He pointed out that she'd had plenty of opportunity to go to the police but had failed to do so, and he told her they knew she'd previously been involved in the British fascist movement.

She tried to hold her nerve: it looked bad, but she wasn't sure if that amounted to much in the way of hard evidence against her. She felt her story still sounded feasible. She was about to recount it when Superintendent Prince held up his hand – *one minute, please.*

'Clearly, we wish to hear your side of the story, but let me tell you this, Mrs Abbott. If you confess now and tell us everything, I can promise you will be treated with a degree of leniency. We would consider a lesser charge than treason.'

He paused to let the words sink in. She felt sharp prickles of sweat and fear all over her body.

'Treason carries the death penalty, as I'm sure you're aware. With a lesser charge and a guilty plea, you'll be surprised at how relatively short the prison sentence could be.'

–

'A word, sir? Only if you have a moment, of course – I can always come back later.' The Scotsman who'd told Prince to call him Douglas was hovering uncertainly, even nervously, in the doorway of the man he'd addressed as 'sir'. Normally such an approach would have come through his own superior and worked its way up the organisation, but he'd taken advantage of the open door.

The man he'd spoken to slowly peered up from behind his desk and removed his spectacles. He was frowning; almost certainly unsure of the name of the man in the doorway.

'Hendrie, sir, I worked with you on the Belgian case.'

'Ah yes, of course. Come in, Hendrie, and do close the door behind you. We don't want the whole world wandering in, eh?' Tom Gilbey had a reputation for being blunt, even rude, but he was also one of the few senior people in the organisation willing to make a clear decision rather than setting up a committee to answer any questions asked of him. He was rumoured to be distantly related to the gin family. He'd been known to joke, somewhat bitterly, that they were the tonic branch of the family.

'You're aware of the German spy we caught last month in Lincolnshire?'

'Wolfgang Scholz, awaiting the hangman's noose at Pentonville. I hear you had some trouble catching him.'

Hendrie nodded. 'Indeed, sir, devil of a job: we feared we'd lost him somewhere between Lincolnshire and London, and you'll appreciate what the repercussions would have been, a German spy on the loose.'

'I would have been one of those repercussions, Hendrie.' Gilbey had closed the folder in front of him and adopted a pose indicating that he'd become interested in what the other man had to say.

'We had precious little in the way of clues, sir. I went up to Lincolnshire and had to reveal our hand to the local constabulary, which we try to avoid, as you know. I shouldn't have worried: the Chief Constable gave me the services of a detective superintendent, a young chap called Prince who turned out to be quite marvellous. We'd drawn a blank, but he was convinced the German hadn't got very far and he felt someone must be hiding him. He had a hunch it would be someone with far-right sympathies but a low profile. He had the bright idea of looking for people in the area who'd previously been members of the British Union of Fascists, and found a woman who fitted the bill perfectly. He managed to get confessions out of both of them before we could even get our hands on them: a breach of protocol, but shows he has initiative.'

'That's an uplifting story, Hendrie, but I'm not sure why you've come to tell me about this chap.'

'I think Prince is wasted in the police. He ought to be working for us.'

'Shaw looks after recruitment: have a word with him.' Gilbey opened the folder again and picked up his spectacles, a sign the meeting was over. Hendrie coughed. He was determined not to waste this opportunity.

'Denmark's one of your responsibilities, isn't it, sir?'

Gilbey nodded. 'Why do you ask?'

'I hope I'm not speaking out of turn, but I understand it may be proving troublesome.'

Gilbey looked slightly surprised at the impertinence of Hendrie's question, but only fleetingly. When he spoke, he sounded pleased to be getting the matter off his chest. 'It's the bane of my life, if the truth be told. We always thought Norway would be the difficult one in that part of the world, but Denmark is indeed proving most troublesome.'

He hesitated, unsure whether to carry on. 'Look, erm… all this is confidential, Hendrie, even inside this building – you understand that, eh?'

'Of course, sir.'

'For one thing, the Danes can't even make up their minds whether they're actually occupied by the Germans in the same way most of the rest of Europe is. And then they think they can handle everything themselves; they seem reluctant for us to help. The SOE are more involved there than we are, but that's the problem: a fundamental failure to distinguish between resistance and intelligence. The Danes seem to think they're one and the same. Their idea of intelligence is to see it as an extension of sabotage. It doesn't feel safe sending people out there at the moment: too many of the SOE chaps we've dropped there have been captured more or less straight away. May be just sheer bad luck, I don't know… but having said that, it is essential I have my own intelligence operation in Denmark. Essential!' He banged his desk with his fist. 'I simply can't get people to take Denmark seriously, Hendrie. Mention the place around here or in Whitehall and it's dismissed as some quaint backwater where they're all terribly decent sorts who produce butter and bacon and we really don't need to worry about it. But we do, we most certainly do! And do you know why?'

Hendrie shook his head and was about to hazard a guess when Gilbey replied to his own question, sounding quite angry as he did so.

'I shall tell you why: because Denmark is of considerable strategic importance. For a start, it shares a bloody land border with Germany, and more importantly, not far from that border is where we think the Germans are producing some of their so-called secret weapons, the ones Hitler is supposed to have up his sleeve and which will win the war for him. Are you aware of these, Hendrie?'

'One hears rumours, sir.'

'Unfortunately, we need to turn what we hear from rumours into hard intelligence. There's talk of them coming up with rockets that can be fired from the Continent at targets in England. I hope I don't need to tell you how critical it is that we get on top of this. I sometimes fear I'm a lone voice, but I think if there's any truth in this rumour, then it could turn the tide of the war against us. And Denmark is crucial: not only is it near where we believe the rockets are being developed, but it seems to be the place where what little information there is on them gravitates to. Sorry to ramble on, Hendrie: what's this got to do with a policeman in Lincolnshire anyway?'

Hendrie opened a file and read from it. '"Richard Marius Prince, thirty-four years of age, born Nottingham." His father was also born in Nottingham, but his mother, Elsebeth, was born and brought up in Denmark, hence Prince's middle name. And, which is why I'm here, sir, I'm told Prince speaks Danish fluently.'

Gilbey nodded approvingly and reached out for the file. When he'd finished reading it, a broad grin crossed his face. 'Well I never... fancy that. Good show, Hendrie. Who was it who spoke of the long arm of coincidence?'

'I don't recall, I'm afraid, sir, but I'm pleased to see you're smiling.'

'*That one may smile, and smile, and be a villain. At least I'm sure it may be so in Denmark.*'

'I beg your pardon, sir?'

'If I recall correctly, that's from the end of Act 1 of *Hamlet, Prince of Denmark*, eh?'

Chapter 2

Denmark; London, October 1942

Not for the first time since the start of the war, Aksel felt there was a distinctly biblical dimension to the decisions he was required to make as leader of the small resistance cell based in Vorning, a rural area north of Randers. He was no longer a religious man, but he'd had enough of the Bible drummed into him when he was younger to be familiar with the story of the binding of Isaac, when Abraham was instructed to take his son to Mount Moriah and leave him there to be sacrificed.

Now it was as if he was preparing to sacrifice his own son. Gunnar was just eighteen, eager to be involved in resistance activities beyond running the occasional errand, and he was about to get his chance. The message from London was clear: on this particular night they were to post lookouts throughout the area and see if there were any Germans around when an RAF plane flew over. There was a small but dense wood spread over a hillside north-east of the village, and Aksel felt this offered the best view of the area. But because of the curfew and the wood's distance from the village, placing lookouts there would be dangerous.

The plan was for Gunnar and Inger, a girl the same age as him, to go to the wood this afternoon and stay there until morning. They were to hide and watch out for German patrols. If caught, they were to pretend to be lovers who'd gone to the woods to find some privacy.

'You and, erm, Inger...' Aksel was finding the conversation with Gunnar awkward. 'Have you ever, um...'

'Have we ever what, Father?'

'Come on, Gunnar – have you ever been boyfriend and girlfriend? You know what I mean.'

'Not as such,' replied Gunnar, smiling and enjoying his father's obvious discomfort. 'But I'm prepared to try if it helps defeat the Nazis!'

–

Gunnar and Inger spent much of the evening enthusiastically ensuring that their efforts to defeat the Nazis were as authentic as possible. They'd created a hideaway in the undergrowth that gave them a good view of the fields beyond the hillside. Their enjoyment came to a sudden halt at a most inconvenient time, Inger suddenly clamping her hand across Gunnar's mouth as he leaned into her again. She raised her head and whispered into his ear.

'Can you hear?'

'No – what?'

'Footsteps, behind us.'

The footsteps could not have been more than ten yards away, pausing before being joined by more. Very carefully, Gunnar and Inger disentangled themselves from each other and edged further into the undergrowth, pulling more branches over them.

'*Kannst du etwas hören?*'

It was a German voice, young and nervous, asking, 'Can you hear something?'

Gunnar and Inger lay as still as possible, convinced that their breathing, heavy from their exertions, was echoing around the hillside and across the fields beyond it. A series of distinct sounds rose behind them: branches snapping as they were stepped on; the strike of matches as cigarettes were lit; the metallic clicks as the catches on sub-machine guns were released.

'*Nur Tiere, denke ich.*' 'Just animals, I think.'

More footsteps joined the group, and then an older voice – one used to giving orders – said something about there being too many trees in the way. Someone else replied, suggesting they move on, and Gunnar and Inger heard movement towards them before the man who seemed to be in charge of the patrol said they should carry on further up the hillside.

-

After that it was quiet, although Gunnar and Inger restricted their defeating the Nazis to watching out for the RAF plane and further German patrols. Around ten o'clock they could make out dozens of German troops moving in the fields below them, and then soon after eleven, there was the low roar of an aircraft approaching from the west. It was a cloudy night, with little light from the moon, so it was hard to make much out, but the shape of the aircraft soon became apparent. It descended to just a few hundred feet, swooping low over the fields, and Gunnar whispered something to Inger about how he hoped the engines wouldn't stall.

The tip of the starboard wing almost brushed the trees on the side of the hill, and then the plane climbed again rapidly, disappearing as suddenly as it had arrived.

The hill seemed to come to life. The patrol that had moved to the top descended quickly and noisily, and at least one other patrol was shouting out to them. From what Gunnar and Inger could gather, they were trying to ascertain whether anyone had seen a parachute. An officer called that they'd seen nothing up there; they'd all need to move down to the fields.

Gunnar and Inger remained in the woods for the rest of the night, using the time to help defeat the Nazis. At first light they returned to the village, through the hidden paths and along the hedgerows they knew like the back of their hands. They noticed German patrols moving through the fields and spotted more than one roadblock. Gunnar arrived home to find his father waiting anxiously for him. He told him what he'd seen, and then his father disappeared to a nearby barn to transmit a radio message to London.

–

It did not take Hendrie long to regret his impulsiveness. He had, he decided, acted quite improperly: one simply did not wander uninvited into the office of someone so senior in the Service. That it was out of character would hardly count as mitigation, and he assumed Gilbey's politeness merely masked his displeasure. Hendrie had little doubt that Gilbey's disapproval would work its way down to Bentley, his own boss. He was certain Bentley didn't like him. There'd been talk of a transfer to India, where they were beefing up the Service operation, and he didn't think he'd cope with the heat.

A week later, an ominous message arrived from Gilbey's secretary: please could he remain in his office after work? Mr Gilbey would like to speak with him.

Hendrie ensured his own office door remained wide open so Gilbey would know where he was. By a quarter to eight, he feared Gilbey had forgotten about him, which might not be such a bad thing. He'd wait until eight and maybe look up and down the corridor.

Gilbey appeared silently in his office, his elegant woollen coat buttoned up, a silk scarf visible at his neck, his dark trilby in place and leather gloves in the process of being adjusted, finger by finger.

'I presume you've not eaten, Hendrie?'

Before Hendrie could reply, Gilbey had made a *come with me* gesture with his head and walked out of the office. Hendrie hurried after him.

'We'll eat at my club. If we get a move on, it might not feel quite so chilly out there.'

It was a pleasant enough dinner, accompanied by a surprisingly sweet Bordeaux. Gilbey talked about his dogs and his wife's family's farm and asked Hendrie just enough questions so as not to appear rude. After dinner, they retired to a room on the upper floor, where an alcove had been reserved for them with a large fire roaring and a bottle of port waiting on the small table between two large leather club chairs arranged close to each other.

'No one will hear a word we say, as long as we don't shout. In any case, if you can't trust members of the same club, who can you trust, eh? This is a rather splendid port, Hendrie, fifty years old. Help yourself.'

Both men settled into their chairs and drank. Then Gilbey leaned forward, the reflection of the flames bouncing around his face.

'Ten out of ten, Hendrie – well done.'

Hendrie appeared confused: was Gilbey talking about the port? 'I beg your pardon, sir?'

'Prince. We've checked him out and he seems splendid, everything you said he was. His speaking Danish – well, about time we had a stroke of luck like that. Your intuition about him being right for us was spot on. His Chief Constable is fighting to keep him, of course, but he doesn't stand a chance. I thought it only fair to tell you I'm taking him on, and obviously you'll mention his recruitment to no one.'

'Naturally, sir.'

There was a long silence. Gilbey poured them each another port and leaned forward, staring into the fire, addressing the flames as if he was talking to someone behind them. 'Apart from this being an opportunity for me to express my appreciation to you, Hendrie, there is something I'd like your help on. I've told Bentley he's to release you for a while. A special project. Are you interested?'

It was a rhetorical question, barely even that. Gilbey didn't wait for an answer. 'When you asked me about Denmark, I may have mentioned how it doesn't feel safe sending people out there at the moment, how too many of the SOE chaps have been captured. There is an undeniable pattern of the Germans expecting our agents, and this is clearly a concern. I need to get Prince out to Denmark – we have a potential first-class intelligence source out there and he is the perfect chap to assess and run them – but I'm not sure we can risk sending him in at the moment. We need to know,' he stretched his feet out so the soles of his shoes were just an inch or so from the fire, 'whether our agents being intercepted by the Germans is simply bad luck, or if there's a problem with our Danish friends or an informer inside the Danish section of SOE here.'

'So how can I help, sir?'

Gilbey straightened himself up and turned to face Hendrie, leaning close. He spoke quietly, and Hendrie had to lean forward too to catch what he said.

'You're being transferred to the Special Operations Executive. As you know, the SOE was formed out of the Service, though it's more or less autonomous now. Nonetheless, we work very closely with them and relations are not bad at all in the circumstances. They tend to operate more with resistance groups, while we concentrate on intelligence-gathering, but obviously there's an overlap and they've tended to be responsible for getting our agents into German-occupied countries. I'm sure you know all this, but you may be somewhat less familiar with the structure of the SOE.'

He slapped Hendrie on the knee and beckoned him even closer. 'The SOE has various departments, but its main work is done through its country sections. The headquarters of the European country sections is at Noresby House on Baker Street. Have you ever been there?'

Hendrie shook his head.

'A few chaps you've worked with in the past are there now – that dreadful so-and-so Arnold, who used to look after our accounts, he's one of them. However, for obvious reasons of security, the actual sections themselves are based in separate buildings, most of them around Baker Street. The Danish section is not far away in Rodmarton Street. That, Hendrie, is where you'll be based.'

31

'Running Prince?'

'No, no, no… I don't want the Danish section to have even the slightest inkling of Prince's existence, let alone the fact that we've recruited him. Looks like we'll have to rely on the SOE to get him into Denmark, but I don't want to ask him to step out of a plane a few thousand feet above the country until we can be sure there's no informer in Rodmarton Street who's arranged for the Gestapo to be expecting him. If there *is* an informer, your job, Hendrie, is to try and find them.'

Hendrie felt a surge of excitement. No longer would he be at Bentley's beck and call, being dispatched around the country to check out every rumour of a German spy. He'd been personally selected for this mission by Gilbey himself.

'Won't it be a problem, me not speaking Danish, sir?'

'Not at all. Half the people there don't speak a word of it, and I'm told the place has plenty of young Danish ladies who do translating and suchlike.' Gilbey winked at him.

'And what's my story? There must be a reason why I'm transferring from the Service to the SOE.'

Gilbey hesitated, looked down at the floor and then up at Hendrie.

'You'll be going there under something of a cloud, I'm afraid. You'll need to adopt the persona of a rather embittered former employee of the Service.'

—

Two days later, Hendrie met his new boss at Noresby House. Lieutenant Colonel Robert Webster ran the SOE Danish section. He had, Gilbey assured him, fought in most of the major battles on the Western Front and there was no question as to his loyalty. 'He's the only one we've confided in about you; he's been very worried himself about the possibility of there being a German agent in his section. Not terribly happy that we're coming in to sort out his mess, but he knows that's the way it is. But even he doesn't know about Prince.'

Webster was well into his sixties, possibly even pushing early seventies, and was one of a legion of senior military and intelligence officers who'd been pulled out of retirement to help in the war effort. He had the slightly irritable air of someone who'd been woken early from an afternoon nap.

'Gilbey's told me everything, Hendrie, no need to repeat it all.' He ran his hands through silver-grey hair slightly longer than most men of his age would wear it, then looked at Hendrie as if, despite telling him not to repeat it, that was nonetheless what he should do.

'My brief is to poke around, sir, as Gilbey no doubt told you. I'm good at being discreet, just observing from the sidelines. It may well be that you're just having an awful run of bad luck with the agents you're dropping in. But if there is someone passing on information to the enemy, I would hope I could spot them.'

'So I understand. You start at Rodmarton Street on Monday. I'm putting you with Llewellyn Tindall; he's our logistics man. There's not much going on in the section he doesn't know about. It's up to him to ensure everything's sorted out for our operations. Awkward character at times, bit of bad luck in France during the Great War, but damn good at his job.'

–

In the three days before he started at Rodmarton Street – there was a weekend in between – Hendrie had drawn a mental picture of Llewellyn Tindall: Welsh, obviously, no doubt short and with a loud voice, probably a socialist of the Methodist variety. He might try to convert Hendrie to socialism or Methodism, or even both.

He turned out to be nothing of the sort. He was tall, with an almost aristocratic bearing, slightly stooped, and he walked awkwardly, as if he were in pain. He spoke with a cut-glass English accent, the words he used sparingly so carefully selected and enunciated they sounded affected.

Lieutenant Colonel Webster had taken Hendrie into Tindall's office on the Monday morning and left him there after the briefest of introductions. Tindall said nothing, nodding his head more in resignation than greeting, and pointed to a small desk opposite his own.

'Miss Poulsen is my Danish secretary: she comes in late and stays late. She sits there.' He tapped a large pane of frosted glass behind him, on the other side of which was a narrow outer office that Hendrie had entered through. 'There are some files for you: read yourself in. It really isn't terribly complicated here. There's a briefing document on Denmark there too. You'll need to look at that. Just remember that Danes are a variant of Germans and you won't go far wrong.'

For an hour Hendrie sat awkwardly, the only sound being the turning of pages, the slight groans made by Tindall every time he moved, and a constant clearing of his throat. Every ten minutes or so he got up and took a few paces around the room before carefully lowering himself back into his chair.

'My mother-in-law was Welsh,' Hendrie said eventually. It was an attempt to break the silence, but as Tindall slowly looked up at him as if he were mad, he immediately regretted saying it.

'Really?' said Tindall. 'I have no Welsh blood in me, thank Christ; never even been to the bloody country – avoided it like the plague. My parents spent their honeymoon there, a week in Aberystwyth. Some years later, when drink had taken a premature but permanent hold on her, my mother confided in me that it had been the worst week of her life. She said it was as if my father were raping her. Can you imagine, her telling me that? She never allowed him in her bed after Aberystwyth. His revenge was to name me Llewellyn when I arrived nine months after the honeymoon: not even a middle name she could use as an alternative. So trying to establish a Welsh connection between us is probably not wise. But tell me, Hendrie, what did you do to queer your pitch at Broadway? Must have been something to be demoted to this forsaken outpost.'

Hendrie remembered Gilbey's instructions. *Obviously don't own up to having done anything wrong as such. That would be too suspicious. They'll wonder why you've not been booted out altogether. More a clash of personalities than anything else, six of one and half a dozen of the other in a row with Bentley and he pulled rank, hence you having to move on. You felt you weren't treated with enough respect; I'll square the story with Bentley in case anyone ever asks him. Perhaps there was a row, raised voices...*

'Well...' said Hendrie, allowing a long pause, hoping to signal a reluctance to discuss the matter. 'I'm not sure this is a demotion, as such. My section head and I didn't quite see eye to eye, and I regret to say a discussion intended to clear the air rather got out of control. Obviously, I apologised, but it was difficult to stay on after that.'

'No hand in the till, then?'

'Good Lord, no!' Hendrie had little trouble sounding genuinely aggrieved, even angry. 'Nothing like that. You may have heard of Bentley, my section head? Rather smart, very well connected; his wife's the youngest daughter of an earl who owns half of Worcestershire. He was at Balliol and is a lawyer, no real record in the Service – didn't even fight in the Great War. Treated me rather like a dogsbody at times and I'm afraid I let my frustration build up. But you know... here I am, a new start and all that.'

Tindall stood up slowly, wincing as he did so. He straightened himself up and walked over to the window, turning his back to it so he was in silhouette when he addressed Hendrie.

'I imagine you and I are somewhat alike, Hendrie: dogsbodies, not really appreciated, taken for granted. This office here, Webster calls it logistics. We're more like a travel agency. Once an agent is selected to be sent to Denmark, I arrange their journey with the considerable help of Miss Poulsen. But Webster takes me for granted, rather as you have been by the sounds of it. You know, he's a lucky bugger is Webster, if you'll pardon my language. Fought on the Western Front throughout the war, front line, trenches and all that, and came through unscathed. Not just physically: if a car backfires, he doesn't even jump. Whereas I...' He was now walking slowly back to his desk. 'I was based at army HQ in Montreuil-sur-Mer, miles from the action. I looked after logistics there too, ensuring supplies reached the front. My one trip forward was in late 1917, when I was sent to Cambrai during the fighting – there'd been a problem with ammunition backing up at a forward depot and I was supposed to sort it out. I was still a few miles from the town, which was taking quite a battering, I can tell you. As we were leaving, heading back to Montreuil, our convoy was hit by shellfire. Lorry in front of the car I was in was destroyed and we were peppered with shrapnel. Not to put too fine a point on it, Hendrie, a piece lodged itself in my balls. I've been in constant pain since that day. Still, probably kept me out of trouble, eh?'

--

At the end of his first week in Llewellyn Tindall's office, Hendrie was summoned to a meeting in Gilbey's office at MI6. He walked to Broadway, south through Mayfair and St James's Park, and when he arrived there, Gilbey and Lieutenant Colonel Robert Webster were waiting for him in reception.

'We'll pop across the road to St Ermin's,' said Gilbey. 'No reason why we can't do this over a decent drink.'

They found a table at the end of the Caxton Bar, overlooking the tree-lined courtyard entrance. 'You know we've got one of the floors here, don't you, Hendrie?' Gilbey was looking up at the ceiling. 'I tried to get my office moved here, but somehow didn't manage it. SOE have a floor to themselves too, don't they, Webster?'

Webster joined the other two peering wistfully upwards, all of them wishing they were based here rather than in the more utilitarian premises that the rest of MI6 and the SOE had to make do with.

'Robert has been of the view,' said Gilbey, 'that the fate of the agents we're sending into Denmark is either an unfortunate coincidence or else the source is in Denmark itself. He has been reluctant to concede that the information is coming from within his own section. I think that is fair, Robert?'

'That was my view, certainly. I have nonetheless come to accept the possibility – no more than that – that perhaps the source may be in Rodmarton Street.'

'What do you make of Tindall?' Gilbey was studying his Scotch as he asked the question. Webster looked uncomfortable.

'If you're asking what I think of him as a person... well, he's not my type. Bad-tempered, unfriendly, not exactly club-bable, clearly has a chip on his shoulder: most of which can be explained by what happened to him in the Great War. But if you're asking my opinion on whether he is a Nazi informant inside Rodmarton Street – no, I really don't think so.'

'Why?'

'It's too obvious, too convenient, wouldn't you agree? He's the man organising the dispatch of our agents to Denmark. He's in far too exposed a position. Certainly if it was him, then he'd make an effort to be more agreeable. Being so unpleasant and openly resentful only draws attention to himself.'

'He's been asking questions about you, Hendrie. He's pally with a chap he was with in the army who works in Registry, and he approached him to see what he knew about you. And it turns out he has a connection with Bentley: his brother was at Balliol with him and he contrived to bump into him at his club. All he wanted to talk about was you.'

'Perfectly normal to ask about one's new work colleague, I'd have thought. Hardly the kind of subterfuge I imagine a Nazi spy would get up to, eh?'

'I agree, Hendrie, but if the source is inside Rodmarton Street then everything points at Llewellyn Tindall; after all, he's the one person who knows every detail of an agent's journey to Denmark. But we have no evidence. We allowed you to go in with this story about leaving the Service under something of a cloud. We suspected Tindall would ask about you, and in fact when he did, what he heard was that far from you being in disgrace, you've actually been transferred to the Danish section on a highly sensitive mission to send in an agent.'

'So carry on as you are,' said Webster, 'acting as the somewhat put-upon and unappreciated dogsbody, and let's see what Tindall does. Be less than careful about what you leave on your desk, and maybe ask him if you can use his safe. In this file' – he passed a thick envelope under the table – 'is all the information you need. You're running a fictitious agent, code name Venice. You're to arrange for Venice to be flown out next Wednesday night from RAF Tempsford in Bedfordshire and dropped north-west of Randers on the Jutland peninsula. The non-existent Venice will be on a Halifax from 138 Squadron; they're part of the RAF Special Duties Service. We'll make sure one of their aircraft does take off as planned – Tindall knows Tempsford well, and he may well check whether there was such a flight.'

'And how do we find out if he's passed the information on?'

'The putative drop will take place near a village called Vorning. There's a particularly trustworthy resistance cell in that area. It's normally quiet, not many Germans. They'll be instructed to keep a careful watch on the drop zone. If there are Germans out there waiting for Venice, then we'll know Tindall's tipped them off.'

Hendrie had played his part, even impressing himself in the process. He spent most of the weekend in the office, a fact that he mentioned to Tindall when he came in on Monday morning and which Tindall later verified with the porter who'd been on duty. He affected an air of preoccupation and even worry, dropping the Venice file, swearing profusely, then concealing it under a pile of papers. When he went out for lunch, he asked Tindall whether he'd mind if he kept something in his safe.

On Wednesday morning, he ensured his rail ticket to Bedford was visible on his desk, and when he left at lunchtime and Tindall asked him where he was going, he replied, 'King's Cross,' before hurrying out of the office.

He spent the night at RAF Tempsford, watching the Halifax take off at nine o'clock, and was in the control tower when it landed after its thousand-mile return trip just before two thirty. Minutes later, the station commander, Group Captain Hanson, escorted him to the crew room, where the young flight lieutenant who'd been in charge of the mission described it rather in the way he might talk about a Sunday afternoon drive in his new sports car.

'Smooth enough flight out: kept to twelve thousand feet over the North Sea, speed averaging a decent two seventy. Bit of flak over German Bight, but I'm not sure we were the target. Crossed the Danish coast at Thyborøn, if that's how you pronounce it, and then headed east-south-east towards the drop zone. Descended to five thousand over the lake north-west of the target zone and then followed normal protocol for dropping an agent: swift descent to six hundred feet, held that in a loop for as long as the engine could bear it, then pulled the hell out of the throttle and up to twenty thousand by the time we were over the North Sea again. Spotted a couple of German night fighters just off the Frisian Front but we soon told them to fuck off—'

'Language, please, Green, we have a guest...'

The pilot looked towards Hendrie as if it were the first time he'd seen him. Hendrie noticed that despite the young pilot's apparent insouciance, there was a noticeable twitch on one of his eyelids and he was constantly clasping and unclasping his hands.

'Sorry, sir, where was I?'

'Just off the Frisian Front, I believe – some German night fighters with whom you didn't see eye to eye.'

'Ah yes. Stepped on the accelerator after that, little bit of a headwind off the Norfolk coast and here we are!'

'And I don't suppose you saw anything on the ground?'

The flight lieutenant glanced at the group captain; both men looked surprised.

'No, sir. We'd chosen a night with a small moon and plenty of cloud, as you know. Wouldn't do for the Germans to have a clear view of no one jumping out of the Halifax, if you see what I mean, but by that same token, hard for us to see anything on the ground.'

Hendrie was driven straight from RAF Tempsford to MI6's headquarters in Broadway. By the time he arrived in Gilbey's office, he realised he'd been awake for more than twenty-four hours. He was on his third cup of coffee when Webster came in just after six, looking like a man who'd had a brush with death.

'Are you all right, Webster?' Gilbey sounded genuinely concerned.

'Do you mind if I smoke, Tom? As you're aware, I'd arranged for the message from the Randers group to be received by the Norwegian section, so no chance of Tindall getting the slightest inkling of it. I say, is there a coffee going?'

He sipped his coffee, alternating with drawing on his cigarette. As he did so, he removed a sheet of paper from his briefcase. 'The message is from the Randers group. It was transmitted at five o'clock this morning our time, somewhat later than I'd have expected, but I think you'll see why. Once it had been decoded, I came straight here. We've changed the times to UK time. It reads: "Bird appeared over nest at approximately eleven twelve last night. Descended to usual height for normal period of time. Ground-to-air visibility poor. Area teeming with German troops – possibly in excess of two hundred – including at least one SS detachment. Roadblocks throughout the area and house-to-house searches carried out in Vorning and surrounding area. Gestapo officers from Copenhagen believed to be involved. Regret unable to transmit before now for reasons of safety and security. Free Denmark!"'

Gilbey held out his hand and Webster passed the sheet to him. 'Could anyone else in your section have known about this, Webster?'

'Not that I'm aware of, sir. Hendrie will know better...'

'I didn't discuss it with anyone else, and the Venice file stayed in the office I share with Tindall. Seems a bit harsh to judge him on circumstantial evidence, though, doesn't it?'

'It's more than circumstantial, Hendrie: it's conclusive,' said Gilbey. 'The only person other than the three of us who knew about the fictitious agent being dropped in the Randers area last night was Llewellyn Tindall. In any case, we've been keeping an eye on him: I've had a team of watchers on him since Monday.'

'First I've heard of that, Tom. Dig anything up?'

'Nothing on Monday. He went straight to his flat in Marylebone; it's in a mansion block on Welbeck Street. On Tuesday he went to his club and then took a cab back to his flat. Incidentally, we searched his flat on Tuesday and there was nothing suspicious there, though frankly I'd have been most surprised if there were. Last night he left his office and walked to Baker Street, then took a taxi to Piccadilly Circus. From there he walked to St Martin's Lane, though according to Treslake, who led the watchers, he didn't go there directly: he went down Haymarket, into Trafalgar Square, all the way round it, then up Charing Cross Road before cutting across. Treslake said he was using a fairly standard technique to avoid being followed: quite good, but obviously not good enough. He walked slowly down St Martin's Lane and then hung around the corner with St Martin's Court, as if he were waiting for someone. After about ten minutes he walked a bit further along and then into Cecil Court, where he was spotted with a young man. They stopped in a doorway, talked for a while and then Treslake said he was convinced Tindall handed the young man a slip of paper. They walked together back into Charing Cross Road, where they split up pretty quick.'

'How many watchers were there at this stage?' Hendrie asked.

'Three, I think. Tindall boarded a number 53 bus and stayed on it as far as Wigmore Street, from where he walked back to his flat. Treslake and one of the other watchers managed to get onto the bus. As for the other chap, he jumped on another bus and just vanished into the night. He must be good: my watchers aren't used to their targets disappearing into thin air. We're not MI5, as you know full well.'

'So when Tindall comes into the office, we take him aside and ask him a few questions, eh, Tom? Seems like he has quite a lot to answer.'

'I don't think we have the luxury of waiting for him to turn up to work. About an hour after he entered his block of flats, Treslake was about to call me to see whether they should stay there when they spotted the same young chap Tindall had met off St Martin's Lane. He appeared out of nowhere and hurried into the block. Treslake called in reinforcements and they've been able to watch the building very carefully: as far as we know, he's still there.'

Gilbey walked over to a cupboard behind his desk. He unlocked it and took out a pistol. 'We'd better get a move on. A car's waiting for us.'

–

Given the speed at which everything happened, Hendrie was surprised how clearly he was later to recall the events of the following hour.

They arrived in Welbeck Street to find that Treslake had a team of six watchers and four armed police officers.

'Tindall's flat is on the third floor, sir. I've placed two men on the landing above and one on the landing below. The rear of the flat opens onto a deep courtyard between this block and the one behind it. I've got one man in there. There's no question both men are in the flat. We can either wait until they come out, or go in: it's your decision, sir, obviously.'

'Obviously, Treslake. We'll go in now; we could even catch them transmitting. Webster, you wait here; Treslake, keep your watchers where they are, and you and the police come with me – you too, Hendrie.'

It was clear to Hendrie that seven men climbing the stairs and moving along the small corridor outside Tindall's flat were bound to make a noise, however much they endeavoured to avoid it. Treslake rang the doorbell and it was a full minute before Tindall's muffled voice could be heard from inside the flat.

'Who is it?'

Treslake explained that he had a parcel, but there was no response. One of the policemen pointed to a spyglass set high in the door and off centre. It was obviously not meant to be seen. Gilbey nodded and Treslake barged at the door.

'It's solid, sir, reinforced. We'll need the hammer.'

It was another minute before they managed to break in. Hendrie was the last to enter, and as he did so, he spotted an open window in the lounge and heard the sound of shouting below it.

'Stay where you are – don't move.'

'Don't be a fool, Tindall, for Christ's sake.'

'Treslake, you need to do something...'

'Llewellyn, perhaps this can be...'

Llewellyn Tindall was standing in the bedroom with his back to a large mirror, the bed in a state of disarray next to him, facing the open doorway. His dressing gown was only loosely done up and he was naked underneath. In his hand, which was shaking violently, was a Webley service pistol, its barrel bouncing around like a conductor's baton. At first he pointed it at the ceiling, then held it down as if he were about to drop it; then he wedged it under his jaw before lifting it up and holding it against his temple.

'Come on, Tindall,' said Gilbey, adopting an almost avuncular tone. 'You're not in any kind of trouble.'

Tindall stared at him in utter confusion: there was no doubt he was in all kinds of trouble. Then, before anyone could move, he pulled the trigger.

He was trembling so much it seemed at first he might have fired at the ceiling after all, but as they all rushed forward, he collapsed in a heap on what was clearly an expensive rug from somewhere exotic. The bullet had blown a large hole just by his ear, and blood was pouring onto the rug.

Hendrie knelt down beside him, and Tindall's eyes swivelled towards him, apparently in recognition.

'Who did you tell, Tindall – who are you working for?' Gilbey sounded nervous now; he kept repeating the question.

Hendrie held Tindall's wrist, feeling for a pulse. 'He's gone, sir. We shall never know.'

–

Two nights later, a drinks reception was held in Whitehall for some American Gilbey had never heard of but who was deemed important enough for a three-line whip: *all invitees will attend*, with the Prime Minister's name used as bait.

These Whitehall receptions were like poisoned chalices in more ways than one, a reminder of how hard it was to know who to trust and an often tiresome exercise in who to avoid.

Tonight was a case in point: Gilbey had found an agreeably dark corner where he had a good view of the gathering and which was also on the route the waiters took from the bar back into the room. He'd seen off some American general with more stars on his shoulder than he imagined was legal when Lord Swalcliffe appeared in front of him.

'What's this I hear, Gilbey?'

No greeting, no pleasantries, no small talk from Churchill's scientific adviser. A boxer throwing an uppercut straight from the bell: typical Swalcliffe.

'I have absolutely no idea, Lord Swalcliffe.' He noticed Swalcliffe didn't have a drink in his hand, which wasn't promising.

'I hear…' Swalcliffe paused, looked round and moved closer – far too close for Gilbey's liking. 'I hear you've been asking questions about rockets: German ones.'

'I ask questions about lots of matters, Lord Swalcliffe. It's part of my job.' Gilbey could have kicked himself. It was a poor response, feeble and defensive.

'Not in this case it isn't. Forget rockets. Good evening.'

Chapter 3

Tom Gilbey was furious, his shouting echoing along the corridor and possibly on the floors above and below his office. In his opinion it was bad enough – even inconsiderate – that Llewellyn Tindall had killed himself before they could interrogate him. But far worse was the other man in the flat – the one Tindall had been seen talking to off St Martin's Lane – somehow managing to escape. That was inexcusable.

Also in the office in Broadway was Webster from the Danish section of SOE, looking even closer to death than he had earlier in the morning. Hendrie was there too, with his section head, Roland Bentley. But the object of Gilbey's immediate wrath was Treslake, the leader of the team of watchers. The fact that they'd managed to follow Tindall around London and spot the young man entering the flat was not mentioned. Such success no longer counted. Their failure to catch him was all that mattered.

'Remind me how many men you had on your team, Treslake?'

'Ten, sir, including myself and the four police officers.'

'All armed?'

'Yes, sir.'

'And I was there too, plus Hendrie, so twelve people, yet somehow this young chap managed to climb out of a third-floor window and disappear!' He struck the desk, causing a teacup to dislodge from its saucer. Hendrie noticed Bentley take a step backwards, strategically placing himself behind Webster. His section head had a career-enhancing knack of stepping out of the line of fire.

'He was incredibly agile, sir, and it was a narrow window; my men had to struggle to fit through it. He managed to climb up a further two floors and then disappeared over the rooftops.'

'But you had a man in the courtyard. What the hell was he doing? Didn't he have a gun?'

'He did, sir, but I'm afraid it jammed.'

'Jesus,' said Gilbey menacingly, his fingers drumming heavily on his desk.

'There is one thing, though, sir, if it's of any help...'

'Go on, Treslake.'

'This has only come to light in the past half hour. You remember I told you how the younger chap had jumped on a number 24 bus heading north on the Charing Cross Road, and how he was so quick my watcher wasn't able to get on it? Well, he was at least able to take the registration number of the bus, and we've now been able to speak to its conductor. He recognised the description of the young man and distinctly remembers him asking if the bus was going in the direction of Marylebone. He told him it wasn't and that he'd need to change on Tottenham Court Road. He also says the man spoke with what he describes as a Continental accent.'

Gilbey looked up, his fingers still drumming.

'I don't suppose he was able to be more specific as to which part of the bloody Continent?'

'I'm afraid not, sir. He just said he was foreign, with a Continental accent – and that he looked nervous.'

–

Later that morning, Gilbey had calmed down somewhat, though he looked no less angry as he paced the office with the pent-up energy of an aggrieved animal. Treslake and Webster had left, and now he was alone with Bentley and Hendrie.

'What do you think, Roland?'

'About what, sir?' Roland Bentley looked wary; he was always nervous when asked to commit himself to an opinion.

'You've heard everything; you know what's going on. I need to get Richard Prince into Denmark. I was worried about using the SOE due to our fears they'd been infiltrated, hence my putting Hendrie in there. Now that it is clear Llewellyn Tindall was the informer, do you think we are safe to send Prince in using the good offices of the SOE?'

'If I may say, Tom – and you'll appreciate I am to a certain extent playing the devil's advocate here – the evidence against Llewellyn Tindall is only circumstantial. Nothing has been found in his flat—'

'Hang on, Roland, he was the only person in Rodmarton Street who knew about Hendrie sending an agent over, and sure enough there was a German reception committee of a couple of hundred troops waiting around the drop zone... and then what about this young chap with a foreign accent whom he met in St Martin's Lane – his German contact?'

'Indeed, Tom, but that's circumstantial evidence nonetheless, and there's nothing to prove Tindall is... was... a German spy. In law, one differentiates between circumstantial and direct evidence. Unlike hearsay, they are both admissible in court, but the latter certainly carries a good deal more weight than the former. And there may be another explanation for this young chap, the foreigner...'

'Go on.'

'This is somewhat sensitive, Tom, as you'll appreciate, but Treslake told us Tindall was hanging around between St Martin's Court and Cecil Court. Well...' Bentley coughed nervously and glanced at Gilbey and then Hendrie, as if unsure whether it was wise to continue. 'On that block is the Salisbury public house. You may not be aware, but that is a venue where homosexual men... meet each other. It is perfectly feasible that this is the reason Tindall met this young man. I believe they call it a pick-up. They went into Cecil Court, which is somewhat less prominent, where Tindall handed him a slip of paper with his address on it and arranged for him to visit him later that evening. Clearly he would not want to be seen travelling with the young man or indeed entering his apartment block with him. The evidence, such as it is, could just as easily point to this having been a sordid sexual encounter: illegal certainly, but hardly in the same bracket as treason.'

Gilbey looked at Bentley, giving the impression that what he said made some sense, but he was nonetheless reluctant to acknowledge it as such. 'What do you think, Hendrie? You didn't think a lot of Tindall, did you?'

'No, I didn't, sir. He was clearly a resentful type, big chip on his shoulder and all that, but whether that makes him a traitor, I'm not sure. As I think I said to you, it's all too convenient, eh?'

'Nevertheless… nevertheless…' Gilbey rearranged a few papers on his already tidy desktop and seemed to come to a decision. 'As long as the possibility remains that Tindall was passing on intelligence about our operations to the Germans, and the young foreign chap is on the loose, we cannot risk using the SOE to send Prince to Denmark.'

'But if the source was Tindall and Tindall is dead, then there's no longer any danger, surely?'

'I know, Roland, but if he was a Nazi spy, what might he have told this young man? We need to get Prince to Denmark by alternative means.'

'Which is difficult,' said Hendrie. 'After all, the SOE has all the expertise in that respect.'

'I know, I know. Tell me, Hendrie – Tindall's assistant, the Danish girl, what's she like?'

'Greta Poulsen? Nice enough. Pretty thing, if rather broad-shouldered. Good legs, though, and a fine—'

'I'm not asking about her physique. What is she like as a person?'

'Quiet, but good at just getting on with things. I know Tindall complained about being used as a dogsbody, but in many respects Miss Poulsen was Tindall's dogsbody, though she never moaned about it like he did. I'm not sure how well things would have functioned without her.'

'Was she in the same office as you and Tindall?'

'Just outside it, sir, in an anteroom. In case you have any worries, she was discretion personified. She always knocked before coming in, and either Tindall or I would lock the office when we left.'

'No, I'm not concerned in that respect. She came through her security clearance with flying colours; I'd already checked that out. The thing is, we need her expertise, but we'd need to get her away from Rodmarton Street. I propose we second her to us while we prepare Prince for his mission.'

–

Gilbey called in a favour or two. He couldn't risk Webster knowing he wanted to use Greta Poulsen to help prepare Prince, so Webster's superior at Noresby House was persuaded to instruct him to dismiss her. 'Sorry, Webster, that part of your operation will have to be shut down: consider it compromised. Don't worry about Miss Poulsen, we'll find something for her to do.'

Next it was his sister-in-law, whose father owned and farmed considerable chunks of Derbyshire. 'It's going to be tricky, Tom,' was her initial response. With her, things were always tricky. Gilbey said that was a shame, because he could be of considerable help with petrol rations – even quite generous. Half an hour later, she rang back: no problem.

The house they came up with was perfect: a decent-sized farmhouse, no neighbours within a mile, situated west of Matlock and on the edge of the Peak District. It was in good condition, used by one of the estate managers until he'd been conscripted a few months previously. No one would have the faintest idea it had been borrowed by the Service. They called premises like this ghost houses: off the books, not known about other than by a very select few.

'You've got three weeks to train him, Hendrie,' Gilbey said. 'You'll go up there to be in overall charge. There's an SOE trainer called Martin to do the nuts-and-bolts stuff, and Miss Poulsen will be there to help with all things Danish. You teach him what it means to be a spy – the theory and suchlike. I imagine you're good at that.'

–

Richard Prince was in a bemused and even confused state when he arrived at the isolated farmhouse in Derbyshire on one of those October days when autumn has taken hold on the trees and the first hints of winter are in the air. They'd left Lincoln early in the morning, and by the time they arrived at their destination, there was still a frost on the ground.

Hendrie was there to greet him, impatiently pacing up and down outside the house as if Prince was late, glancing at his watch and fussing unnecessarily about who'd carry which case into the house. The journey had given Prince an opportunity to reflect on his recruitment and the fact that he was now working for British intelligence. His bemusement was at the pace at which everything had happened and the fact that he'd had relatively little say in it. His agreement had been assumed: one moment he'd been a policeman in Lincolnshire, the next he was in his Chief Constable's office, the room thick with cigarette smoke. Hendrie was making the whole business sound somewhat matter-of-fact.

'A couple of months, Prince, that's all. Come and work with us for a couple of months.'

The Chief Constable had been sitting behind his desk, his face red and his demeanour that of a man who'd clearly lost an argument. 'I've said two months must mean two months, Prince, don't you worry. If I could afford to lose my best detective, I'd have allowed you to join up in 1939 as you wanted to, but Mr Hendrie is insistent.'

Prince had turned to Hendrie, whose demeanour was the opposite of the Chief Constable's: a man who'd clearly won an argument. Hendrie shifted his chair away from the angry gaze of the Chief Constable. 'Look on it as a matter of duty, Prince. Clearly we cannot force you to work for us, but for what we have in mind, you're undoubtedly the best person.'

And while he could have conceivably said no at that point, he knew he'd have regretted doing so. Every time he saw a soldier or an airman, he felt a pang of conscience, a sense that he wasn't playing his part in the war. He knew that but for Henry he'd have joined up long ago.

'Two months you say, sir?'

'More or less, yes. I mean, clearly we won't be counting days as such, but...'

The Chief Constable made a snorting sound.

Prince took a deep breath. 'Well, I suppose so, yes...'

Hendrie had stood up rather too fast and walked over to him and clasped his hand with both of his own. 'Welcome on board, Prince. Perhaps you and I can find somewhere to have a chat?'

–

In other circumstances Richard Prince would have described the three weeks near Matlock as being rather pleasant. The house was very comfortable, a couple employed by the Service were there to look after the place and cook the meals and the countryside was stunning. A man called Martin gave him firearms and self-defence training along with sessions on communications. Hendrie's job, apart from fussing around and worrying about security, was to brief him on the mission and initiate him – as he put it – in the ways of an agent on a clandestine operation. A Danish woman called Greta was there from time to time too: her job was to help construct his new identity and ensure he was familiar with all things Danish.

Prince and Greta Poulsen became close during her visits to Derbyshire. He wasn't able to tell her anything about himself and she only knew him as Thomas – Hendrie was the only person there aware of his true identity. But she was friendly, in contrast to Martin's businesslike approach and Hendrie's fussing around. They went for long walks in the countryside and after a couple of days she would link her arm through his. Soon after that, she took to kissing him on the cheek when they met and when they parted.

Prince hadn't anticipated how much this friendship would mean to him, and he even came close to telling her about his circumstances. He thought about it as they walked down the lanes and across the fields: of course he wouldn't give his name or any other details, but he could hint at a recent tragedy involving his wife, and maybe even refer to a child – he'd avoid saying it was a son. It might help explain a certain reticence she'd have been bound to have spotted in him. He didn't want her to think of him as being rude.

But then he remembered how Hendrie had warned him to tell no one anything. *All you need is one person you trust to let slip to someone else they trust a seemingly innocent detail and they tell another person – who they also trust – and the next thing you know you're in a damp basement having to explain yourself to the Gestapo, which is not something any amount of training can really prepare you for.*

In fact, they had tried to prepare him for such an eventuality. They'd brought up a couple of MI5 interrogators, with whom he spent an unpleasant few hours in a barn, and then a Danish army officer had come to interrogate him in Danish. He was roughed up a bit, then blindfolded and forced to stand in the dark with his hands and feet bound for what felt like hours. The consensus was that he handled these mock interrogations very well: he was unflappable, managed to think before he answered without any undue hesitation, demonstrated a degree of physical bravery and had quickly mastered his backstory – the legend, as they insisted on calling it. 'You're jolly good,' Hendrie told him when the interrogation training ended, as if he was surprised. 'However, you need to understand that unfortunately that doesn't count for an awful lot once the Gestapo get their hands on you. The most important thing is to use this training to stop yourself falling into their hands. Don't be cocky: they'll smell that a mile off. That and fear.'

Greta Poulsen was spending more time in Derbyshire now, though every few days she'd return to London, where she was helping with preparing his documentation.

'Important you feel comfortable speaking Danish,' Hendrie told him.

'I always have done, sir. The language came naturally to me and I always spoke it with my mother.'

'Even so, you'll have to speak it under pressure when you're there. Take advantage of Miss Poulsen being around, but do be careful about how much you let on. Remember, Mr Gilbey and I are the only people who know all the details of your mission.'

–

The last three days at the farmhouse moved at a frantic pace. Greta returned to Derbyshire on Sunday, and she seemed to have caught the solemn mood. For two hours she sat in a room with Prince and Hendrie as they went through everything that had been prepared for him: the clothes with Danish labels, the Danish toiletries, the odds and ends and scraps of paper to go in his pockets and wallet.

'And here's your identity, Thomas: you're Jesper Holm. In this envelope is your identity card – your *legitimationskort* – in that name along with various other documents. And here,' she handed him a file, 'is Jesper Holm's story.'

Prince opened the file, but Hendrie put his hand on top of it. 'Later. You'll need to read this, absorb all the information and commit it to memory. Remember, your life depends on it. It's not just a matter of memorising the information; you must absolutely believe it and live it. By the time you leave here you need to *be* Jesper Holm. Greta's done a splendid job. It's a first-class identity and absolutely rock solid.'

When they finished, Prince went for a walk in the paddock alongside the farmhouse. He was leaning against a fence when Greta joined him. She stood apart from him, gazing into the distance.

'Are you ready for your mission, Jesper? You have to get used to being called that.'

'Not yet, but I imagine I will be once I've read up on him.'

'Do you go this week?'

He shrugged. 'I really don't know, Greta, I—'

'I'm sorry. I shouldn't be asking you these questions.' She glanced at him and then away again. They didn't speak as they walked back to the house.

–

The following morning, Tom Gilbey arrived along with a young Royal Navy officer he introduced as Jack Shaw.

'I gather things have gone rather well?'

'I hope so, sir.'

'Nervous?'

'Naturally. I suspect I'd be nervous if I wasn't nervous, if you gather my meaning.'

'Very good. Now then, you're going to be travelling to Denmark by sea, and young Shaw here will be your escort.'

They ate that night in the dining room, the first time they'd used that room since arriving in Derbyshire. It felt very formal, like a farewell dinner, with an atmosphere to match. There were four of them round the table: Prince, Gilbey, Hendrie and Shaw. When they'd finished their meal, Gilbey asked Shaw and Hendrie to leave.

'I return to London tonight, Prince. You'll leave here in the morning. Shaw's terribly good: we've borrowed him from Royal Navy intelligence and they rate him very highly. I know he looks like a schoolboy, but then they all do these days, don't they? You've had all your briefings, eh?'

Prince nodded, wondering whether he dared help himself to another glass of claret.

'Any... problems?'

'Only that I'm leaving my son, sir. Of course, I realise everyone has to make sacrifices because of the war, but he is all I have, and perhaps more to the point, I'm all he has. But Mr Hendrie says it will only be a couple of months, and once I'm back...' He stopped speaking as he tried to compose himself, his head dropping down.

Gilbey allowed a few moments of silence before he spoke. 'Of course, one understands, but as you say, we're all making sacrifices. Do have another glass of wine; there's very little not helped by that.'

He waited while Prince poured a large glassful. 'I do worry that when we train our agents, we cram their heads full of information and it's sometimes hard to see the wood for the trees. I always try and send them off with a short summary of what the mission is about so they can be clear as to what I expect.'

He stood up and circled the dining table before sitting down next to Prince.

'The tide of the war has turned in our favour, no question about that. But we mustn't be complacent; there's still an enormous amount of fight in the Germans. They're a formidable enemy and a clever one. The biggest threat to this country could well be from these long-range rockets they're developing. They could cause us untold damage; they could even reverse our fortunes. I'm not suggesting they could cause us to lose the war on their own, but if the rumours are close to the truth, they could set us back months, quite possibly even a year or two. That would be a disaster. However, there's a worrying degree of scepticism in some quarters. There are people in Whitehall – some of them quite influential – who insist these rockets pose no threat, or that the threat is exaggerated, and they're trying to influence Winston accordingly.

'Recently our head of station in Stockholm was approached by a Danish businessman, whom we call Agent Horatio. He travels to Berlin frequently for his work and claims that while there, he's picked up something about the rockets. But there's a limit to what we can do with him from a neutral country: I need my own man on the ground in Copenhagen to run him. First, though, you'll need to check him out – we cannot even be sure we trust him. In the end, it may well be a matter for your judgement. If you think he passes the test, I want you to milk him for whatever intelligence he has.

'I don't think I'm exaggerating, Prince, when I say that this mission is of the utmost importance: if half of what we hear about these rockets is true and they extend the war by even a couple of months, that could be a disaster. And there's something else: Denmark is also very well placed to gain information about the rockets. The Germans are developing the damn things at a place called Peenemünde, which is on the Baltic coast, very close to Denmark. They're even test-firing some of them into Danish territory.

'So that's your job, Prince. Run Horatio, find out what you can about the rockets, supply me with the evidence I need to persuade the fools here that this is a genuine threat. Do that and you'll be a hero.'

There was a period of silence. Prince was not sure if the conversation had come to an end. Gilbey stood up and walked towards the large stone fireplace.

'Have you seen that film *The Great Dictator*?'

'The one with Charlie Chaplin, sir? Yes, we saw it at the Regal.'

Gilbey nodded. 'It's certainly amusing, but the problem with it is it makes the Germans out to be clowns, and I'm afraid broadly speaking they're anything but that. You're making a very grave error if you think the enemy are fools, but too many people in London do make that mistake. Your Danish background and ability to speak the language is a great asset, Prince, and you have a very good Danish identity, but I don't want you to feel that it makes you safe, if you get my drift. Always be alert, never be complacent. The Gestapo see through most cover stories, sooner or later. Main thing is to avoid falling into their hands.'

There was another period of silence. Gilbey sat down again and both men concentrated on their wine glasses. Gilbey started to speak a couple of times but paused, giving Prince the impression he was unsure of what he was about to say. 'One final thing,' he said eventually. 'As you may have gathered, I'm somewhat sceptical about the Danes. I think we've been lulled into a false sense of security what with them being so friendly and so hostile to the Germans. Be very careful who you trust. Hendrie's briefed you about Agent Osric? At least Osric is reliable.'

He leaned back in his chair, studying Prince very carefully, running his finger round the rim of his wine glass. 'I'm going to be frank with you, Prince. There is something I've been in two minds about telling you.'

Prince was startled. This sounded ominous.

'When we started, I wasn't sure how you'd turn out. Nothing personal, you understand; it's how I approach all new agents. It's one thing getting top marks in training and quite another cutting it in the field. Very hard to predict – until you send an agent into enemy territory, you simply have no idea how they'll perform.

'However,' Gilbey sat up at this point and leaned closer, so close Prince could smell the wine on his breath, 'one does get an instinct for the quality of a person. I like to describe agents I know I can trust implicitly as *cum laude* – that's Latin for "with very great distinction". You're a *cum laude* agent, Prince.'

'Thank you, sir, I—'

'No need to show me gratitude, we're not in some bloody Oxford college. What it means is that had I not decided you're a *cum laude* agent, I would not have told you what I'm about to tell you. We have a further source in Copenhagen, one so highly placed and so important to us that you are only to approach him in the most extreme of circumstances: if Agent Osric is unable to help you and if your life is in danger, not if you've run out of milk. Do you understand this?'

'Yes, sir.'

'Just three people in this country know about this source, including myself. If he's compromised, it would be a disaster for this country. His code name is Browning. Under no circumstances are you to approach him directly. Now, you'll need to concentrate, Prince. I'm about to tell you how to contact him.'

Chapter 4

The North Sea, November 1942

When Prince came down for breakfast at seven thirty, Jack Shaw was already at the table, looking slightly nervous and smiling as if genuinely pleased to see him. His hands shook slightly as he poured his own tea and a cup for Prince.

'We'll leave here at nine, maybe a shade earlier if the driver gets here before then.'

'So we sail today?'

'I'm afraid I'm only permitted to advise you of our arrangements one stage at a time, sir. In any case, you'll not be going straight to the port. Mr Gilbey has arranged a stop on our journey.'

They left the house near Matlock just before nine and headed east. Throughout the journey Shaw was continually glancing around, peering in the wing mirror, trying to see through the back window and instructing the driver to let any car coming up behind them overtake. On at least four occasions he told him to pull into a lay-by, and they waited there in silence, apart from the driver drumming his fingers on the steering wheel. They drove south of Mansfield and crossed the Great North Road near Newark before joining the road to Hykeham, heading north towards Lincoln. Prince could feel his heart beating fast. He now had an inkling of where they could be going.

Instead of going to his own home, however, they turned north-east when they entered Lincoln, soon pulling into the driveway of a house off the Lindum Road. Shaw turned round, addressing Prince in his public school accent, no longer nervous.

'Your son has been brought here for you to visit him, sir. Mr Gilbey didn't think it would be wise for you to be seen at your own home. It's now, what... eleven o'clock. The plan is for you to stay here until three. You'll be able to play with Henry – apparently there's a large garden with a swing in it – and have lunch and spend some time together. Mr Gilbey said it was because you might not see him for a while.'

There was a pause as Shaw's final words hung heavy in the car. *For a while...*

'That is very nice of Mr Gilbey,' said Prince. 'Though four hours isn't terribly long, is it?'

'I'm afraid it's as long as we can spare, sir. There is one other thing: Mr Gilbey said to remind you you're not to utter a word about where you're going and what you're up to.'

'For Christ's sake, Shaw, Henry is three years old! If you seriously think I'm going to discuss my mission with him...'

–

By the end of the visit, Prince wondered if it wouldn't have been better if it hadn't taken place at all. Henry had been thrilled to see him, and for the first hour it had been fine: they'd played in the garden, kicked a football around and played with a large black cat that gave the impression they were in its territory and should respect that. Then it had started raining, so they came inside, where there was less to distract them, and sat in a slightly formal lounge with a couple of jigsaws that were far too difficult for Henry. Shaw was in the kitchen but popped in every so often to ask if everything was all right.

Prince's sister-in-law was also there, and she hovered nearby.

'Evelyn, perhaps if you could let Henry and me have a few minutes on our own?'

'Lunch will be ready soon.'

'Well, a few minutes before lunch then, eh?'

He'd never got on particularly well with his wife's sister, who since Jane's death had appeared put out that she'd not been asked to be more involved in Henry's life. It was as if she felt she ought to replace her sister as Henry's mother, something Prince wasn't keen on.

However, when he was recruited by Gilbey, he felt he had no alternative but to ask her to help out. After all, Gilbey had assured him it would only be for a few weeks. She'd had to make do with a brief explanation about a project to do with port security.

Since they'd arrived in Lincoln, he'd been thinking about how he'd broach the subject of his absence with Henry. 'Daddy's going to work for a few days. When I come back, we'll go somewhere very special. Where would you like to go?'

'Can we go and see Mummy and Grace?'

He didn't know how to respond. Henry had been just a year old when his mother and sister were killed. He had no memory of them, and Prince had felt it was best left that way. He'd tell him when he was older. He guessed Evelyn must have been talking about them.

There was a bag with some books in it, and Henry thrust one in his hands for him to read. It was the story of a little bear whose father goes to find food and gets lost in a forest. The little bear appeared to spend all his time looking out the window for his father to return. He couldn't have chosen a worse book.

Prince was on the edge of his emotions for the remainder of the time in Lincoln, doing his best not to show how upset he was and praying for the weather to improve so they could be alone in the garden. At two thirty, Shaw came into the lounge, tapped his wristwatch and told him there was half an hour to go. Five minutes later, the rain stopped and the sun broke through. He and Henry put their coats on and went outside, his son clutching his hand.

'You know I told you I'm going to work for a few days, Henry?'

Henry was kicking leaves and looking for the black cat and didn't appear to be paying attention. Tears welled up in Prince's eyes and he was grateful his son was distracted.

'Just remember this: Daddy loves you very much and you're very special to him. You understand?'

The boy might have noticed the catch in his father's voice, its unfamiliar cadence. His grip tightened and he looked up, smiled and nodded as if he did understand, although Prince wasn't sure that wasn't wishful thinking on his part.

—

They left Lincoln at three, as planned. Prince cuddled his son in the hallway and then left the house quickly.

They headed north out of Lincoln, towards Market Rasen. It was a road Prince knew well. An hour or so later, they arrived in Grimsby, driving through the town and onto the docks. A policeman on a motorbike was waiting for them at a security gate and they followed him as he drove past a large wooden sign for *Fish Docks No. 3* barely covered by a frayed sheet of tarpaulin. The enormous Dock Tower loomed in the distance as they headed to the furthest part of the docks, close to the sea wall. They drove slowly along North Quay, the sea wind buffeting the car, until the policeman stopped, his arm outstretched, pointing to a small building.

They climbed to the top floor, to an office warmed by a large oil fire and with views of the dock to one side and the Humber Estuary to the other. Their driver followed them in with their bags and then left.

'It's getting dark. We'll need to close the blackout and put the lights on,' said Shaw. 'Before we do, though, come over here.'

He was standing by the window overlooking the dock. Immediately below was a trawler that to Prince looked quite old, possibly not even seaworthy, though he'd be the first to admit he was no judge of such matters. It was painted almost entirely black, with a narrow white band running horizontally around the hull and the name of the ship picked out in white – *Northern Hawk, Grimsby* – along with its registration, GY512. The same registration was painted on the stern. The deck was blackened with soot and grime, the wheelhouse a dirty white.

'At the start of the war there were around four hundred and sixty trawlers sailing out of Grimsby,' said Shaw, who was evidently more relaxed close to the sea. 'We requisitioned the best ones and they've done a splendid job with the convoys. They make excellent minesweepers and rescue ships and the crews are second to none. As the war has gone on, we've released more of them back for fishing. The *Northern Hawk* is ostensibly one of those: it may look like it's not up to it, but actually that's deliberate. If it looks like a rust-bucket, the Germans are less likely to be interested in it. In fact, it has a brand new engine and is in tip-top condition; its rather sorry-looking exterior is as much a camouflage as anything else. Ah, there we are – you see those two men coming down the gangplank?'

Prince could make out two figures dressed in black.

'That's the skipper, Bert Trent, and his first mate, Sid Oliver. They both have top-level security clearance but obviously don't know what you'll be up to in Denmark; they only know you as "Tom". It goes without saying that you don't breathe a word about your mission while on board. In a moment I'll give Bert the coordinates for the rendezvous point with the Danish trawler: that's as much as he needs to know. But he's absolutely reliable and this isn't the first time he's undertaken something like this for us. Here they are.'

The two men who entered the office were both quite short and built like boxers, their weather-beaten faces making it impossible to pinpoint their ages. They moved in the somewhat deliberate way sailors do on land, each smoking a pipe and looking at Prince with a mixture of suspicion and curiosity, studying him without saying a word. Shaw did the introductions and both men crossed the room to shake hands in a rather formal manner. Then he passed Trent an envelope. The skipper put his pipe down while he opened it, read its contents carefully, then handed it to his first mate.

Shaw indicated that they should both join him at a table covered in charts. For a while Trent didn't say a word as he held a large ruler over the charts and made calculations with a pencil. Then he muttered something to Sid Oliver, who shook his head and pointed to another part of the chart. Trent looked up.

'It's very close to Denmark, Jack, very close. They realise that, I presume?'

'That's the coordinates we've been given, Bert; we can't change them now. I think it must be because they don't want to risk the other ship having to come out too far.'

'I don't imagine they do. Very well then. The rendezvous point is here – only just outside Danish territorial waters, west of the North Frisian Islands.' His forefinger tapped part of the North Sea on the map. 'Sid and I will do more detailed calculations before we set sail, but I'd estimate it being some two hundred and fifty nautical miles from Grimsby. We'll travel at seven knots; we're capable of more but that could draw attention to us. Best they see us as a harmless old trawler unable to go any faster.'

'When will we get to the rendezvous point?'

'Hard to say, Jack, hard to say: two hundred and fifty nautical miles assumes we travel in a straight line, but it doesn't tend to work like that. The sea conditions could knock us off course, and then we have the German navy to worry about...' He paused, bouncing his pencil on the chart. 'Today's what – Tuesday – and my estimate is a minimum of thirty-five hours once we leave Grimsby, but according to these instructions the rendezvous should be between midnight Thursday and two in the morning Friday. I don't want to get into the area too early, it could arouse suspicion.'

'What do you reckon then?'

Sid Oliver spoke. 'High tide's at about eight fifteen tonight. I think we should delay our departure to midnight. Rather than going in a straight line through Humber and German Bight – they're shipping areas, Tom, here and here – I think we should head north up through Humber into Dogger and from there down to German Bight. Bert's right, we don't want to arrive too early.'

'I hope you don't mind me asking, but...' Prince hesitated, aware that he sounded awkward, 'aren't we sitting ducks for the Germans – U-boats and all that?'

'You're right to mention that. The danger is from U-boats heading out to the Arctic or returning from it. Their two main bases are here, Trondheim, in Norway and here, Kiel on the Baltic. Fortunately, their routes should keep them north of us. The U-boats based in Hamburg – here – tend not to bother with a lone trawler these days: they worry about exposing themselves, giving away their position, and it's not worth it for an old rust-bucket like us. It's not unknown for trawlers to be used as decoys to tempt U-boats to the surface and then attack them. But that's no guarantee of our safety.'

They set sail a few minutes before midnight, the *Northern Hawk* slipping silently and unseen through the dock gates into the Humber Estuary, the world around them pitch black, with only an occasional distant flickering light to remind them they were not alone in it.

Shaw and Prince shared a tiny cabin next to the skipper's, just below the wheelhouse. They remained there the rest of that night and throughout the following day, when the *Northern Hawk* moved into Dogger and cast its nets. 'It's important they keep up the pretence of being a working trawler,' Shaw explained. 'And if we leave the cabin, we'll just get in the way.'

When night fell on Wednesday, they ate in the trawler's galley and then Bert Trent asked Prince if he'd like to join him in the wheelhouse.

For a while neither man said anything. The sea was calm and the same colour as the sky; impossible to tell where one ended and the other began. The gentle swell gave the impression that they were in the middle of an enormous shifting field, with the suggestion of hills rising far in the distance.

'First time at sea, Tom?'

'I guess it is really, yes.'

More silence. The skipper peered through the window to his right and then checked his dials. 'We're making good progress. We're above Dogger Bank, you know. Wonderful fishing ground. They say that thousands of years ago this was all land, connecting Britain to the Continent – all the way from Lincolnshire to Jutland! You wouldn't have needed us then, would you? Mind you…' Another long pause; it seemed as if the skipper had lost his train of thought. 'If we were still connected by land, the war would've been over long before now.'

'Maybe it would never have started.'

'Who knows.'

'Were you in the convoys, Bert?'

The other man nodded.

'And were they as bad as they say?'

'Worse, far worse. We've lost dozens and dozens of men.'

'You must have known some of them.'

The skipper nodded, staring hard ahead of him, his hands gripping the wheel. 'My brother and brother-in-law.'

'I'm sorry, Bert.'

Another long spell of silence. When Trent spoke again, his voice was barely audible above the hum of the engine and the crashing of the waves against the trawler. 'And my son.'

Prince stepped to the rear of the wheelhouse. The thought of his own son overwhelmed him. He could feel the tears welling in his eyes, and all the time the *Northern Hawk* was taking him further away from Henry.

–

Late on Thursday afternoon, the *Northern Hawk* changed course and headed south from Dogger into German Bight, closer now to Denmark. The wind was against them and they'd increased their speed to eight knots, but the first mate thought he might have seen a periscope in the distance, and there was certainly a ship on the horizon, so they dropped their speed and cast their nets for an hour in case anyone was watching.

At eleven o'clock that night, Shaw called Prince into the cabin. A final check, he said. They went through the rucksack Prince would be carrying to make sure there was nothing that could link him with Britain, and then his papers to confirm they were all in order. Then Shaw quizzed him on the details of his new identity – where Jesper Holm was born, his date of birth. Finally Prince prepared for the rendezvous, wrapping his rucksack in an oilskin and putting on a lifejacket.

'Wait here,' said Shaw. 'It could be any time now.'

He left the cabin and went to the wheelhouse. There was the noise of activity on deck and Prince could sense the trawler's speed being cut. More activity in the wheelhouse: from what he could tell, Shaw was now in charge. 'That's them, it's the right signal!' he heard the young Royal Navy officer shout.

A few minutes later there was a knock on the cabin door and Sid Oliver popped his head round it. 'Come on, Tom, it's time now.' He looked behind him and quickly thrust a small flask into Prince's hands. 'Rum: drink that and everything'll be fine.'

When Prince reached the deck, Jack Shaw was coming down from the wheelhouse. He led him to where the deck-hands were hanging tyres over the side of the trawler. Out of the darkness, a shape loomed into view. As it came closer, he could see it was a Danish trawler: *Lena, Esbjerg.*

The skippers of the two trawlers took five minutes to manoeuvre the boats alongside each other. The tyres ensured they came together smoothly, and then ropes were lashed at the bow and stern, held in place by deckhands on either vessel.

'You've got everything?' A wind had picked up and Shaw was shouting to be heard above it. Prince said he had, and with that, he was helped over the side of the *Northern Hawk* and then more or less hauled onto the wet deck of the *Lena*. Even before he'd clambered to his feet, the two trawlers had separated and the *Northern Hawk* was pulling fast away from the Danish boat. One of the Danish crew pointed to an open hatch. 'Down there – quick.'

–

They arrived in Esbjerg a few hours later on the high tide. Prince was uncomfortable from being kept in the hold throughout the journey, and he reeked of fish. He was grateful for the rum Sid Oliver had given him. He waited below deck while the fish was unloaded. A period of silence followed, and he wondered if they'd forgotten about him. Then one of the crew came down, opened a door and led him into the engine room. Another pointed to a small hatch. 'Go in there: just a few minutes. Not a sound.'

It was the shape and size of a coffin, the air limited and suffused with the smell of diesel and fish. Prince could hear people walking past and talking. He could make out that they were speaking Danish, although not what they were saying; he could also have sworn he heard some German. Half an hour later, the hatch door opened.

'Out you come.' It was a man in his sixties, distinguished-looking, with an irritated air about him. 'I trust you had a successful trip. What fish did you catch?'

What fish did you catch? Prince knew he was safe. This was Niels, his contact in Esbjerg.

'Only haddock, I am afraid.'

'Don't worry. Haddock is more plentiful than cod at this time of the year.'

Prince felt relieved. Niels looked at him expectantly, his eyebrows raised: *Carry on…*

'Oh, yes… and no plaice either.'

'Good,' said Niels, 'but you mustn't hesitate like that. Your safety – and ours – depends on it. You need to be more fluent. Anyway, welcome to Denmark. I'm Niels.'

'Were some Germans here before?'

'They were, yes. A routine search apparently.'

'Do they search every trawler coming in?'

'Sometimes. Still, they found nothing. We'll take you to your safe house soon. Let me see your identity documents, please.'

Prince passed over his Jesper Holm identity card and the other papers. Niels studied them carefully.

'This is the only identity you have?'

Prince nodded. Niels shook his head.

'I'm not happy with this. They really should have given you more than one identity: one for your journey, one for when you reach your destination. I've told London this so many times, but as usual they ignore what I say. Stay here while I sort out a new identity card for you. I'll come back soon to take your photograph and we'll have the card ready by lunchtime. That will be a better time anyway to take you to the safe house – it's always busy then.

'This card,' he handed the *legitimationskort* back to Prince, 'keep it safe. We'll sort out somewhere to conceal it soon – and don't use it until you arrive in Copenhagen.'

Chapter 5

Denmark, November 1942

Days later, on the train from Odense to Nyborg, Prince had fallen into a deep sleep when he was woken up by a loud voice shouting for tickets a few rows behind him. For a moment he had trouble remembering quite where he was, the rocking effect of the train creating a hypnotic sense of confusion. And then he spotted Henry in a seat diagonally opposite, smiling and staring straight at him.

The sense that his son was opposite him was so intense, Prince leaned forward to speak to the boy. The words were half formed, but just as he opened his mouth, the ticket inspector appeared in the aisle and the spell was broken. By the time he'd checked the tickets, the boy had turned round. He no longer looked like Henry.

At that moment, Prince would have happily betrayed the whole world just to spend five minutes with his son.

-

In Richard Prince's first year at grammar school, morning lessons were spent in a classroom overlooking the main entrance, where from his window desk he'd watch the almost ceremonial arrival each day of Mr Marquis, one of the classics masters.

Towards the end of the first period, a dark car would appear on the school's improbably long gravelled drive and proceed at almost funereal pace to the front entrance. A woman Prince assumed was Mr Marquis's wife would emerge and help him out. He would spend a while sorting himself out, checking his briefcase and adjusting his hat, before she guided him by the elbow the short distance to the steps at the entrance of the school, where a boy from the Lower Sixth would be waiting to take over. He would lead Mr Marquis up the steps and into the school, from where he would be taken to a classroom for the start of the second period.

On Wednesdays, this would be Prince's class. Mr Marquis would be handed over to the teacher from the previous lesson, who would take his hat and coat and help him with his briefcase before placing him in the right position facing the pupils.

Mr Marquis would remain in that position for the duration of the lesson, his only apparent movement being that of his left hand across the papers spread out on the table in front of him as he spoke in a near-endless monologue. He paused only to ask an occasional question of the class, and gave the impression of being thrown off track if a pupil asked anything of him. He could spend a whole lesson reciting the poetry of Homer, switching without a pause from ancient Greek to the English translation, his head tilted back as he spoke in a quiet voice the boys strained to catch, his unseeing eyes darting from left to right, sometimes filling with tears: the blind teacher reciting the words of the blind poet.

At the end of the period, another Lower Sixth boy would appear to escort Mr Marquis to his next lesson, and that would be the pattern of his day: being led from place to place, never quite sure of where he was, his journey always in the hands of someone else, his destination taken care of.

Prince now had some appreciation of how the teacher must have felt. Since being sent to Derbyshire, he'd had to entrust every stage of his journey to someone else, unsure of where he was going next. It was as if he was blindfolded. Now Niels had told him to be ready to leave Esbjerg first thing in the morning.

'Am I going straight to Copenhagen?' He assumed Niels was in charge of the resistance group in the port: he had an undoubted air of authority about him and he was the only person he'd seen on more than one occasion.

'It's best you know nothing about your journey. You'll be told as much as you need to know at the right time. It's safer that way.'

A woman around the same age as Prince arrived early the next morning at the tiny attic flat in the shadow of the port. She busied herself making breakfast before joining him at the table.

'You have your new *legitimationskort*?'

Prince nodded and handed the card to her. 'I'm Hans Olsen, a sales representative from Aarhus. Do I look like a Hans Olsen from Aarhus?'

'Well you certainly look like a sales representative. Listen, we have no time to joke. Your other identity card is sewn into the top part of your rucksack. When you get to Copenhagen, switch to that one and destroy the Olsen identity. Understand?'

He assured her he did.

'Here are your tickets. I'll travel with you on the train for the first part of your journey, as far as the ferry port. When the ferry docks, there'll be buses waiting: take the one to Odense. When you arrive there, head towards the train station. It's only a short walk. Remember what Niels has told you: act normally, don't keep turning round, and walk at an even pace. Assuming you're not being followed, a man will approach you and ask if St Canute's Cathedral is worth visiting. You are to reply that it dates back to the eleventh century. Then you will accompany him. If you suspect anything, apologise and say it is your first time in Odense.'

'And what will happen if he thinks I have been followed?'

'Then he won't approach you.'

They took the second train of the day from Esbjerg to Lunderskov, and from there it was a short bus journey to the small port, where the ferry to Funen was already waiting to cross Kolding Fjord. Prince's *legitimationskort* was checked twice on the journey: once on the train by a Danish policeman, who passed it on to a German plain-clothes officer; the second time at the port, when he was just one of three men in the queue asked to show their cards.

The atmosphere in Odense felt considerably more menacing than that in Esbjerg or elsewhere on the journey. The station forecourt was swarming with German troops and there was a palpable air of tension as soldiers pushed through a crowd that was noticeably reluctant to give them clear passage. The Danes were not exactly impeding the Germans, but nor were they making things easy for them, and there was much pushing and shoving. As the passengers from Prince's train joined the melee, matters seemed to get worse. Some of the younger German soldiers were beginning to look edgy; a woman in her fifties shouted to one of them in German that they were to show manners. *Remember where you are!*

Before he realised it, Prince found himself in the midst of a group of Germans. He'd been too distracted by what was going on around him and hadn't been watching where he was going. An officer stopped him by placing his palm against his shoulder.

'Pass!'

Prince produced it; the officer barely looked at it.

'Search him!'

A young soldier frisked him, pulling a packet of cigarettes out of a jacket pocket.

Always carry a packet of cigarettes: decent ones, mind – ideally two packets, in fact. They're a great way of relieving tension in difficult moments.

Prince could feel his throat tightening. The officer had the cigarettes now and clearly didn't want to let go of them.

'Take them, please.' As soon as he said it, he wondered if he'd gone too far, like he was obviously trying to curry favour. He was unsure whether to carry on, so he paused.

'What the hell are you waiting for, your king to turn up on horseback?'

The other soldiers laughed obediently and Prince thought it best to smile.

'Go on, fuck off!'

He hurried out of the station, everything around him giving the sense of being wreathed in gloom and fear.

The thought of what he'd do if no one turned up in Odense had occupied him throughout the ferry crossing and the subsequent bus journey. He needn't have worried: the man who eventually approached him near the station in Odense was smartly dressed and well-spoken and gave the impression of actually being pleased to see him. He told Prince to call him Marius and took him to a restaurant in the lee of the cathedral, where most of the diners were German officers. As they walked through the restaurant, he greeted some of them in German in a familiar, even friendly manner, stopping to share a noisy joke with one of them and slapping another on the shoulder. To Prince's relief, they were taken to a small area upstairs where the only other diners were a table of elderly ladies, whispering as they picked at their food like nervous birds.

'You'll stay with me tonight,' said Marius, pouring them each a glass of beer from a large bottle that had been waiting for them on the table. 'You'll find out where you're going next just prior to your journey tomorrow. Don't worry, you'll be fine. Have a cigarette.'

He lit one and handed it to him. It was a Danish habit and it gave the impression it would be discourteous to refuse. Prince had smoked more cigarettes since he'd been in Denmark than in the whole of the previous year. Marius gestured to the floor.

'Don't worry about what happened downstairs with the Germans.' He leaned back and inhaled deeply, blowing the smoke out through his nose. 'I supply them with luxuries that make their lives here a little bit easier. So they trust me, they think we're friends. I pick up information from them and that information is useful to us!' He laughed loudly, causing the elderly ladies to turn and glance disapprovingly in his direction.

'Denmark is probably the easiest assignment anywhere for a German officer at the moment: even easier than Germany itself. You know…' a pause while he finished one cigarette and lit another, then one for Prince, 'this is barely an occupation. The Germans treat us almost as a neutral country rather than one they've invaded. We pretty much run our own affairs; you're probably aware of that, eh? We have our own parliament, we have elections, the King is still the King, even our Jews are still at liberty and we hear such dreadful things about what is happening to them elsewhere in Europe. We have our police, our army… we're even allowed to keep some of our own food. To be honest, I'm not sure how long this will last. Too many Danes are complacent about it all. You've heard about the King upsetting Hitler last month?'

Prince shook his head, and they fell silent as the waiter placed plates of herring and potato salad in front of each of them. He couldn't recall they'd even been shown a menu.

'Hitler sent King Christian a lengthy telegram to congratulate him on his birthday. The King replied with just a few words – "My best thanks, King Christian", something like that. Hitler was furious, and now he's brought in a real Nazi called Werner Best to keep us in check and ordered all of our troops out of Jutland. Mark my words,' Marius put his cigarette down briefly as he forked up some herring and continued talking as he chewed it, 'next year, we'll know what an occupation feels like.'

Prince hardly slept that night. Marius was so friendly that in the early hours he decided – for no logical reason – that he'd actually been *too* friendly and this was suspicious. As a consequence, he lay awake most of the night, listening for every sound, convincing himself the Gestapo was about to hammer on the door.

The following morning, Marius told him they were about to leave for the train station. 'Here's your ticket. You're going to Nyborg. The train departs in twenty minutes. I'll walk to the station and you follow me. When we're on the main concourse, I'll go to another platform. You'll be travelling on your own; you won't see me again. When you arrive in Nyborg, a woman will be waiting by the news kiosk in front of the station. She'll be wearing a long dark red coat and a dark beret. Don't speak with her or acknowledge her at any point. Only approach the kiosk if her handbag is in her right hand, understand? At the kiosk ask for a copy of the *Berlingske* newspaper and some chocolate so she will know who you are. Christ, this sounds like something out of one of those detective novels I used to read at university in preference to Old Norse. Did you read those kinds of books?'

Prince shrugged. He thought it better to avoid the subject of detectives.

'Where were we? Ah yes, then you follow her. She'll take a bus to the port. Don't follow her once you're there. She'll go into a café; you'll buy a ticket for the ferry to Zealand.'

'And then?'

'If someone calling themselves Egon approaches you, do what they say. No more questions, please: everything is being taken care of for you.'

The train had barely pulled out of Odense station before Prince dozed off, and it was when he was woken up by the ticket inspector that he imagined Henry was opposite him. That short encounter quite unsettled him: for the remainder of the journey he leaned against the cold window, staring at the Funen countryside rushing past him. He was thoroughly depressed, bitterly regretting agreeing to this mission, cursing his willingness to please people and his inability at times to say no. He should have stayed with Henry.

At the ticket barrier in Nyborg station, his *legitimationskort* was checked again. This time he had good cause to feel singled out: as far as he could tell, no one else's card was being checked.

'Name?'

'Hans Olsen.'

'Place of birth?'

'Aarhus.' Prince felt his heart beating fast. He couldn't remember if the card said he was born in 1906 or 1908.

'Occupation?'

'Sales representative. I sell tools and—'

'Off you go.' The German soldier thrust his card back at him, a fleeting look of disappointment on his face.

The woman in the long dark red coat and dark beret was waiting by the kiosk and he duly followed her to the ferry port. The voyage across the Great Belt, the narrow strait dividing the islands of Funen and Zealand, was a choppy one, the waves tossing the small ferry in every direction, and it was with some difficulty that Prince climbed below deck, where he found an empty table. He laid the *Berlingske* in front of him and began to read it, breaking off a piece of his chocolate as he did so. After a few minutes a large man with a full and messy beard joined him, his enormous arms resting on the newspaper and taking up much of the table between them.

'I do this journey twice a week and it's a long time since I've known it as bad as this. I'm surprised we left port, to be honest. I'll tell you what: I'll swap a cigarette for some of that chocolate.'

As Prince broke off a chunk of the chocolate, he noticed the man opposite him looking around before leaning closer and speaking more quietly.

'You're going to Copenhagen?'

Prince wasn't sure how to reply. He assumed he was going to Copenhagen, but he was no longer the master of his own destiny and he didn't know if he could volunteer that information. The man lit a cigarette and handed it to him. Prince paused as a German plain-clothes officer stopped at their table.

'*Legitimationskort.*' He was talking to Prince, ignoring the other man. Prince handed over the card, relieved he'd checked the year of his birth. The German looked at it, angled it against the light, glancing back at Prince.

'Name.'

'Olsen. Hans Olsen.'

'Place of birth?'

'Aarhus.'

The German nodded; another look of disappointment as he tossed the card back on the table. 'I'd better see your card.' He'd turned to the man opposite. He gave the card a cursory glance, said nothing and moved on.

'I wonder why they picked me out?'

'There's no method to their madness. Look, I have a van on the deck full of cheese, which I'm taking to Copenhagen. I like to have company. If you give me some more chocolate, I'll drive you there.'

Prince told him that sounded like a good idea, even though he wasn't sure it was. Had he made a mistake? Seeing the boy who reminded him of Henry, and all the *legitimationskort* checks, could well have affected his judgement.

'That's a deal then. By the way, my name's Egon.'

–

Copenhagen. Richard Prince – or Marius, as his Danish relatives insisted on calling him in memory of a great-grandfather he'd never met – had never been fond of the city, though of course he knew better, even as a young child, than to express such feelings.

He'd first visited the place when he was three or four, and he and his mother would spend the whole of August there every year, so by the time he was sixteen, he'd been there a dozen times, becoming quite fluent in the language. His memories of the city were predominantly of the interminable train journeys to and from the country across northern Europe, the stifling formality of his grandparents' house, and Sundays spent at a series of services in the local Lutheran church. The smell of mothballs surrounded his grandfather, while his grandmother appeared to have sprayed her clothes in especially pungent lavender.

His grandfather had been a clerk at the enormous Carlsberg brewery in the centre of the city, but as he had worked his way up in the company, the family had moved in a similar direction through the more middle-class suburbs to the north of city. For most of Prince's childhood they'd lived in Hellerup, and his grandmother – not someone given to any obvious displays of emotion – found it hard to conceal how thrilled she was to be resident in such a smart area.

But the atmosphere in the house was a difficult one. Prince was forced to drink sour milk, which his grandmother insisted was good for him, and his grandparents were forever criticising both him and his mother. Nothing she did was good enough, and behind closed doors there were muffled arguments most evenings. She would often come to check on him in his bedroom afterwards, her eyes moist with tears, and occasionally she would make a remark along the lines of 'Maybe now you can understand why I left Denmark.'

The visits ceased in 1925 following his grandparents' deaths from influenza within days of each other. Prince's mother barely managed to disguise her relief. The last time he'd been to Copenhagen was in 1928, when he was twenty and already a sergeant. It was his cousin's wedding, and he and his parents flew from Croydon Airport to Amsterdam and from there on to Copenhagen on one of Danish Airlines' new four-engined Farmans. And now he was back.

For someone who claimed he liked to have company, Egon had been surprisingly taciturn during the two-hour drive to the city. Prince reckoned he must be nervous; it was something he'd picked up with other members of the resistance since he'd arrived in Denmark. As benign as the German occupation was, helping a British agent was still punishable by death.

At no stage in the journey did he say where they were going. As in England, there was an almost complete absence of road signs, but eventually Prince recognised where they were, passing through Brondby and entering Copenhagen through its southern suburbs, heading towards the centre. It was getting dark when they reached Vesterbro, which he remembered well: it was where the Carlsberg brewery was based, and where his grandparents had lived until they started to climb the social ladder.

Despite her obvious snobbery, his grandmother could never quite leave Vesterbro entirely behind her. Although it was a working-class area, with factories and tiny cottages, it was the place she knew best and, he sensed, the area where she felt most comfortable, where she didn't need to put on airs and graces. Most Saturdays they would take him to the Enghaveparken: if he was well behaved and sat still as they listened to whatever was being performed on the bandstand, not only would he then be allowed to visit the play area, but he would also be bought an ice cream.

Egon drove past Enghaveparken and on to Carstensgade. They were now in the north of Vesterbro and he was clearly having difficulty finding his way around. Prince was worried they were driving too slowly: nothing looked more suspicious than a vehicle crawling along, pausing too long at junctions. As they passed the street where Prince's great-aunt had lived, and then the school his grandmother had gone to and which she always made a point of showing him, he was tempted to ask Egon what he was looking for, but thought better of it. He was, he remembered, the blind man being shepherded by others.

Egon let out a sudden and triumphant 'Ah!' and turned the van sharply into a narrow entrance, driving into the centre of a neat courtyard surrounded by identical white-painted apartment blocks, each eight storeys high, with heavy wooden doors. From under his seat he removed a small package and handed it to Prince.

'These are your keys. The big one opens the main door to that block there – block D. You're to go to the top floor, to apartment 30, understand? If there is a newspaper tucked under the door of the apartment, under no circumstances enter it. Leave the building immediately. But if there's nothing under the door, use the smaller key here to enter. Lock the door when you're inside but don't bolt it. That is important. Understand?'

Prince said he understood, but Egon, whose nervousness was now all too obvious, made him repeat his instructions.

'You go in now. I have to leave.'

He had restarted the engine and reached over to open Prince's door. Prince hesitated; he wanted to ask Egon what he should do if there was a newspaper under the door. It was all very well being told to leave the building immediately, but where should he go? It was clear that Egon wasn't going to hang around to give him a lift anywhere.

'Please, you need to go in – now!'

–

When the trawler docks in Esbjerg, you will be in the hands of a Danish resistance cell we trust implicitly. Do as they say, don't ask questions. When the time is right, they will get you to Copenhagen. When you arrive there, that resistance cell will have no more to do with you. They will have done their job. From that moment, you become Agent Laertes. Once you are there, you wait. Don't be impatient. Agent Osric will find you. You may have to wait a week in the place you are taken to, maybe even longer. Agent Osric will identify themselves with the quote and you will respond with yours. I'm sure you won't have forgotten them.

The apartment block was silent, as if abandoned. Prince stood for a while trying to get a sense of the building. As he climbed the stairs, he began to hear some muffled signs of life behind the apartment doors: a baby crying in one, a piano being played in another, voices on a radio...

There were four apartments on each floor, but the top floor had a sloping ceiling and just two doors. There was no newspaper under the door of number 30. He let himself in and locked it from the inside.

—

You may have to wait a week in the place you are taken to, maybe even longer.

Prince was reconciled to having to wait for at least a week. If it was going to be less than that, he assumed they would have said so. He'd decided he would not start to worry for ten days. He was like that: not setting his sights too high, avoiding being unrealistic.

It was a small apartment, but perfectly comfortable, even quite cosy. No one had said anything about whether he should disguise the fact that he was there, which he thought was odd. He took precautions nonetheless, walking around in his socks, keeping the curtains drawn as they had been when he entered the place, not making much noise. The kitchen was well stocked: plenty of tins of fish and meat, potatoes and a box of vegetables, biscuits, even a large cake in a tin with a picture of a castle on the lid. In the bedroom someone had laid out clothes more or less his size on the bed.

The first thing he did after looking round the flat was to unpick the lining of his rucksack and remove the Jesper Holm identity that had been sewn in there. He then stood by the kitchen sink trying to gather his thoughts. Hans Olsen felt reliable: he'd got through four identity checks and he was reluctant to confine him to ash. But his instructions had been clear, so he cut up the *legitimationskort* he'd used since Esbjerg, and all the papers that went with it, and dropped them in the sink before setting light to them.

He was now Jesper Holm again, an accountant from Copenhagen. The fact that he'd always been bad at mathematics felt like the least of his concerns.

Doing nothing for hours on end in the half-light of the day and the dark of the night had a strangely relaxing effect, especially for someone who was always on the go and hated wasting his time. He ought to have been on the edge of his nerves: a British agent in enemy territory, on his own in an apartment with papers unlikely to fool the Gestapo for very long. He must have been through the hands of a dozen members of the resistance since landing in Esbjerg – plus the men on the trawler – and all it needed was for just one of them to be arrested to bring the rest down like dominos. He didn't like the fact that the plainly nervous Egon knew where he was, though Hendrie had given him a long talk about how he mustn't look for flaws he could do nothing about, because no espionage operation was ever flawless.

But the isolation had the opposite effect: he felt calm, able to sit for long periods of time in the large armchair doing little more than allowing his mind to wander in no particular direction. Inevitably it often wandered in the direction of his family. On the second afternoon he was convinced Jane was sitting opposite him, but he didn't feel any pain – not even when he saw little Grace next to her – just the warmth of Henry sitting on his knee, his head leaning back against his shoulder.

On his fifth night in the apartment, he woke in the early hours of the morning, wondering if he'd heard some movement outside the bedroom. He checked his watch, which showed it was just after three, and listened carefully, his ears so attuned he imagined he could hear all kinds of noise. He thought about getting up, but it was so cold he decided against it, and after ten minutes or so he fell back into a doze, still in the half-sitting position he'd hauled himself into.

He was still in that position when the bedroom door opened, the person framed in the doorway barely lit by the light from the kitchen.

'Who is it?' Foolishly, he spoke in English. He quickly repeated the question, this time in Danish. He could hear the fear in his own voice, his mouth and throat dry.

'*Your lordship is right welcome back to Denmark.*'

He found himself breathing fast and realised he was gripping the sheet, as if to prevent himself from falling off the bed. This was the first line of the code Agent Osric was to use, the code he was meant to respond to. But hearing the voice had shocked him, and in his confusion, he had to think carefully about his reply, despite having rehearsed it a dozen times each day.

'*I am satisfied in nature, whose motive in this case should stir me most to my revenge.*'

It was like being back at school, forced to the front of the class to reluctantly recite Shakespeare.

Osric took a step into the room. '*How is it, Laertes?*'

He was ready now with his response, the final part of the code. '*Why, as a woodcock to mine own springe, Osric. I am justly killed with mine own treachery.*'

Agent Osric turned on the bedroom light. 'Let's hope not.'

'What do you mean?'

'That bit about your own treachery. He wouldn't approve, would he?'

'Who?'

'Oh, come on – your William Shakespeare. He wouldn't approve of us changing Hamlet round like that, would he?'

Prince was out of bed now and putting on his dressing gown. He couldn't take his eyes off Osric. 'I think Shakespeare would approve; he'd understand the circumstances.' He realised he was talking too fast.

He followed Osric into the small lounge, where they sat facing each other, working out what each was about.

'But I'm not sure,' said Prince, 'Shakespeare would have wholly approved of the part of Osric being played by a woman.'

She laughed, tossing her head back and allowing her long dark hair to fall on either side of her shoulders.

Prince had assumed Agent Osric would be a man: nothing they'd told him in England had given him cause to believe otherwise. He was worried his obvious surprise might be seen as disapproval. She was perhaps in her mid-thirties, more or less the same age as him. She had dark eyes, which darted around, a noticeable turn to her lips, and jet-black hair. She spoke with a cultured Copenhagen accent, and as friendly as she appeared, there was an almost familiar authority to her voice. She was, unquestionably, someone who was accustomed to telling people what to do.

Chapter 6

'We need to have a proper talk.' Agent Osric leaned back in her armchair, relaxed but alert, her eyes carefully working him out. She'd propped her right elbow on the arm of the chair, holding it upright so her lit cigarette pointed to the ceiling, a spiral of grey-blue smoke looking as if it came from her forefinger.

Prince leaned forward, ready to concentrate on what she was about to say.

'Not now,' she continued, 'it's far too late. Or too early: I never really know whether four o'clock in the morning counts as early or late.' She looked at Prince as if she half expected him to decide for her.

'But there's a curfew, isn't there? How could you get here during the curfew?' Prince hesitated, worried he might be sounding anxious.

'We'll talk about all these things in the morning, or at least later in the morning. I need to get some sleep before then. I've been up since six o'clock; that's getting on twenty-four hours.'

'How come?'

'Work.'

'What do you do?'

'Later: we'll talk about all that later. There are two things I want to say before I get some sleep. Firstly, this is the last time we speak in English. It's too risky and I'm told your Danish is excellent. You need to be speaking it all the time, though. You must get out of the habit of speaking English. Understand? *Forsta?*'

Prince nodded and said he understood. What was the second thing she wanted to mention?

'How about you sleep on that couch and I take the bed?'

-

When Richard Prince had joined the police as an enthusiastic eighteen-year-old, he'd spent the first few months after his initial training on the beat. He didn't last long walking the streets of Lincoln: early on, his superiors spotted him as a very bright grammar school boy who could easily have gone to university and clearly was destined for greater things. Before he'd completed his first year in the police, he was already a detective.

Life on the beat, as brief as it was, had a pre-ordained quality to it. Pinned on the inside of his bedroom door in his lodging house was his rota: he knew weeks in advance whether on any given day he'd be on a shift starting at six in the morning, two in the afternoon or ten at night. And when he arrived to start his shift at the police station in Church Lane, in the lee of the cathedral, the large board by the duty sergeant's desk informed him which beat he'd been allocated to: West Common; South Commons; Castle & Cathedral; Station and St Mark's; Canwick; Washingborough, or one of half a dozen others. And then there were the carefully drawn maps of each beat he'd tuck inside his notebook, showing a suggested route, which streets to pay special attention to, and the pubs to keep an eye on.

As his career progressed, he was pleased he'd moved on from the regimented life of being told where to go and when to go there. But in recent years he'd had more mixed views: perhaps having your life carefully mapped out weeks in advance was not such a bad thing. Being moved around Lincoln like a piece on a chessboard had its attractions.

Now he felt like a chess piece in Copenhagen.

He was woken at seven thirty by the noise of running water in the kitchen and crockery being moved around. He hauled himself up from the sofa and caught a glimpse of Agent Osric wrapped just in a large towel. Moments later she came into the lounge, still draped in the towel, her hair wet, a lit cigarette sticking out of her mouth and a tray in her hands, which she placed on the small table by his sofa.

'This coffee isn't bad; it's about as good as you'll get in Denmark these days. Drink it while I get dressed. Then we can talk.'

When she returned, she was dressed but her hair was still damp. She ran her fingers through it as she relaxed in the armchair, her legs casually folded under her. She lit another cigarette, then paused briefly to drink her coffee in one go, all the while watching him and sizing him up in a manner that felt familiar but which he couldn't quite put his finger on. She didn't say a word, and when she'd finished her cigarette, she dropped the stub into the remains of her coffee and lit yet another. Only then did she speak.

'You show me yours and I'll show you mine.' This was followed by a quick smile.

'I beg your pardon?'

'Don't look so shocked. It's a saying, though maybe it doesn't have the same meaning in English. It's a childish way of saying you tell me about yourself and I'll tell you about myself.'

'Are we allowed to do that?'

She shifted in the armchair and waved her hand in front of her in a dismissive manner. 'Look, we're going to be working very closely together. Do you imagine we'll be going round Copenhagen with you addressing me as Agent Osric? You don't think that could sound suspicious?'

'I suppose you're right. So what do I call you?'

She unfurled her legs and straightened herself up, leaning closer to him. She examined the end of her half-finished cigarette and placed it on the saucer of her coffee cup. 'The way I operate is by deciding whether I trust someone or not, and if I do, by being very honest with them. But I set out rules, the code by which we'll operate. You understand that?'

Prince nodded, though he wasn't absolutely certain he did.

'I'll explain: London would have told you they trust me totally. I'm very secure, I operate on my own. My links with the Danish resistance are indirect and very much on my terms. London clearly think that using me to plant the occasional bomb or find out which German units are in which garrison is a waste of my talents. So I've been totally undercover. My only contact with them has been through the MI6 station in Sweden, and even that has been intermittent. But because I know no one in Copenhagen suspects me, I have to be certain that whoever I work with here is safe. I have to know I can trust them. I cannot afford to be compromised.'

She reached out for the cigarette, checked it was still alight and inhaled deeply.

'I've watched this apartment ever since you arrived. Indeed, I was even keeping my eyes on you when you got here. If you'd been followed or if you were a traitor, believe me, I'd have known. So now I'll be open with you. Come.'

She stood up and beckoned him to follow her into the kitchen. She went over to the sink and turned on the taps. 'Perhaps an unnecessary precaution, but who knows? This is the only time I will tell you my real name. You are never to use it. That should be obvious, but the reason I tell you is because sometimes not knowing something can be more dangerous than knowing it. And by the same logic, knowing my true identity could also help you. It is a difficult judgement to make, I accept that. London would be horrified, but they're not here, are they? My name is Hanne Jakobsen. In case you're wondering, I'm not married. Apart from my elderly father, I have no one in the way of family. You now tell me as much or as little about yourself as you see fit, but I have to know the identity they've given you – obviously.'

Prince passed his *legitimationskort* to her. She examined it carefully, holding it up to the light, dabbing it with water, even sniffing it before finally allowing an approving nod.

'This is very good. So you're Jesper Holm, an accountant from Copenhagen. I presume you had no problems with it on your journey across Denmark?'

'I didn't use it.'

'How come?'

'My contact in Esbjerg felt I should use another identity for that journey. I had papers in the name of Hans Olsen, a sales representative from Aarhus.'

'And everything was fine?'

'Yes… I was stopped quite a few times, but there didn't seem to be any problem when they checked the *legitimationskort*.'

'And what happened to Hans Olsen?'

Prince tapped the sink. 'He ended up as ashes in here.'

She frowned. 'That was probably a mistake. It's a shame to waste a good identity. Never mind, Jesper Holm is good too. You don't need to tell me about your life in England, but do tell me this: is this your first operation?'

'Yes and no. It's my first overseas operation, but I was involved in an operation back in England. I caught a Nazi spy and his British contact. I was a police officer; I suppose I still am a police officer. On secondment, I think you'd call it.'

'A police officer – but so am I!'

'Really?'

'Don't sound so surprised, Jesper Holm. In Denmark we have many female police officers and we don't just look after cases to do with children. I investigate some very serious crimes. I hold a senior rank.'

'What is that?'

'It's called a *vicepolitiinspektor* – I'm not sure what the equivalent is in England. Tell me your rank.'

'I'm a superintendent – a detective superintendent. It sounds as if I might outrank you!'

She shot him a disapproving look. 'Well, we'll see about that. We need to talk about your mission. What have you been told?'

Prince hesitated. 'I'm not sure how much I'm...'

'Look: we have to trust each other. This is the only way the mission will work. Let me help you. Agent Horatio...'

'I've been told he's a Danish businessman whose work frequently takes him to Berlin. Apparently on a recent trip there he came across intelligence about the German rocket programme. Up to now he's been handled by Stockholm, but London want him to be run from Copenhagen; they think that'll be safer. My job – our job – is to find him, decide whether we think he's genuine and then run him. London is desperate for whatever intelligence he has on the rockets.'

Hanne had turned the taps off as Prince spoke and walked back into the lounge. 'And do you know any more about him?'

'No. I don't even know his name or where he lives; I was told you'd know that. Once we're ready, I'm to approach him in the street and ask him where the Amalienborg Palace is and—'

'Hang on. Jesper Holm is from Copenhagen and he doesn't know where the Amalienborg Palace is? Couldn't they have come up with something more imaginative?'

'Maybe, but we can't change it now. I ask him where the Amalienborg Palace is, and he is to reply asking whether I'd prefer to approach it from Frederiksgade or Amaliegade, then I say, whichever one is nearer to the church with the big dome.'

'Very well then – it's not the way I'd have chosen to do it, but there we are. I've already checked out Agent Horatio and I'm as sure as I can be that he's genuine. He's a businessman called Otto Knudsen, fifty-three years of age, lives on his own in a smart apartment block in Gammelholm, overlooking the Nyhavn canal in the centre of the city. He doesn't have a criminal record and because of this we don't have too much on him, but thanks to the Gestapo, we have records of political affiliations in the 1930s at our headquarters, and certainly at the time of the general election in 1935, he was registered as a supporter of the social democrats. I was also able to check the municipal records, which show he was divorced many years ago and has no children. He works for a specialist engineering company based in Copenhagen called Mortensen Machinery Parts. He's a salesman, and this job takes him to the other Scandinavian countries and into Germany. He therefore had good reason to be in Berlin and an excuse to be in Stockholm, where he contacted the intelligence people at the embassy. Stockholm gave us the dates he told them he was last in Berlin – the trip where he claims to have found out about the rockets. He told them he flew there. I have a friend who works at Kastrup airport; we were at police college together. I've told her I'm working on a sensitive case and she's promised to let me see the passenger lists covering that period.'

'And then?'

'Is that the time? I need to get a move on, I really do. I need to be in the office at half eight. If it turns out Otto Knudsen did fly to and from Berlin when he says he did, I have one more check to make on him. If he still looks trustworthy after that, then you can approach him. Hopefully in three days we should know one way or the other. Until then, you stay here.'

—

It was six in the evening by the time Vicepolitiinspektor Hanne Jakobsen arrived at Kastrup airport on Amager island, south of the city centre. There'd been no flights for a few hours, but the small police station next to the terminal building was still open. Her friend Margrethe was the officer in charge; she'd sent one of the other three officers on duty for a meal break and told the other two to check the terminal building. She led Hanne into her office.

'You have half an hour, Hanne, no more than that, though it's extremely rare for the Germans to come in here. There are plenty around when there are flights, and they patrol the runway and perimeter, of course, but it's best to be quick in any event. You asked for all of August, right?'

'Yes.'

'They're all here.' She tapped two large ledgers on her desk. 'The blue book is passengers leaving, the green one passengers arriving. These are just for Danish citizens, you realise that? Germans and other nationalities are in other books. There's a separate one for Jews, even though they're allowed to travel.'

'I'm only interested in Danish nationals, thank you.'

'You don't need to tell me anything, of course, but just in case anyone asks anything, though that's highly unlikely...'

'Just say it's a financial crime. Hopefully they'll find that boring. I'll be fine on my own, thanks, Margrethe.'

She'd written nothing down, of course, but she remembered every detail of her conversation with George Weston. Weston was the MI6 head of station in neutral Sweden, who'd inherited Hanne when MI6 hurriedly shut down its operation in Copenhagen at the start of the war. On a visit to Stockholm in 1940, he'd told her to lie low. *No one knows about you. Let's keep it like that, eh? Don't do anything that's going to draw attention to yourself. I'll call you when I need you, and when I do, rest assured it will be most urgent.*

Weston had been counting the months to his retirement when the war started, but his fluency in Swedish and Danish ensured he was too valuable to let go. Having spent the two or three years prior to the war becoming increasingly raddled in appearance and testy in spirit, he'd now found a second wind and was enjoying every moment. At the end of October 1942, he'd summoned Hanne to Stockholm. They met in the main bar of the Grand Hotel on Södra Blasieholmshamnen and exchanged pleasantries. He insisted she try a turquoise-coloured cocktail, his hand resting on her knee, even when she tried to move it. 'Part of the cover, dear: be a good girl, eh?' He continued in that manner once they left the hotel and walked by the harbour towards Skeppsholmsbron.

'Danish chap popped in to see us the other day. Move a bit closer, dear.' His arm reached round her waist, guiding her towards him. He allowed it to rest on her backside. 'There we are. Now we don't look like a couple having a row, do we?'

'I'm young enough to be your daughter!' she'd replied.

'All the more reason to look lovey-dovey, eh? Now this Danish chap – we're calling him Agent Horatio, by the way – sells ball bearings. I'm not terribly sure what they do, come to think of it, but evidently, he's important enough to travel outside Denmark to sell the bloody things. Smile as I talk to you, dear, perhaps link your arm in mine. That's it. He told me he'd spent the first week of August in Berlin, and while there he'd picked up some intelligence about these long-range rockets the Germans are developing. London are terribly excited, practically wetting themselves. They want to know more about this chap and then ensure we run him as an agent. I've told them to calm down. Chap's a walk-in after all, and I'm most sceptical about people who wander in off the street and offer us intelligence. Having said that, he did come across as credible, and although the fact that he waited the best part of three months to make contact is annoying, it actually rather works in his favour. Apparently he was waiting until he had a business trip to Stockholm, so that makes sense. Anyway, London insists we make contact with this chap. The first thing you need to do is check out his story. Best to start with his visit to Germany in August.'

'What do you mean?' she'd asked.

'Check he actually made it. I'm not certain of the dates, but he did say "Four nights in the Reich is as much as anyone can manage", so it's a reasonable supposition that he flew out on Monday the third, returning on the seventh. You'll find an envelope in your handbag, dear; in it are Horatio's details. You'll obviously destroy it once you've committed them to memory. And there's one other thing...' He had paused and looked around. 'Assuming Horatio turns out to be who he says he is,

London plan to send out an agent. They think running Horatio will be a full-time operation – too much for you to cope with along with your job. Your role will be to look after this agent. Should be rather splendid for you to have some company!'

Now she checked the blue ledger for the names of all passengers on the daily 10.00 Deutsche Lufthansa direct to Berlin. Otto Knudsen's name wasn't there on Monday the 3rd or indeed any other day that week. She checked the previous week, but he wasn't there either. She turned to the green ledger for returning Danish citizens and checked the 18.05 flight from Berlin: no sign of Knudsen. It looked as if his story was about to fall apart. They should have asked her to check him out before sending Agent Laertes over. Reluctantly she called her colleague into the office.

'I'm sorry to involve you, Margrethe, but the person I'm looking for was supposed to be on direct Deutsche Lufthansa flights to and from Berlin, but I can't find his name anywhere.'

Margrethe leaned across, flicking the pages of the ledger. 'Here, there is another direct Deutsche Lufthansa flight, but it shows as the Oslo service. It leaves Oslo at 14.55, lands here at 16.44, then takes off again for Berlin at 17.25, landing there at... here... 19.25. Same with the return: it leaves Berlin at 8.40 in the morning, lands here two hours later and forty minutes after that flies on to Oslo. A lot of people prefer this flight.'

And sure enough, on Monday 3 August, an Otto Knudsen was on the Oslo/Copenhagen flight to Berlin, returning from the German capital that Friday on the Copenhagen/Oslo flight. Even more helpfully, the ledger also contained his *legitimationskort* number.

–

Now she'd established that Knudsen's journey to Berlin was indeed as he'd described it, there was, as she'd told the Englishman, just one more check she needed to make.

Knudsen lived in an apartment in one of the elegant six-storey painted houses on the Nyhavn canal. The building was on the south side of the canal, on the block between Heibergsgade and the Nyhavnsbroen bridge. It wasn't difficult for her to gain access to Knudsen's top-floor apartment. It took her just a minute to pick the lock, and she allowed herself ten minutes to look around.

She wasn't searching for anything in particular, but she'd developed a good sense for whether something wasn't right. For a start, there were no obvious signs that this was where a German sympathiser might live. The bookshelf contained no right-wing literature; there was nothing on his desk that appeared suspicious. The apartment was clearly that of an affluent man: well-kept and clean, with good furniture. She checked the drawers in the bedroom: a few letters and papers, nothing unexpected. There were three large paintings in the lounge, modern interpretations of boats on the canal.

Her ten minutes were up. Her gut feeling was still that Knudsen was who he'd said he was. Nothing she'd seen in his home disabused her of that.

Agent Laertes could now approach him.

-

She returned to the apartment off Carstensgade around eight in the evening, entering it so silently, as always, that he was aware of her presence only when she appeared in the lounge. There were few pleasantries; she only wanted to know everything was in order. She was concerned with security: any strange noises outside the apartment, that kind of thing. Then it was down to business.

'From what I can tell, Agent Horatio is genuine, although of course that can't be guaranteed. I've watched him the last two mornings and he appears to have a routine – the time he leaves his apartment, the route he takes to his office, the café he stops at on the way for breakfast. You'll bump into him on that route; I've identified the best place to do it. I'll explain.'

Prince could feel his heart beating fast. It was a feeling of fear mixed with a growing excitement. It also meant he'd be able to leave an apartment he'd been confined to for too long. The walls had begun to close in on him.

'When will I be bumping into him?'

'Tomorrow morning.'

–

From the north bank of the Nyhavn canal he watched Otto Knudsen leave his building on the south bank. Everything was precisely as Hanne had described it. Knudsen, a tall, smartly dressed man in a dark trilby-style hat with a wide brim and a long light brown raincoat, left the building a shade after eight o'clock. He turned left and walked briskly along the canal, past the junction with Heibergsgade and towards Kongens Nytorv, a large square where Prince recalled having lunch with his grandparents in another life.

Agent Horatio will enter the square and turn right. He'll then turn left and go into one of the cafés on the north side. If you follow him, you'll be able to see where he goes. Try and approach him as he goes into the café. If it doesn't feel right, wait until he leaves it.

Prince fell into step with the other man. As they approached Kongens Nytorv, Knudsen quickened his step. Only when it was too late did Prince notice a queue in front of him on the north side of the canal, as Nyhavn joined the square.

It was a German checkpoint.

He had no alternative but to stay in the queue, gathering his thoughts as he did so. He realised he now wouldn't be able to pick up Knudsen before he entered the café. Hopefully he'd be able to spot which one he was in and approach after he'd left it. He tried to remain calm. He was confident he knew every aspect of his Jesper Holm identity; after all, he'd had plenty of time in the apartment to study it over and over again.

And he remembered what he'd been told in Matlock: *Check-points are routine in occupied Europe. Unfortunately, they're part of everyday life. The most important thing to remember about a checkpoint is not to panic. Do not under any circumstances try and leave the queue – they watch out for people doing precisely that.*

So he waited his turn, agreeing with the old man next to him that it was indeed warm for the time of year and smiling perhaps a shade too pleasantly at the German sentry who hurried them along. The soldier appeared to be suffering from a heavy cold, wiping his dripping nose with the sleeve of his greatcoat. He looked at Prince's identity card, then at Prince himself, and once more at the card.

'Name?'

'Jesper Holm.' He wondered whether to add 'sir' but decided against it.

'Let me have a look.' A short German wearing civilian clothes moved forward, one of a group of three observing the checkpoint: Gestapo. The soldier handed him the *legitimationskort* and he studied it carefully, then looked at Prince, appearing to go onto his tiptoes to get a better view. He turned round and said something to his colleagues, and before Prince could fully grasp what was going on, his arms had been grabbed from either side and he was being hauled away. He must have pulled against them, because a fist punched him hard in the ribs and he doubled up.

By the time someone spat in his ear that he was under arrest, he'd already gathered that might well be the case.

Chapter 7

Copenhagen, November 1942

He'd been blindfolded and bundled into the back of a car, so had no idea where they were going. His only impression of the vehicle was the tan-coloured seats he'd glimpsed under the blindfold and the aroma of leather and stale tobacco.

There was a man on either side of him and another in the front alongside the driver; he was able to work that out from the different voices as they argued about where he should be taken, clearly unaware he spoke German.

'I'm telling you, we take him to our headquarters on Kampmannsgade. There's no question about him. This is so clearly a case for the Gestapo. This name has been on our watch list!'

'But the protocol is that all Danish citizens have to be processed by the local police first – you know that as well as I do, Klaus. The last thing we want is another row with these precious Danes.'

'But according to our information, he's probably not Danish. Let's go straight to Kampmannsgade and *then* deal with the bloody Danes. We're far too sensitive about their feelings as it is.'

'Look, let's go to the main police headquarters on Polititorvet, get him processed as a priority and then we can have him back at our place within an hour.'

–

Having that conversation in front of him had been their first mistake, the first of a number the Gestapo made that day. The second was throwing him in a cell with someone else in it, a boy around eighteen years of age with a mop of blonde hair and a large bruise under one eye that he wore like a badge of honour. He told Prince he'd been arrested for throwing an apple core at a German armoured car. Prince told him he had no idea why he'd been arrested: a misunderstanding over his *legitimationskort* perhaps. He wasn't even sure where he was.

'This is the main police headquarters on Polititorvet. At least they've brought you here. If they offer you an all-expenses stay at the Gestapo place on Kampmannsgade, turn them down.' The boy came and sat next to him on his bench and spoke quietly in a conspiratorial manner. 'Do you have anything to worry about?'

'I'm not sure what you mean.'

'I mean, you say they arrested you over your *legitimationskort*. Was that at a checkpoint?'

'Yes.'

'And did they arrest anyone else?'

'Not as far as I could tell.'

'And your identity... do you have anything to be concerned about it? I mean, is it genuine?'

At Matlock they'd told him to be careful of plants, seemingly sympathetic people who'd appear to be your friend, on the same side, and who'd lure you into revealing too much. With his innocent looks and obvious pride in his bruise, the boy didn't look like a plant, but Prince knew he couldn't risk it.

'Of course it's genuine – why wouldn't it be?'

–

Perhaps they'd realised their mistake, because soon after that, he was moved to another cell, this time on his own. It was tiny, lit only by a small amount of daylight diffused through the opaque window. The darkness and the solitude gave him time to reflect.

He remembered Gilbey's warning – *The Gestapo see through most cover stories, sooner or later* – and realised he needed to act fast.

His opportunity came half an hour later, when he was marched up two floors and into an empty interview room, one not wholly dissimilar to the ones he'd spent so much of his career in. A Danish policeman guided him to a chair on one side of a large wooden table and secured one part of his handcuffs to the side of the chair.

In the corridor outside, an argument was being conducted in German. Someone was telling another person to get on with it. The other person replied in poor German that he'd be as quick as possible but there was a procedure to follow. Moments later, that person came into the room: a tall man in plain clothes carrying a large notebook. He seemed nervous as he sat opposite Prince, constantly adjusting his wire-framed spectacles, all the while nervously coughing. As he opened the notebook, Prince could see his Jesper Holm *legitimationskort* interleaved between the pages.

'Your name is Jesper Holm.' It sounded like a statement rather than a question, but Prince nodded nonetheless. Then every detail on the *legitimationskort* was checked: profession, address, date of birth.

More questions: where did he work; his father's name; his mother's name; which school he'd gone to. As nervous as he was, Prince had little trouble answering.

'The problem is that for reasons they don't share with us' – Prince detected a hint of bitterness – 'the Gestapo not only had the name Jesper Holm on a watch list, but also a description matching you, and that means we really have a very limited role in dealing with you, I'm afraid.'

A long pause. *I'm afraid* – a hint of sympathy, possibly.

'In a case where the Gestapo has an interest in a suspect, our job is simply to process you – fill in a few forms – and then hand you over to them. That way we maintain the pretence that the Germans aren't really our occupiers.' The man held up his hands as if to indicate there was no more he could do.

Prince knew full well that the Jesper Holm identity was unlikely to survive a Gestapo interrogation. The fact that they were looking for someone who matched his description would explain why he'd been stopped so often on the journey from Esbjerg. Fortunately, the man they'd stopped then was Hans Olsen rather than the Jesper Holm they were looking for.

'I'm sorry.' The Danish policeman sounded sincere, allowing an embarrassed smile to cross his face. 'Would you like a cigarette?'

In the apartment, when she'd surprised Prince by telling him her real name, Hanne had justified it by saying that knowing her true identity might help him. Now he was about to put that to the test. He leaned across the table as far as the handcuffs would allow, looking up into the face of the police officer as he coughed nervously once more.

'I need your help.'

The policeman's eyes widened, more in fear than anything else.

'It's essential I avoid the Gestapo. I have a contact with you – with the police. I beg you to tell that person I'm here. I'm risking my life telling you this… and theirs.'

A long silence. The man's eyes narrowed. He removed his spectacles, studied them, then put them on again. 'You're risking my life too, telling me this. Who is your contact?'

Maybe he should be brave. Maybe he should risk a Gestapo interrogation after all. He could rely on his cover story, and if that failed, at least he could protect Agent Osric and Agent Horatio. They were more important than him. He'd sacrifice himself. But then he thought of his son and realised he had to do everything he could to escape.

'Hanne Jakobsen – Vicepolitiinspektor Hanne Jakobsen.'

The policeman leaned forward in shock. 'Hanne? Hanne is involved with you?' His hands were shaking. He closed his notebook and opened it again, clearly unsure of what to do or how to react.

'Would you know how to contact her?'

'She's two floors above us.'

–

After that, the Gestapo made another mistake. The policeman went into the corridor and in poor German informed the waiting Gestapo officer that there was a minor problem and he needed to get a colleague to sort it out. It shouldn't take too long. They wouldn't want the paperwork to be incorrect.

'Hurry up,' had been the response. And then the Gestapo officer decided it had taken long enough already and he was going to get something to eat. 'It's twelve fifteen now. I'll be back at one to collect him: paperwork or no paperwork!'

Once the Gestapo officer left, Hanne was summoned. She seemed remarkably calm when she entered the room. Certainly she shot Prince a disapproving look, but it was more like a parental look of disappointment rather than one of anger.

'Give me a minute, please, Jens,' she said to her colleague. Once the policeman had left, she sat opposite Prince. 'So what happened?'

He explained.

'And it couldn't have been Agent Horatio informing them?'

'I can't possibly see how – he'd have had no idea I was following him from the other side of the canal. And the check-point was a random one; the queue was already quite long when I joined it.'

She nodded. 'Nonetheless, it seems the name Jesper Holm was on a watch list and you match a description they had. You must have been betrayed. We have to get you out of here.' She chewed a nail and looked at her watch. 'We have half an hour at the most. Let's see what we can do. I can't tell you how fortunate it is Jens was questioning you. He's a friend and I trust him. I can't say that of everyone here.'

He was left on his own for five minutes, still handcuffed to the chair. When Hanne returned, it was with Jens and two uniformed Danish policemen. The handcuffs were released and Hanne explained the plan.

'Go with these two officers. They'll drop you somewhere safe. You know where to return to. Once there, stay put. Wait until I come, which may not be today. Understand?'

He was hurried down to the basement and into the back of an unmarked van. The van drove around for an hour, then it stopped, the rear doors opened and he was told to get out quick. Without so much as a goodbye, he was on his own, by the entrance to Enghaveparken. Ten minutes later, he was in the apartment off Carstensgade. Only when he locked the door and sank into the armchair did he appreciate the state he was in: drenched in sweat, his heart beating fast, mouth dry, and alternating feelings of dizziness and nausea. He was about to get up for some water when a wave of emotion hit him in a way he hadn't experienced, not even when told of Jane and Grace's deaths.

This was not so much shock, more profound fear and sadness. He thought of Henry and whether he'd ever see him again. He realised how close he'd come to falling into the hands of the Gestapo. The fact that he had apparently been betrayed only added to the emotion, and for a full hour he sat in the armchair and, for the first time since he was a child, sobbed his heart out.

–

At police headquarters on Polititorvet that afternoon, various careers came to rapid ends. When the Gestapo officer returned from his meal break and found Prince was missing, Jens was summoned. He explained, with an admirable degree of plausibility, how there had clearly been a misunderstanding. He had assumed that once he'd sorted the paperwork – which thankfully he had – he was to send the suspect direct to the Gestapo headquarters on Kampmannsgade.

'So he's there now?'

'Yes – he must be.'

A delay while calls were made. There was, it transpired, no sign of the suspect at Kampmannsgade. What arrangements had been made to transfer the suspect?

He'd been sent down to prisoner transport, explained Jens. Prisoner transport, it transpired, had undergone a shift change. It would take some time to check exactly what had happened to the suspect. It was possible he might have been put on a transport to Roskilde, by mistake of course.

It was around this time that the Gestapo officer – a squat man with bad skin and a distinctive Swabian accent – began to realise how much he was to blame for the suspect going missing. He knew full well he should not have left the prisoner on his own. Going for a meal break, notwithstanding his considerable hunger, was tantamount to desertion.

When his senior officer arrived at the police headquarters, he took a similar view. The squat Gestapo officer with bad skin and a Swabian accent was dismissed on the spot. At one point his senior officer pinned him against the wall. 'I promise you that within twenty-four hours you will be on your way to the Eastern Front: see how many fucking meal breaks you get there!'

Jens's boss agreed that his officer had, quite uncharacteristically, made a serious error, albeit one arising through a misunderstanding. Jens would of course resign and no further action would be taken against him.

And all this time Hanne Jakobsen was not involved. Her name was never mentioned, and the Gestapo had no idea who she was.

They decided this was an example of typical Danish incompetence. They'd find Jesper Holm sooner or later anyway, and at least they now knew he was in Copenhagen. After all, how long could a British agent survive once his identity had been blown?

Early the following evening, Hanne appeared, as silently as ever. She looked for all the world like a busy housewife returning home, a shopping bag in each hand and even a pleasant smile to greet him. But she didn't say a word until she'd double-bolted the front door and led him into the lounge, taking her usual seat in the large armchair, tucking her legs under her and lighting a cigarette.

'I cannot believe we got away with that,' she said eventually, shaking her head in disbelief. There was another period of silence, during which she pulled hard on her cigarette before finishing it and lighting another one. Prince began to say something, but she held up a hand, as if stopping traffic. *Wait, let me speak.* 'Thank Christ I told you my real name. I knew it was a risk, but if I hadn't… who knows what the Gestapo would have done to you by now. And who knows what you'd have told them.'

'You can trust me, I wouldn't have—'

'Wouldn't have what – told them anything? Listen: those bastards at Kampmannsgade have broken the most hardened resistance fighters in a matter of hours. You cannot begin to imagine what they do to you. By now, everything could have been blown – you, me, Agent Horatio, the people who helped you in Esbjerg and on the way here. As it is…'

She paused again, walked over to the window and pulled the drawn curtains aside before returning to her chair.

'As it is… what?'

'As it is, the situation is bad enough. Potentially, I'm compromised. Fortunately, Jens is to be trusted: he won't say anything. He's not a well man and he wasn't far from retirement as it is, so for him to lose his job over this is a very small price to pay. He's the only one who's really aware of my connection with you.'

'What about the policemen who drove me back to Vesterbro?'

'I didn't say we were safe, did I?' She sounded annoyed. 'Jens said they're trustworthy, but who knows? In any case, it wasn't as if they dropped you here, was it? Our real worry is you. Tell me again what happened this morning: everything.'

Prince told her every detail, and she listened thoughtfully. When he had finished, she went into the kitchen, came back with a glass of water, walked round the apartment, back into the kitchen and then came to sit down before starting her now familiar cigarette routine.

'We need to get you a new identity. But the fact that they know what you look like is a concern. The only way we can do it is by changing your appearance. Your hair is quite dark, especially for a Scandinavian. We can certainly make it lighter; that should be easy enough. Have you ever grown a beard?'

'No.'

'Any idea how long it would take you to grow one? It would need to be a proper one, though.'

Prince was stroking his chin, trying to assess how long it would take. 'I don't know really. My guess is at least three weeks, perhaps a month.'

'Very well then: I'll get a message to Weston in Stockholm and he can tell London there's been a delay. They don't need to know more than that; they'll just have to be patient. I'll speak to someone about a new *legitimationskort*, but we can't actually prepare it until we can get a photograph of you with lighter hair and a beard. In the meantime, you stay here. You'll just have to be patient. Would you like a cigarette?'

'I would actually, thank you.'

She lit one and passed it to him, noticing as she did so how his hands were trembling. 'Are you all right?'

'Yes, thank you.'

'You don't look all right.'

Prince looked down at the rug between them, his eyes filling with tears as he did so. He watched as a couple of them dripped onto the ornate pattern, and then wiped his eyes.

'No, it's just been a terrible shock, that's all. I'm sure I'll be fine.'

Hanne said nothing, but she leaned forward and wiped a tear from under his eye with her thumb.

–

Hanne's work was split between the police headquarters in Polititorvet and the police station in the Nørrebro district, where the unit investigating high-value robberies was based. A week after sending the message to London via Weston in Stockholm, she made one of her regular lunchtime visits to the Assistens cemetery.

The cemetery was a popular place to visit. Some people came to see Hans Christian Andersen's grave and those of other notables, but most just came to enjoy the grounds, with their avenues of tall trees and well-tended shrubberies. It was particularly popular at lunchtime, and so there was nothing unusual in Hanne strolling round, picking a quiet bench to eat her sandwich or just looking for some peace and quiet amongst the graves.

She made a point of going there every two or three days, though for obvious reasons she avoided having a routine. On this particular day she entered the cemetery on Jagtvej and strolled for ten minutes or so before pausing for her lunch. There were three graves she needed to see, none of them belonging to notable people. The first was clear, but the second – chosen like the other two for its shaded setting – had a chalk mark on the side of the stone. It was not obvious and was hard to make out, so much so that she had to go to the rear of the stone to check for a second, more distinct mark. It was there: a casually drawn chevron. It confirmed that a message would be waiting for her elsewhere. She would now have to try and get away from work a bit earlier than planned. Checking that no one was watching, she took off her scarf, spat on a corner of it and quickly erased the marks.

On her way home, she got off the bus a stop before her normal one and went into the small grocery store to buy some apples. By the time she'd left the shop, she was sure no one had spotted her. She hurried along until she came to the abandoned warehouse. She allowed herself one glance behind her and then turned left down the side of the building. As she walked across the rubble to the large gap in the wall that had once been a doorway, she cursed herself for once again forgetting to change her shoes. Inside the building she paused for a minute: she could hear her own heartbeat, and rats scurrying around. At the far end of the building, near where the roof had caved in, a pair of pigeons were flapping frantically. She had an excuse ready in case she'd been followed: she was desperate for the toilet and was looking for somewhere private.

But no one appeared, so she picked up a wooden chair, placed it against the wall and climbed onto it. Stretching up, she felt around inside the rusty junction box above her and retrieved a slip of paper.

She read the message three times, holding it against her chest as she repeated it to herself as if reviewing for an exam. Satisfied that she'd memorised its contents, she lit a cigarette, used the match to burn the letter and continued on her way.

–

That one gesture – when Hanne had wiped the tear from his face – had a disarming effect on Richard Prince. Until that moment he'd have described their relationship as businesslike. She was not unfriendly, nor was she cold, but she could appear brusque and somewhat distant. He was not unfamiliar with such behaviour, where someone was very focused on a serious task in hand and had little time to devote to those around them, not least because he knew he was often guilty of it himself. He was sure that was how he must have come across to Jane, when he put his work before her feelings and needs.

But that gesture, which he assumed was meant innocently, seemed to signal a relaxation in tension between them. He sensed a growing closeness and managed to convince himself the feeling was mutual, though it was never more than a comforting hand on an arm, or sitting closer together on the sofa, and once or twice when she'd visited there'd been a fleeting kiss on the cheek, followed by a warm smile.

After a week of checking the growth of his beard almost every hour, Hanne agreed it was looking good. 'Maybe another two weeks rather than three. What do you think?'

'It has to look like a proper beard, though.'

'Let's see. In the meantime, we have a problem.'

'Go on.'

'London weren't satisfied with the message about a delay. They've told Weston he has to find out the reason for it. They are angry we've not contacted Horatio yet.'

'How do you know this?'

'I picked up a message this evening on the way here.'

'You saw someone?'

'No, it's a dead letter drop system. I burn the messages once I've read them.'

'And what did this message say?'

'I've told you, don't you listen? They want to know the reason for the delay.'

'Maybe we should tell them.'

'Tell them what – that you were arrested by the Gestapo, by some miracle we managed to effect an escape, and by the way, you probably ought to know there's a traitor over there who's not only told the Germans what you look like but has also given them details of the Jesper Holm identity? Once they hear that, they'll order us to abort the mission.'

'But surely we ought to tell London. If there's a traitor there, they need to know, don't they?'

'Can you think of anyone?'

'Not really, no.'

'Exactly. I say let's keep them in the dark and rely on our own judgement. In the meantime, think carefully about everyone you met in England who knew about Jesper Holm. It's not as if you haven't got plenty of time, after all.'

–

Hanne began to spend more time in the apartment, stopping by most evenings. By the end of the second week, with his beard making good progress, he felt emboldened to ask her some questions.

'Do you live nearby?'

'You want to know where I live?'

'Well, yes.'

'You have no idea?'

'No, how could I know?'

'Go over to the window and have a peek through the curtain.' She waited until he was there. 'What can you see?'

'The courtyard and more of these apartment blocks.'

'And what's the apartment block directly opposite this one?'

'B, I think it is. Yes, B...'

'You're telling me you've never watched me leave to see where I go?'

'No, you tell me to stay away from the window.'

He returned to sit opposite her. She lit a cigarette and one for him. 'I live in block B. My apartment faces this one, though I'm two floors below you, on the sixth floor. This apartment belongs to my father. He's in a home now, and that's where he'll remain, but I've told people he may return here, which gives me an excuse to keep the flat on. It also gives me an excuse to keep popping over, to check everything is all right. I rented a flat in the block opposite so I could keep an eye on him.'

'And Weston doesn't mind you using this place?'

'He just said find a good safe house, and as far as I'm concerned, this is a good safe house. The only other apartment on this floor is empty too: the couple who live there spend all their time in the country. They only come back for a few days in the summer. So this really is ideal.'

At the weekend, Hanne spent most of Sunday in the apartment. They had lunch and then spent a long afternoon talking about their police work, both genuinely interested in what the other had done. Prince mentioned how he had at one stage been responsible for keeping an eye on political extremists in his area.

'Another coincidence! When was that?'

'Around 1938, 1939.'

'I was involved with political extremists in 1934. There was a group of students at Aarhus University who'd broken away from one of the traditional nationalist clubs and set up what was basically a Nazi cell. The local police were concerned enough to want to infiltrate the group, but middle-aged policemen tend not to make very convincing students. I was younger and a woman, and no one there knew me, so I enrolled at the university and managed to infiltrate the group. They were very hard-line, a really nasty bunch. I know we Danes have a reputation as decent people, but I can tell you our Nazis are as bad as the German ones; it's just fortunate there are so few of them.'

'So what happened?'

'It took me two semesters to fully infiltrate the group, by which time I'd found out about everything they were up to. There was a lot of talk about how to support Hitler; they'd convinced themselves the population of Denmark was waiting to rise in support of him. But then they came up with a plan to burn down the synagogue in Aarhus on Passover, when the building would be full of people. They gathered all the materials they needed and drew up diagrams. At that point I tipped off the local police and a dozen of them were arrested. I even have photographs of the group somewhere. I keep my old photo albums in the hall cupboard; there's more storage space in my father's flat than in mine. Let me get them.'

They looked through the albums together. Some of the photos showed Hanne when she first joined the police, on patrol in Copenhagen, behind a desk, with a horse. A couple of pages she turned over very fast; those seemed to show her with a man of her own age. Then came the photographs of her as a student in Aarhus, posing outside a university building, standing windswept in a courtyard.

'We used to go on hikes into the countryside. This was their idea of providing cover: we were a nationalist hiking group, would you believe. They also felt it was important to connect with nature. Here, this is the whole group. See if you can spot me.'

'Not difficult. I could spot you anywhere. The Nazis aren't nearly as good-looking as you!'

They were sitting on the floor, their backs resting against the sofa, the albums stacked in front of them. She patted his knee, as if in thanks. But Prince didn't notice. He was staring at the photo, oblivious to everything else, a chill running down his spine.

'What is it? You look like you've seen a ghost!'

He said nothing, turning over the page to look at more photos of the group. One in particular was very clear, taken in good light, the faces more in focus.

'Who is that?' His voice sounded uneasy.

'That's Greta. Greta Poulsen. She was one of the most active Nazis. In fact, she was the one who originally came up with the idea to burn down the synagogue. She served four or five years in prison. Why do you ask?'

He didn't reply, instead picking up the album and taking it to the table to study it more closely. There was no question it was her: the hair, the eyes, the lips... all the same. 'You know you asked me to think of someone who might have betrayed me?'

Hanne nodded.

'Well, I've found them.'

Chapter 8

Copenhagen, November 1942

They argued long into the night, at one stage having to stop themselves when they realised they'd actually been shouting.

'Of course we have to tell London,' said Prince. 'Greta Poulsen is clearly a Nazi spy working at the heart of British intelligence: she helped create the Jesper Holm identity and then betrayed me. It is unconscionable to allow her to continue to operate when we know who she is. Apart from anything else, what about other agents she might be betraying?'

'Let's be a bit more rational. Your thinking is too ABCD. That's what I learned in my detective classes at police college: don't think in an obvious manner, in a straight line, as one of my lecturers described it. Sometimes you should think more smartly. Didn't they teach you that at your police college?'

'I didn't go to police college.'

'So how did you learn to become a policeman – and especially a detective?'

'We learned on the job.'

'And we think the British are so clever. Look, we retrieved the *legitimationskort* for Jesper Holm. The Nazis may think you still have it. It's unlikely, but as long as it is a possibility, they'll carry on looking for Jesper Holm as well as someone matching your description. That will help protect you once you have a new identity – they'll be looking for someone else. However, if we let London know and they arrest Greta Poulsen, there's a good chance news of her arrest will get back to the Gestapo, and then they'll know Jesper Holm has disappeared.'

Prince didn't agree but he could see Hanne wasn't going to concede, and she was the one who controlled communications with London. They would need to concentrate on sorting out his new identity.

—

Ten days later, they agreed that his beard looked like a proper beard rather than the result of not having shaved for a few days. Hanne had bought a dye, and after using it a few times, his hair was a noticeably fairer shade. She had a friend who had a photographic studio just a few blocks away; despite Prince not having a *legitimationskort*, they felt they could risk walking there. 'We have to take some risks: if we didn't, we wouldn't be in this game, would we?'

At the studio, Hanne produced a pair of spectacles – large lenses with thick black frames.

'Try them on.'

He squinted as he peered in the mirror.

'Don't worry, it's a very low prescription and you'll quickly get used to them. Wear them whenever you're out. It would be too risky for them to have no prescription at all; if anyone checked, they'd know something was up. They certainly change how you look.'

She asked the photographer if there was anything he could do to make the beard appear fuller, and he produced a lotion that, when mixed with water, had something approaching the desired effect.

'I know it doesn't look too good in here, but in the photograph you won't be able to tell the difference. My advice is to keep the beard a bit messy, avoid the temptation to trim it. Like this, whoever's looking at you will see your beard rather than your face.' With that he let out a loud laugh that echoed around the small studio. The birth of Peter Rasmussen had begun.

Four days after the photo session, they were sitting at the table in the apartment, a *legitimationskort* and assorted other papers in front of them.

'You look like a Peter Rasmussen.'

'I look like a man with a beard.'

'Good, that's the idea. Peter Rasmussen from Helsingør.' She was holding the card; he could barely recognise himself. 'With your beard and glasses you look rather unremarkable, even quite unattractive.'

'And without the beard and glasses?'

She smiled briefly and then pointed to the papers. 'Concentrate: do you know anything about Helsingør?'

'Isn't it a port?'

'Correct. It's north of Copenhagen. If you were to drive there from here it would take around an hour, possibly slightly longer. It's on the narrowest point of the Øresund, just two miles from the Swedish town of Helsingborg. In English it's known as Elsinore; that's what your Shakespeare called it in *Hamlet*.'

'Is this another literature lesson?'

She continued. 'Please, your life is going to depend on this. Peter Rasmussen was born on the eighth of July 1901, making him forty-one years of age.'

'I'm thirty-four and people often comment that I look young for my age. It's pushing it to make me seven years older.'

'You don't look so young with a beard and those glasses, I promise you. Also, it just feels better having someone who's not in his thirties. Your occupation is ship worker. Helsingør used to have dozens of ferries crossing to and from Sweden each day. Now there's only one or two, so many of the ship workers have come down here to look for work.'

'And if someone wants me to describe my job? I barely know one end of a ship from the other. I'm not even sure what the difference is between a ship and a boat.'

'But that was the same with Jesper Holm being an accountant: this identity is to allow you to move around, that's all. I'm going to get hold of more clothes for you, the kind a ship worker might wear. For the next two days you need to study everything here about Peter Rasmussen. I'll find you something to read on Helsingør and on ships too. Then you'll finally be ready.'

'Ready for what?'

'You've forgotten already? Ready to meet Agent Horatio.'

–

The routine aspects of espionage were so time-consuming. It would take her the best part of an hour and a half to deposit her message and then go to the cemetery to leave a mark to indicate that she'd made the drop.

The only way to do it was with an early start, so she woke up at six, made as strong a cup of coffee as was possible these days and then put on a pair of gloves before sitting down to reread the letter she'd written the night before.

> *Dear Father,*
>
> *Thank you for your recent letter. I am sorry I've not been able to reply sooner, but we've all been so busy here, and what with the usual coughs and colds there's so little time!*
>
> *Unfortunately, Viggo's cold turned into a nasty bout of 'flu (it's always the same with men!) so he's been out of action for a while. The good news is that he's now a lot better and in fact he looks like a new man! He is hoping to visit Uncle Kristian very soon. We'll pass on your regards and of course let you know if Uncle Kristian has any news.*
>
> *I promise I'll write soon.*
>
> *All my love,*
> *Gerda*

London would have to be happy with that. She was telling them she'd received their message; that all was well and there'd been a delay – they wouldn't appreciate her not going into detail, but hard luck. Then she was informing them Agent Laertes had a new identity, which would worry them, but they'd hopefully be reassured that he was finally about to meet Agent Horatio.

She read it through once more and was satisfied. It was as much as they needed to know. Then she removed her gloves – there would be no danger of her leaving fingerprints – broke up the pencil with which she'd written the letter and removed the five sheets below it on the pad. These were deposited in her rubbish bin, which she'd empty on the way out. A quick bath, the same clothes she'd worn the previous day, another coffee and she was on her way.

She used a different dead letter drop for her messages. It was ten minutes' walk to the church, which was closer to where she lived than she'd have liked, but its doors opened early and closed late, meaning she could go there at more or less any time. By seven o'clock there were already a dozen or so worshippers, but the morning service had yet to start, so they were scattered around the large seating area. Her preferred pew towards the back was unoccupied; she sat down and allowed herself five minutes of apparent prayer and contemplation before giving one final look around, then removing the plain envelope from her handbag and placing it inside a prayer book. She remained sitting for another five minutes until she spotted an elderly woman a few rows in front get up to leave and decided to follow her.

From there she caught a tram towards the Assistens cemetery, getting off one stop after it, stopping at a news kiosk to buy a paper and check she hadn't been followed before doubling back.

She left her chalk marks on one of the same graves as Weston's courier used. She often wondered how wise this was, and she also questioned the sense of having to carry a bit of chalk in her handbag. How, she'd once asked Weston, would she explain that away? He'd patted her on the knee and told her he was sure she'd think of something. His courier would walk past in the next day or two. She had no idea who he or she was, or how they managed to get her messages to Stockholm for Weston to encrypt before transmitting them to London.

She did think she'd spotted one of his couriers a few months previously. It was a Monday lunchtime and she was walking through the cemetery to check the graves when she saw an elegantly dressed man, perhaps in his late sixties, walking ahead of her with a dog. He'd paused in front of one of the three graves and taken a step towards it before turning to check no one was around. When he saw her, he moved back onto the path and walked away in the direction she was coming from. For a brief moment their eyes met, perhaps with a fleeting understanding of what the other was doing there. Hanne saw him hesitate before carrying on, and she felt an irrational urge to run after him and say something, to have a word with someone who'd understand.

Espionage was not only tiring, it was also very lonely.

–

'How is your revision going, Peter?' She'd been calling him Peter ever since revealing his new identity, and he was becoming rather fond of the name. He felt he was more of a Peter than a Hans or a Jesper. There'd been a Peter in his year at school who'd been captain of both the rugby and cricket teams, as well as being the first in their year to have a proper girlfriend. Naturally he'd also gone to one of the better colleges at Cambridge. Prince had always aspired to being Peter.

'I beg your pardon?'

'Your homework: how's it going?'

'Very well, thank you. I've memorised every detail I can on Peter Rasmussen and I now know the difference between port and starboard thanks to the children's book on ships you brought from the library. And as for Helsingør, what do you want to know? I can tell you all about King Eric of Pomerania and describe St Olaf's church in great detail.' He was patting a pile of books next to him.

'You'll meet Agent Horatio tomorrow. You know what to do?'

He nodded.

'I ought to be getting back to my apartment now. I won't see you in the morning. I hope the meeting goes well. Are you all right, Peter?'

'Yes, I'm fine, thank you. Obviously a bit apprehensive...'

'What happened last time was an unfortunate coincidence. You'll be fine, you're well prepared.'

There was a long silence. Prince started to talk, then stopped himself. He came and sat next to her on the sofa. 'Can I ask you something?'

'Of course.'

'Do you have any family?'

'Is it wise for us to be having a conversation like this?'

'Is it wise not to?'

It was her turn to be quiet. She edged closer to him and rested her hand on his thigh, gently patting it as if in reassurance.

'I've told you about my father – he's in a home. He suffered a stroke a few years ago. My mother was killed when I was very young. My father brought me up on his own, though of course he had help. He and I are very close. And before you ask, I've never been married and I don't have children. I've told you that already.'

'Can I ask how your mother was killed? I hope you don't mind...'

She removed her hand from his thigh and moved slightly away from him. 'I don't normally talk about it, Peter, it hurts too much. She was killed crossing the road. A lorry hit her. I was seven years old and had a twin brother. He was with her and was also killed, though not immediately. He died a few days later.'

'You weren't with them?'

'No. Even to this day I don't know where I was. I was in shock for weeks, perhaps months. My father and I never discussed it. I remember just the one conversation with him about it, very soon after my brother died. He said the only way we'd survive was by getting on with our lives and by not looking back, which is what we did. I do remember it was around then that I decided to become a police officer. I must have thought in my grief that maybe I could prevent that kind of thing happening.'

'I'm sorry. I understand how dreadful it must have been for you.'

'Really? But that's the thing, Peter. People say they understand, but they can't. Unless you have been through something like that, you simply have no way of understanding.'

She moved further away from him. She'd spoken in an admonishing tone and looked annoyed. She'd clearly felt he was being intrusive.

'But you see, I have been through something just like that. My wife and daughter were killed in a car crash two years ago. And I have a son who wasn't with them. He's three. So I do know how you feel.'

They both sat in silence, during which time it grew dark, the room lit only by the light from the hall.

There was no need for either of them to say anything, but they did move closer to each other again.

It was perhaps not the best way for Prince to prepare for his meeting with Agent Horatio the following morning.

–

They'd agreed that this time he should approach Otto Knudsen well away from Kongens Nytorv, the square where he stopped for breakfast and where Prince had been arrested. They knew that after leaving the café Knudsen would head west towards his office, walking for about ten minutes in the direction of the university.

Not too near Kongens Nytorv. Not too near his office. Nowhere near his apartment on Nyhavn.

It wasn't going to be easy.

He decided to wait on Gothersgade, which was the road Hanne had said Knudsen was most likely to take after leaving the café. It was a busy road, full of cyclists and people hurrying to work. Prince felt self-conscious and kept stroking his beard: it was the first time he'd been out for weeks, he was close to the place where he'd been arrested and he was dressed as a ship worker. It was half past eight and he hoped he'd got his timings right. If he had, Knudsen should be walking past in less than five minutes.

It happened much quicker than he'd expected. He was toying with the idea of going into a shoe shop, from which he'd be able to look into the street, until he noticed two German officers in there. He was about to cross the road when he spotted Agent Horatio coming in his direction on the same side as him. Knudsen was much taller than he'd appeared to be from the other side of the canal, and as such he was easy to pick out in the crowd. He was dressed as before, with a dark trilby-style hat and a long raincoat. He was carrying a black umbrella and wore the kind of half-smile that seemed to be a permanent feature of naturally jovial people. Peter Rasmussen was about to find out if this was true.

'Excuse me, sir.'

Knudsen paused, still smiling. He raised his eyebrows in response. *Can I help you?*

'I was wondering if you could tell me where the Amalien-borg Palace is?'

Prince had wondered whether he should add that he was from Helsingør, but Hanne had advised against it. *Stick to saying what he's been told you'll say. If you deviate from it, he may think something's wrong.*

Knudsen bowed his head as if to indicate he was happy to help. 'It depends on whether you'd prefer to approach it from Frederiksgade or Amaliegade.' Another smile.

'I'd like to approach it from whichever way is closest to the church with the big dome.'

Knudsen nodded his head and the smile faded. 'Walk a while with me. We are actually walking away from the Amalienborg, but never mind, no one would have heard us. We obviously cannot talk now. Do you know where I live?'

Prince nodded.

'I'll make sure I'm back there by five thirty this afternoon. There's a rear entrance, which you can access through Heibergs-gade. I shall unlatch that door at five thirty-five. Let yourself in and reset the latch. Maybe if you carry a parcel that will help. Come straight up to my apartment.'

Prince doffed his cap and thanked Otto Knudsen very much. The older man was pointing, as if giving directions. His other hand was gripping Prince's forearm; he could barely contain his excitement. 'I'm so pleased you've finally made contact. We have so much to talk about! I was expecting to see you weeks ago. Whatever happened?'

Chapter 9

London, November 1942

It had been raining for three days and four nights and Tom Gilbey – not a religious man, despite dutifully accompanying his wife to church most Sundays – was beginning to agree with colleagues describing the constant downpour as being of biblical proportions.

The surface of Whitehall had a layer of settled water on it, with dips in the pavement creating puddles deep enough to cover his ankles. By the time he reached Downing Street, his shoes were sodden. They were a particularly expensive pair, hand-made in Jermyn Street earlier that year and meant to last a lifetime, and now he was convinced they'd been ruined before they'd been properly broken in. But the nature of the summons he'd received earlier that morning ensured the state of his shoes was the least of his problems.

He turned right just before Number 10, down the path that would take him to the rear entrance, where a policeman nodded him through. Once inside, his papers were checked before he was escorted to Sir Roland Pearson's office.

Sir Roland was the Downing Street intelligence chief. His role was to act as an umpire between the various intelligence and security agencies; to keep the internecine disputes and rows over who was responsible for what to manageable proportions. His office was deep inside Downing Street, looking out over an internal courtyard.

'Come in, Tom, glad you could drop by.' Pearson was a man given to understatement. *My office, Gilbey, eleven thirty* had been the message: hardly a cordial invitation to drop by.

Gilbey removed his coat and hat, the carpet below him dampening as he did so. When he sat on the chair opposite Pearson's desk, he could feel quite how drenched his trousers and jacket were. He was beginning to feel most uncomfortable.

'This report of yours, Tom...' Pearson was tapping a dark green folder on his desk.

'Which report is that, Roly?' They'd been at boarding school together, Pearson a couple of years above him. Gilbey felt he could get away with Roly, but he did omit the Poly that came after it in his school nickname. Pearson had been fat even at school.

'The one on Agent – what's his name – ah, here we are... Horatio. Winston appreciated the classical references, though. It amused him for almost a minute.'

'What about the report, Roly?'

'The thing is, Tom, it has rather set the cat amongst the pigeons, I'm afraid.'

Silence in the office. The only sound Gilbey could hear – and he hoped it was imagined more than anything else – was that of water dripping from various parts of him. He wasn't in the mood to make matters easier for Pearson by asking *why* his report had set the cat amongst the pigeons. Instead he indulged himself with a quizzical frown to indicate he wasn't sure what all the fuss could possibly be about.

'Let me explain, Tom. Winston prefers clarity to confusion. He doesn't appreciate being given conflicting advice; he simply does not have time for that. Hence my role here in Downing Street – and indeed Lord Swalcliffe's.'

Gilbey nodded. Now he knew why he'd been summoned and after their encounter at the Whitehall reception, it was no great surprise. Lord Swalcliffe – first name Edward, surname he couldn't quite recall, but the man was originally from

Luxembourg and he seemed to remember the name had an unfortunate Germanic edge to it – was Churchill's principal scientific adviser and seemed to have the ear of the Prime Minister in a way few of his other confidantes did.

'Winston is distressed at the degree of rancour existing between the various departments, agencies and individuals with whom we work. I realise that to an extent he encourages it: he realises disagreement can sometimes lead to honest opinions being expressed, which he sees as being better than suppressing one's views. He doesn't like matters being bottled up, like in some miserable marriage. Swalcliffe is very good at...' Pearson hesitated, searching for the precise word, 'distilling differing opinions and coming up with clear and concise advice, which is why this report' – this time he held up the dark green folder and waved it in Gilbey's direction – 'has caused such a fuss. Lord Swalcliffe's consistent and considered opinion has been that there is no threat from German long-range rockets: he does not think they're feasible. That is the advice he has been giving Winston. Now you send in a report saying the contrary. He tore a strip off me last night and instructed me to sort it. So we're going to go from here into a secure room in the basement and thrash it out. Swalcliffe will be there, of course, plus Air Vice Marshal Frank Hamilton of RAF intelligence and one of his chaps, and Long from the Ministry.'

Pearson hauled his considerable frame up from his chair and gestured to Gilbey to do the same. He paused by the door to regain his breath, turning to Gilbey and gripping him by the elbow.

'Don't let Swalcliffe rile you, and certainly don't underestimate him, Tom. People do that at their peril. He's terribly bright and misses nothing. He tends to take a contrarian view: he's an original thinker, and Winston likes that. As difficult as he can be, he's right far more often than he's wrong. Best not forget that.'

There were six of them in a room that would have been a tight squeeze for four. It was more of an interview room than one suitable for a meeting. Given that all the attendees bar Pearson had been caught in the rain, there was an unpleasant fug about it. No sooner had the soundproof door been closed from the outside with some degree of ceremony than Lord Swalcliffe started speaking, dispensing with any need for introductions.

'Well, Gilbey, I thought I'd suggested you steer clear of rockets? All this nonsense – and I didn't know you had agents in Denmark. There's a turn-up for the books!' He spoke with the very faintest of accents, a hint of the Continent. Had Gilbey not known of his background, he doubted he'd have spotted it.

'There we are then, Lord Swalcliffe.' He'd thought about addressing him as Edward, but decided against it.

'Meaning?'

Meaning you don't know everything.

'Meaning we do have agents in Denmark.'

'I was under the impression all our agents over there had been rounded up?'

'You're probably thinking of the SOE, Lord Swalcliffe. Our service is perhaps more accomplished.'

'Very well then.' Swalcliffe paused to put on a pair of reading spectacles and open a folder in front of him. 'One of your agents has met a man who knows someone else who knows a chap whose colleague may have overheard a German mention the word "rockets": ridiculous!' He closed the folder as if resting his case.

'If I may say – with the very greatest of respect, Lord Swalcliffe – that is an unnecessarily cynical interpretation of what happened. We have—'

'Perhaps it would help,' said Pearson, leaning forward uncomfortably, 'if Tom explained the situation and then you can respond, Lord Swalcliffe, along with our other colleagues, of course.'

Gilbey launched into his explanation before anyone could protest. 'Back in August, Stockholm station had a walk-in: a Danish businessman who claimed to have picked up intelligence about the German V-rocket programme while in Berlin.' He paused. Lord Swalcliffe was looking at his folder, impatiently bouncing his pencil up and down on it. 'George Weston handled the chap himself and decided he merited serious attention, gave him the code name Horatio. We recruited an agent here – Agent Laertes – and sent him to Denmark to work with Horatio. We already had an agent in Copenhagen called Agent Osric who we've been keeping under wraps for something of this importance. Osric has been in a good position to check out Agent Horatio and is satisfied, as far as one can be sure, that he is who he says he is. Therefore, we were able to move to the next stage of the operation: for Agent Laertes to meet with Horatio. This happened last week, and it is that meeting that forms the basis of my report.'

He hesitated. He wished he'd been better prepared. It was typical of Pearson to have thrust this briefing on him. At school Roly had a reputation as a particularly devious cricketer, known for running out his own teammates.

'Let me say at the outset that Agent Osric watched Laertes enter the building where the meeting took place – Horatio's apartment block, as it happens – and kept an eye on it throughout the meeting. When Laertes left, Osric followed him back to his safe house. They are certain he was not being watched or followed.'

'Which doesn't guarantee it's not a set-up, does it?'

'No, Lord Swalcliffe, it doesn't, but everything does seem to point in the direction of Agent Horatio being who he says he is.'

'The Germans could just be smarter than your agent, Gilbey.'

Gilbey looked around the table before continuing, hoping for some support. Roland Pearson wore a studied expression of impartiality; Air Vice Marshal Frank Hamilton had an impassive air about him, as did the young wing commander sitting next to him, while Long from the Ministry, who would certainly be his ally in this case but was evidently biding his time, was smiling weakly.

'Perhaps if I summarise Agent Laertes' meeting with Horatio? Agent Horatio is a sales representative for a Danish engineering company. He—'

'For heaven's sake, Gilbey – a sales rep!'

'He's hardly a door-to-door salesman selling vacuum cleaners or encyclopaedias, Lord Swalcliffe. The company he represents manufactures specialist components for the engineering industry. Weston's original understanding was that they make ball bearings, but according to Agent Laertes, they are far more sophisticated than that. They specialise in manufacturing small parts for engines and are particularly skilled at fabricating components that can withstand very high temperatures. Agent Horatio was on a business trip to Berlin in the first week of August to discuss an order for parts for a factory making tanks. One night his contact took him out for dinner, where they were unexpectedly joined by another guest, who turned out to be an *Oberst* in the Luftwaffe. You'll correct me if I'm wrong, Frank, but as I understand it, an *Oberst* is more or less equivalent to a group captain in the RAF?'

'That's right, Tom: he'd be somewhat junior to me but would outrank Tim here.' The air vice marshal chuckled as he patted the arm of the officer next to him. Gilbey was relieved: the tension in the room appeared to have dropped by as much as one degree.

'The *Oberst* was introduced to Horatio as Kurt. I imagine that's not his real name, but he—'

'Hang on, Gilbey, hang on – you imagine Kurt is not his real name but somehow you're sure he's an *Oberst*? For heaven's sake: you've seriously been wasting Winston's valuable time with all these fanciful stories?' Lord Swalcliffe slammed his pencil onto the table, causing the lead to snap.

'Edward, perhaps if we let Tom finish his account, then we can draw some conclusions. Wouldn't that be a more... scientific approach?'

Swalcliffe didn't reply, and Gilbey continued. 'According to Kurt, the Germans are actually developing two long-range rockets, both designed to be fired at targets in England from the Continent. These rocket programmes are called V-1 and V-2. The V apparently stands for *Vergeltungswaffen*, which translates as "vengeance". Frank, you'll forgive me if I show technical ignorance here, but the two programmes differ from each other quite substantially. I know you've read the report and perhaps you'd be able to explain the essential differences? But before you do, I want to mention a distinction between the two that we'd not appreciated: while the V-1 is being developed by the Luftwaffe, the V-2 is being developed by the army. This has led to intense rivalry, which in turn is causing problems with the production of the rockets. We should seek to exploit that rivalry. Over to you, Frank.'

'Thanks, Tom. Wing Commander Carter here is our expert on the German rocket programme, so I'll ask him to explain the technical details. But I want to emphasise the importance of realising that the two programmes are not version one and version two of the same weapon. The intelligence you've given us that they are being developed separately by the Luftwaffe and the army is most interesting – if true, of course. They also differ in terms of the technologies they use. I'll ask Tim to explain this and I should acknowledge we've been able to update our intelligence on these programmes thanks to the report you've put together. Tim?'

'Thank you, sir. As you say, we're talking here about two very distinct programmes. In layman's terms, the V-1 is essentially a pilotless aircraft with a maximum speed of around four hundred and fifty miles per hour and carries a one-ton warhead. It has a range of just over two hundred miles, so to target London and the south coast ports, it would be fired from somewhere in – say – northern France and the trajectory and other settings would, the Germans hope, ensure it hits its target area, most likely London or the south coast ports. According to your report, the V-1 carries a one-ton warhead.

'The V-2, on the other hand, is a very different beast. It's a rocket rather than a pilotless aircraft. One of our boffins has come up with a term to describe it: a guided missile. It's launched high into the sky, possibly as high as seventy miles. Its engine is then cut at a crucial moment by means of a radio signal from the ground and this causes the rocket to fall onto its target. Like the V-1 it carries a one-ton warhead, and it has a similar range, around two hundred and twenty miles, but it travels a great deal faster – possibly around three and a half thousand miles per hour. Mr Gilbey's report was able to furnish us with considerably more detail than we'd had up to now.'

Lord Swalcliffe was coughing vigorously, clearly impatient to make his case.

'One moment, Edward,' said Pearson. 'I have one question: if we are to believe what we're being told, what are the implications for Britain?'

'Potentially devastating,' said Hamilton. 'While we'd stand a reasonable chance of intercepting a V-1 rocket, I doubt we'd get much of a shot at a V-2, not going at that speed. Our Spitfires are being updated all the time, but their top speed is currently not much more than four hundred miles an hour.'

'Which is a flaw, isn't it?' Lord Swalcliffe spoke with the air of a barrister at last allowed to begin his cross-examination. 'Why bother with the so-called V-1? If this V-2 rocket is so bloody good, they ought to be putting all their resources into that, surely? All this rivalry nonsense we're expected to buy...'

'The V-1s would be much easier and certainly cheaper to produce,' Hamilton replied. 'They'll be able to fire far more of them at us.'

The young wing commander chipped in. 'And also, who knows how the technology would work out? The rockets are still being developed, after all. This is an area we really need to know far more about. The report says the *Oberst* implied that both weapons are proving problematic in their development stage. This is something we'd really like to have far more detail on.'

'Well the technology is at the heart of my very considerable reservations about all of this nonsense.' Lord Swalcliffe waved a hand dismissively at the folder in front of him. 'I simply cannot see how they are going to launch a one-ton warhead, let alone keep it in the sky. The missiles – both of them – simply aren't big enough, and even if they were, the correct fuel systems for them don't exist. They'd need solid fuels to carry those warheads and the rockets would have to be many times bigger than what we're being told they are. And the idea that liquid fuels could be used... well I simply don't accept it. And then there's the question of where the damn things are being developed. If they actually existed, it would need a massive site, and we'd easily be able to identify it. My view,' he was standing up now, as if making his closing speech, 'and I've told Winston as much, is that this is all a hoax, and not a terribly sophisticated one at that. It's designed to get us all excited, to devote an enormous range of resources to combating these so-called V-1 and V-2 rockets and in doing so take our eye off the ball. We'll be so distracted by peering into the sky for rockets that are never going to appear that we'll miss some other trick the Germans are preparing for us. This is both fanciful and madness.'

'Surely not so fanciful?' Pearson shifted in his chair. 'After all, we know the Americans are currently developing a bomb that would be considerably more lethal than—'

'That subject is most certainly NOT for this room, Pearson!' Lord Swalcliffe looked furious, banging the table. 'It has the highest possible classification and is not for discussion here. In any case, it is an altogether different system, as I know personally. I would ask that no reference is made to this in anyone's notes.'

'There is one concern I have,' said Hamilton, 'and I do think it needs to be addressed if what the *Oberst* says is to have any credibility. We need to establish what his motives are. Why would he come out with all this highly sensitive information at a dinner, passing it on to a Danish businessman? My wing commander here is right, of course, that we need further technical information, but we also need to be satisfied as to why this Kurt is passing on secrets to a stranger. Until we can be sure of that, a question mark hangs over whatever else he's told us.'

—

The discussion continued for another half an hour. Just as Sir Roland Pearson was about to bring the meeting to some kind of conclusion, a hitherto unheard voice emerged from one end of the table. It was Long from the Ministry.

'My minister is of the view that we have to be prepared. He has told the Prime Minister as much, and as you know, they spent the weekend together. He feels one can allow one's scepticism to get in the way of the need to be vigilant.'

'It seems to me,' said Pearson, 'that we need to find out more. Maybe get some answers to various questions that have emerged here this morning. Don't you agree, Tom?'

'According to what he told Agent Laertes, Horatio is due to return to Berlin on another business trip next week, the first week in December.'

'How long is he going for?'

'Around four or five days, I gather.'

'Well then,' said Pearson, 'say we send him over there with some company?'

'And who did you have in mind, Roly?'

'Agent Laertes would seem to be ideally placed, wouldn't you agree? Nothing like getting intelligence straight from the horse's mouth. Send him over with a clear brief: to check out the *Oberst*, get as much technical detail as possible and—'

'And see if we can find out where these bloody rockets are allegedly being developed. If we can find that out and go and have a look at the place to verify it, even I might be persuaded. And if I'm persuaded, Winston will be too.'

'Of course, Edward. I was just about to add that requirement. I suggest we reconvene once Agent Laertes returns to Copenhagen?'

A nodding of heads around the table.

'Assuming the poor bugger gets back, of course,' said the air vice marshal.

—

They walked in line through the narrow corridors and up the steep staircases to the ground floor of 10 Downing Street. The two RAF men left, as did Long from the Ministry. Tom Gilbey was about to follow them when Lord Swalcliffe grabbed him by the elbow, causing him to stop.

'Well done, Gilbey, one nil to you. But we haven't even got to half-time yet.'

Gilbey bowed his head in what was meant to come across as a magnanimous gesture.

'One thing, though. This Agent Osric in Copenhagen, the one you describe as being well placed?'

'What about them?'

'She's a woman, isn't she?'

'How the hell...?'

'Pronouns, Gilbey, pronouns. You studiously avoided using male or female pronouns when talking about Agent Osric. You did it again just now.'

With that, Swalcliffe disappeared through the door, the rain now little more than a drizzle.

Gilbey stood there with a bemused look on his face – a chess player defeated by an ingenious move he never saw coming.

'Those damn foreign types who become fluent in English, eh, Roly? They develop a precision in our language that can put them at an advantage over us native speakers. That French geography teacher at school, the one who broke Mogg's nose in the staff versus pupils rugby match… what was his name?'

'Leclerc?'

'That's it, Leclerc: always on about our use of the subjunctive.'

Pearson patted him on the shoulder. 'Don't take it so personally, Tom. I told you he was clever, didn't I?'

Chapter 10

My dearest Gerda,

The family and I were delighted to receive your letter, and we were especially thrilled to read Uncle Kristian's news – it seems almost too good to be true! We're so pleased Viggo finally managed to see him. It's good to hear Uncle Kristian is visiting his cousin in Jutland again. I think Viggo should accompany him on that trip. It will do him the world of good to get into the countryside and I'm sure he has plenty of questions for his cousin! Maybe you'll write again as soon as he and Uncle Kristian return from Jutland.

The garden is looking terrible at the moment. I find so little time for it these days, and in any case those fat black cats from next door are under the impression it belongs to them! Next week I hope to start painting the hall, although I have yet to decide on the colour.

With my fondest love,
Father

'And that means I have to go with him to Berlin? Are you absolutely sure?'

'Yes, I'm absolutely sure, Peter. I keep telling you: Uncle Kristian is Agent Horatio, you are Viggo, Jutland means Berlin and the cousin will be Horatio's contact there, the Luftwaffe officer. "It seems almost too good to be true" will be London's way of saying they want the intelligence Horatio brought back from Berlin corroborated. It doesn't mean they don't believe it, but they want to know more, which is understandable.'

Prince paced up and down, finding it hard to disguise his nervousness. He'd assumed his role would be confined to being Horatio's contact in Copenhagen, which was dangerous enough. It hadn't occurred to him he'd have to go to Berlin. He felt hot and sweaty and his mood wasn't helped by Hanne looking tense and edgy herself.

'And what's all this about the garden and cats and painting the hall – what on earth does all that mean? Am I supposed to try and arrange tea with Hitler?'

'It means nothing. The last paragraph of London's communications are meant to be trivial domestic news; the idea is for the letters to appear as mundane as possible in the unlikely event someone comes across them. I'll reply and confirm you're going and I expect London will then send a briefing for you – what to ask Kurt, for example.'

–

Prince was struck by just how calm Agent Horatio was. He'd watched him come home from work, standing on the other side of the Nyhavn as the tall Dane strolled along the canalside and entered his apartment block at around a quarter to six.

Prince waited five minutes and then walked slowly along the canal, crossed it on the Nyhavnsbroen and walked back in the direction of Agent Horatio's building. This time he couldn't enter through the rear because he wasn't expected, but going through the front entrance would be risky. He waited near the entrance, leaning on the railings as he slowly lit a cigarette. The longer he waited, the more exposed he'd be, and for some reason the area seemed to be especially busy with German troops, most just strolling along. After five minutes he spotted his opportunity. An elderly lady with shopping bags in each hand approached the building and paused at the door, putting the bags down and removing a bunch of keys from her pocket.

Prince walked up to her. 'Let me help you.'

'You're so kind. I just need to find the right key. Please don't go out of your way.'

'It's no problem. I'm taking this parcel to a friend.'

Upstairs, Otto Knudsen opened the door and beckoned him in as if he was expected. The Dane had peered over his shoulder to check no one was behind him on the small landing.

'Is everything all right, Peter?'

'It is – there's no need to worry. Everything is fine.'

'So have you popped in for a chat?' Agent Horatio smiled. He'd led Prince into the smartly furnished lounge, and each man was sitting in one of a pair of very modern-looking armchairs. Prince had never seen anything like them in England. 'Coffee maybe – or perhaps a beer? I can offer you an aquavit, but you'll excuse me if I don't join you. I can't stand the stuff!'

'There's no time for a drink. We need to talk. London received the information you gave me about your Berlin trip and what Kurt told you. They were very grateful and have asked me to pass on their thanks.'

'But? Surely they wouldn't risk sending you here just to say thank you?'

'They feel they need to know more. There are questions they have for Kurt.'

'Give me the questions and I can ask him if I see him next week. I'll need to wait until I'm there and then ask my contact to arrange a—'

'They want me to go with you.'

'Really... to Berlin? Is that such a good idea? I need to have a think.'

Horatio walked around his lounge, pausing by the bookcase to put a couple of books back in line. Then he went over to his desk and removed a diary from his briefcase before sitting down.

'I was planning to fly out next Tuesday night – the first of December. I was only intending to stay until Thursday. I try to minimise my time in the Reich. It's not exactly pleasant, you know.'

'Will two nights be enough?'

'I'm not sure, Peter. My contact would probably need longer than that to arrange the meeting with Kurt – I wouldn't want to risk asking him before I see him in person.'

'Of course not. Can you bring the trip forward?'

'Probably not. The Monday flight is always fully booked. But we could take the ten o'clock flight on the Tuesday morning and come back on the Thursday evening. That gives us two nights and the best part of three days. Hopefully it will be enough time to get to see Kurt. And we need to think about you. You'll need a visa and accreditation too, as well as tickets for the flights, and then there's the hotel...'

Otto ran his hand through his hair; he was as close to being stressed as Prince had seen him. But he didn't look so much worried as someone enjoying the challenge of seeking a solution to a problem.

'Tomorrow's what... Wednesday. First of all, let me see if I can change my flight and see what we can do about you. Here, let me have a look at your *legitimationskort*.'

–

They'd arranged to meet at lunchtime on Thursday at a café close to where Agent Horatio worked.

'Will it be safe, a public place like that?' Prince asked as he was leaving the apartment. He'd assumed he'd return there to discuss the travel plans.

'It will be safe enough. It will be better than you coming here again; I don't think we can risk that. One or two of my neighbours are of the nosy variety.'

At the café, Horatio had his excited look about him. He was very pleased with himself, he announced. The café was so noisy they had to lean very close to each other, their heads almost touching.

'Congratulations, Peter! You're now an employee of Mortensen Machinery Parts. Well done.' He patted Prince enthusiastically on the shoulder as if he was congratulating him at the end of a gruelling selection process. 'I'm very senior in the company,' he continued. 'I've worked for them for years and I'm by far their best salesman. I have a lot of influence and of course I know who's sympathetic and won't ask questions. Most Danes are opposed to the Nazis; it's just a matter of being aware of the small number to steer clear of. I told my managing director I needed to take someone with me to Berlin next week and he said he was fine with that as long as it didn't cause problems for the company.'

'What kind of problems?'

'Don't worry, there shouldn't be any. The important thing is that I'm getting papers sorted for you and we're applying for your visa. You'll be an engineer with a background in shipbuilding, which means your *legitimationskort* will be fine. The cover story is that I need your expertise with the company we're working with in Berlin; we may need you to spend more time at their factory next year. I've sent a telegram to my contact in Berlin telling him I'm arriving on Tuesday and confirming we'll meet him the next day. I expect to have all the papers and tickets sorted by Friday. Let's meet on Saturday, say twelve noon outside the Restaurant Grøften in the Tivoli Gardens. Hopefully it won't be raining.'

-

The terminal building at Kastrup airport at nine fifteen on Tuesday morning, the first day of December, was a bleak place. The civilian passenger building had been closed over the weekend and no one appeared to have bothered as yet to turn the heating back on. Deutsche Lufthansa flight number 29 to Berlin was the only flight scheduled before noon, so a building that could comfortably accommodate well over two hundred passengers today held only a dozen or so. Most sat on their own, well away from anyone else. There were two or three pairs of passengers, people who obviously knew each other. One of those pairs was Otto Knudsen and Peter Rasmussen, the latter now dressed in more formal garb than the ship worker's clothes he'd been wearing before.

'It's good we didn't arrive first,' said Knudsen, who was not quite as calm as Prince had previously seen him. 'The Gestapo look out for early arrivals, I'm not sure why. You see those two over there?' He indicated with a slight nod of his head two men strolling in front of the seating, one short and fat, the other tall and thin. Both wore long coats and wide-brimmed hats. 'They're Gestapo. They're always here. They look so unhealthy.'

'If you were making a film about the Gestapo, you'd choose two people like that, wouldn't you?'

'If you chose those two, it would be a comedy film! Don't worry, though. They'll just be *Anwärters*; that's the lowest rank in the Gestapo. They're probably just here for show as much as anything else. This is what will happen next. Very soon that desk over there will open. We go and show our tickets, and they'll give us another ticket that allows us onto the plane and shows us which seat we've been allocated. Then we go through the first security check; you can see the tables just behind the check-in desks. They'll search your bags, but they do that with everyone. You have nothing on you to be concerned about. Then you go to the Gestapo desk, where they will check your *legitimationskort* and your travel documents and ask you questions: again, don't worry, they ask everyone questions. By the way, Peter, I should have asked you: do you speak German?'

'I do. I'm mean, I'm not fluent in it by any means and it's nowhere as good as my Danish, but it's not bad.'

'Don't use it, if possible. Best stick to Danish. The Gestapo officer will be Danish-speaking but will start off in German.

If he has any concerns about you, he'll bring in a Danish policeman to help him, but they prefer not to do that.

'It's usually a Junkers Ju 52 on this flight, which carries seventeen passengers. My guess is it's pretty full today, so hopefully the Gestapo will get a move on. After you've been through the Gestapo desk, we wait in the departure lounge. Then we board the plane. From then on, act as if you're in Germany. Don't say anything to me about the mission, however irrelevant it may seem. Any German is a threat.'

'Do many Germans travel on this flight?'

'Civilians, yes; military personnel usually take a Luftwaffe passenger aircraft, but occasionally some will be on this one. The Gestapo tend not to bother with them too much!'

They sat in silence for a few minutes. The terminal building slowly came to life. There were hints of the heating having been turned on, and two or three people in bright blue uniforms were preparing the check-in desks.

'Can I ask you a question, Otto?'

The Dane turned round and smiled. 'As long as you don't do it too loudly.'

'Why do you do this? Helping us?'

Knudsen raised his eyebrows and pursed his mouth, as if to help him find the right response. 'I'll answer you in a very Danish way, Peter, by asking *you* a question: why would I *not* do this? It is my duty. I'm not a political man, though I've always been a supporter of the social democrats. For me, like most Danes, having the Germans occupy our country is an anathema, a terrible thing. But compared with the rest of occupied Europe, we don't suffer much. What angers me most is what the Nazis are up to elsewhere in Europe. They must be defeated and I swore to myself that if I found I was in a position whereby I could assist the British, I would have no hesitation in doing so. I rationalised it like this: I wouldn't go out of my way to find out something, but if something found me, so to speak, I would not ignore it. And that is what happened with

Kurt, the Luftwaffe officer. He told me things I knew would be of interest to the British. And here we are! I've been divorced for many years and I have no close family. I've lived a good life, a very comfortable one. It would not be the end of the world if it was sacrificed for a greater cause. I hope that doesn't sound too sanctimonious, but you did ask me.'

'But your contact, how did he know to put you in touch with Kurt?'

'That's a good question, Peter. Maybe by the time we return we'll know the answer to it. Look, we'd better move. Not too fast, though; let's make sure we're at the end of the queue. That way they'll be in a hurry by the time they get to us.'

–

'Date of birth?'

The Gestapo officer was a good two or three inches taller than Prince and appeared to be standing on a small platform behind his desk. He towered over the passengers in the queue.

'Eighth of July 1901.'

'Birthplace?' Given the circumstances, he didn't sound especially unpleasant.

'Helsingør.'

'Occupation?'

'I'm a ship worker.'

'Why is a ship worker flying to Berlin?' A bit more unpleasant now, a hint of a sneer.

'I'm actually a maritime engineer: my company is doing some work at a locomotive manufacturing plant in Berlin and my expertise is the operation of large boilers – industrial ones: the type you get on ships and trains.' Prince could feel his stomach tightening. The Gestapo officer looked just like the kind of person who spent his leisure time looking at boilers, the industrial variety.

'Your age?'

This is when they get serious; when they mix up the questions, go back on ones they've asked before but in slightly different ways.

'I'm forty-one.' *No need to add anything; just answer the question. Sound respectful, but not too much. Don't sound as if you're in a hurry, but neither as if you have all day.*

'What day were you born?'

'Eighth of July 1901.'

'That's not what I asked. I asked what day you were born; what day of the week.'

One or two identity cards in occupied Europe state the day you were born, but most don't, and it's a favourite trick of the Gestapo to ask. They'll check it out. Best not to get it wrong, old chap, eh? If you've forgotten or aren't sure, say you don't know. You may just about get away with that; surprising how many people don't know which day of the week they were born on.

'A Monday. My mother always said she spent the whole weekend—'

The Gestapo officer held up his hand like a traffic policeman: stop. He was consulting something behind his desk, evidently checking whether 8 July 1901 was indeed a Monday.

Looking slightly disappointed, he thrust Peter Rasmussen's papers back at him. 'Very well, continue.'

Chapter 11

Tempelhof had been nerve-racking. Although he'd steeled himself for it, passing through the airport's various layers of security felt like climbing an uncharted mountain: he'd reach a ridge and discover he was still in the foothills.

He recalled Hendrie telling him how important it was to adopt a frame of mind that there was nothing about him that could cause people to be suspicious, while at the same time remaining alert.

At the time he'd thought that would be easier said than done, and so it proved.

—

'At least we're past the first hurdle, eh?' The U-Bahn train was almost deserted on the short journey from the airport to Koch Strasse station: just three stops up from Flughafen, then a short walk to their hotel. He was quickly put in place by Agent Horatio.

'I've told you, be careful.' Knudsen looked furious, his angry whisper just audible above the metronomic sound of the wheels on the track. He stared out of the window rather than at Prince. 'Keep quiet until we're somewhere safe. Believe it or not, getting into Germany is the easy part. The real danger begins once you're in the country – and when you try to leave it.'

Agent Horatio's instructions not to discuss anything about their mission during the flight had turned out to be academic. Despite sitting in one of the rear rows, the considerable noise from the two wing-mounted engines close to the cockpit rendered any conversation near impossible.

The pilot's intercom was just about loud enough to break through the racket. Because of a strong prevailing wind, he told them, they'd take off in a northerly direction and head up the Øresund, banking south once they reached eight thousand feet. This would take about ten to fifteen minutes; they'd then climb to around nineteen thousand feet, crossing the German coast at Stralsund and heading south, keeping to the east of Berlin and flying close to a maximum speed of around one hundred and sixty miles an hour.

All the passengers had been handed copies of *Völkischer Beobachter*, the mouthpiece of the Nazi Party. Prince read a long article on the brave defence being put up in Stalingrad. Things must be going badly for the Germans in the battle; anything less than positive in the *Völkischer Beobachter* usually meant bad news.

An hour later, the pilot was back on the intercom: the wind was against them, he announced. They were descending to fifteen thousand feet and one hundred and thirty miles an hour. They were unlikely to land at Tempelhof before eleven fifteen. He was sure the passengers would all understand.

His final announcement came at eleven twenty: passengers may have noticed they had not landed he said, sounding rather pleased with his little joke. They'd been told by air traffic control to fly as far south as Schönefeld before turning north towards Berlin.

Just before their final descent, a steward came round to check all the curtains were drawn over the portholes. They were not to be opened in any circumstances, he instructed them. Otto

Knudsen leaned over and whispered in Prince's ear: 'There are military planes here; they don't want anyone to see them. Especially those bringing casualties back from the east.'

It was a shade before half past eleven when the Junkers Ju 52 pulled off the runway, crossed the apron and shuddered to a halt in front of the arrivals hall. It was a short walk from there to the building, where non-German nationals were pointed in the direction of a separate entrance.

'Let me go in front,' said Knudsen. 'I'll be talking in German but it's probably better if you don't let on you speak or understand more than a few words.'

When it was his turn, Prince was searched and his suitcase emptied on a trestle table where a bored-looking woman in a light brown uniform checked every item. He noticed half a dozen men, presumably Gestapo, spread out around the perimeter of the room, their backs to the wall, observing everyone and everything. He caught the gaze of one of them for a few unblinking seconds. Prince smiled politely and the man continued to stare.

Eventually the woman finished her search. She indicated he should repack his suitcase and pointed to a desk where a man in his fifties with improbably thick spectacles looked as if he was genuinely pleased to see him.

'*Sprechen Sie Deutsch?*'

The man called Peter Rasmussen frowned and smiled: he didn't understand.

'*Sprechen Sie Deutsch?*' The German no longer looked pleased to see him and pronounced the words loudly, with the pause reserved for uncomprehending foreigners between each one: '*Sprechen… Sie… Deutsch?*'

A nod of slight understanding from Peter Rasmussen, who nonetheless then shook his head. '*Ich spreche nicht Deutsch.*' He pronounced it badly and repeated it three or four times. '*Kein Deutsch.*'

The Gestapo man with the thick spectacles tried a different tack. '*Verstehen Sie Deutsch?*' Did he understand German? He was looking quite annoyed now.

Prince shook his head and managed to look disappointed. '*Ein bisschen*' – a little.

'*Unterlagen.*' An exasperated sigh as the Gestapo man pointed at the papers Peter Rasmussen was clutching.

The German moved his spectacles to the top of his head and one by one held each of the papers close to his face, checking them slowly. Every few seconds he licked his lips in a disconcertingly meticulous manner: the lower lip first, right to left, then the upper lip, left to right. First the *legitimationskort*: a nod, Rasmussen's identity was in order. Then the flight ticket, followed by his exit card from Denmark and his entry visa for Germany: more nodding, not quite enthusiastic enough to be interpreted as a sign of approval, but acceptable nonetheless. The final two documents were his letter of accreditation from Mortensen Machinery Parts and the telegram from the hotel confirming his reservation. The Gestapo man studied these more carefully before calling over a colleague and handing them to him.

'*Warten Sie dort,*' he repeated several times to Peter Rasmussen, pointing to a bench where he was apparently supposed to wait.

After ten minutes, Prince wondered whether this was routine or whether he should worry. As far as he could tell, Otto Knudsen had already passed through security. He clasped his hands together to stop them shaking and wished he could get up to walk around. There seemed to be far more security people in the building than passengers, and it was easy to think they were all looking at him. For the first time that day he thought of Henry, and of how he could have allowed himself to be placed in such jeopardy. He was a Lincolnshire police officer sitting in the arrivals hall of an airport in Berlin, being questioned by the Gestapo. The situation was so ridiculous he found he was grinning to himself.

He recalled one of the many briefings in Matlock – the tutorials, as Hendrie liked to call them. 'Remember, old chap, a chain is only as strong as its weakest link. Rather a cliché, I know, but a very wise one nonetheless and one you'd be well advised to keep in mind. At any and every stage of your mission there's bound to be one part of your cover – your story, if you like – that is not quite as robust as the other parts. Be prepared for that.'

And now – possibly too late – he decided the accreditation letter from Mortensen Machinery Parts was the flaw, Hendrie's weakest link. It was all well and good Agent Horatio sorting matters out with his managing director, but what would happen if the Gestapo called the switchboard and they replied that they had no employee called Peter Rasmussen?

'*Kommen Sie her!*' The Gestapo officer was calling him and Prince could feel his throat tightening, convinced there was a menace to the man's voice. As he walked back to the desk, he noticed a couple of SS officers standing in front of the exit; he was sure they'd not been there when he last looked.

But the man with the improbably thick spectacles nodded his head to indicate all was in order and handed the papers back to Peter Rasmussen. '*Willkommen im Reich.*'

Prince bowed very slightly in gratitude and muttered, '*Vielen Dank*,' with a slightly better pronunciation than was perhaps wise. When the Gestapo officer enthusiastically shouted, '*Heil Hitler!*' he decided the wisest course of action was to respond likewise.

–

They were in Kreuzberg now, and it was a five-minute walk from the Kochstrasse U-Bahn station to Askanischer Platz. 'We ought to assume we're being followed,' Knudsen said. They were crossing Wilhelm Strasse, and he had his head down as he spoke. 'As I said, getting into Germany is not so difficult. It's easier to break into a prison than out of one, isn't it? They will be keeping a close eye on us, certainly for the first twenty-four hours. They'll want to know what we're up to while we're here. There are rumours they let in people they know are here to cause trouble just to see who they meet with and what they get up to. So we'll do nothing suspicious. In fact, I'm making it easy for them to keep an eye on us.'

Prince glanced around him. He'd been shocked enough on the streets of Denmark at the ubiquity of the Nazi occupation: the flags, the soldiers, the weapons. But this was altogether different and considerably more sinister than Denmark. At least there it was reasonable to assume that most people around him at a checkpoint or in the street were opposed to the Nazis. It was hard to underestimate how reassuring a slightly raised eyebrow, a frown or a hint of a smile could be. But here he had to assume everyone he encountered was the enemy: the mother pushing a pram, the old lady weighed down by her shopping, the limbless veteran of the Great War. It was far more unsettling than he'd anticipated.

They were now on Anhalter Strasse, with Anhalter station – the gateway to Munich and Frankfurt – to their left and on their right an enormous and rather ornate building.

'That building on your right – please don't stare at it, just keep looking ahead or at me – is the headquarters of the Gestapo. This is the rear of the building; the main entrance is on Prinz Albrecht Strasse. The high iron gates we're just walking past are where prisoners are driven in. They say very few who enter that way leave it alive. Here's our hotel.'

Prince was overwhelmed by the size of Hotel Excelsior as they climbed the steps to the entrance. Armed soldiers in grey greatcoats stood on either side of enormous doors. From the parapets hung flags the size of houses, giant swastikas set against a blood-red background, draped like the sails on a Viking ship.

'Five hundred rooms, nine restaurants, the largest hotel in Berlin,' said Otto. 'I like to think there's a degree of anonymity in staying here, but I don't doubt I'm deluding myself. There are Gestapo everywhere.'

While they waited to check in, Prince noticed a woman standing behind them, apparently studying a noticeboard with that day's menus pinned to it. He'd glimpsed her as they walked into reception and something about her caught his attention, but he couldn't be sure what it was. He turned round again, and this time the woman was facing the reception desk, though not looking in his direction. She had extraordinary dark eyes that darted around, and was wearing a turban-style hat. Ignoring Prince and Knudsen, she caught the attention of the reception clerk they were about to deal with. She spoke in a gentle accent, quite a cultured one. Could he check once more about her table reservation, please?

They signed the register and were allocated rooms next to each other on the fourth floor, overlooking Saarland Strasse. Before they went upstairs, the concierge called them over,

'Have you been in Berlin during an air raid?'

Both men shook their heads. Prince resisted the temptation to mention that he'd most probably seen the bombers as they left their Lincolnshire bases.

'We haven't had any raids recently, but if there is one, I urge you to take it seriously.' The concierge dropped his voice and moved closer to them, as if he was imparting something confidential. 'Last September they destroyed Potsdamer station, just across the road from here. Most of our windows were blown out. Of course,' he smiled, exposing a mouthful of yellow teeth, all at different angles, 'we are defeating the enemy, but in the unlikely event of a raid while you are our guests, there are three bomb shelters in the hotel. Please allow me to show you where they are.'

–

'Just keep walking, Peter. We'll have a proper chat once we're in the park. In the meantime, it's not a particularly good idea to stare for too long at the bombed buildings, and don't take too much notice of soldiers either – especially if they're wearing black uniforms like those over there: they're the SS. Remember, we're most probably being followed, so this needs to look like two colleagues out for a stroll.'

After leaving the hotel, they'd headed up Saarland Strasse to Leipziger Platz and then north along Hermann Göring Strasse. Apart from the pale yellow trams, almost all the traffic was military, lorries moving noisily through their gears, armoured cars acting as if the road belonged to them, and the occasional long black Daimler or Horch with curtained rear windows and a motorbike outrider. Ahead of them loomed the Reichstag, its grim blackened exterior setting the mood for the surrounding area.

No one made eye contact and everyone seemed to be in a hurry: it was as if every pedestrian had been permitted an unreasonably short period of time in which to reach their destination. Prince couldn't quite place it, but there was an unfamiliar smell to the city.

'What's the smell – it seems unusual?'

'I'm not sure. I always notice it too: it's got worse as the war's gone on. I think it must be a combination of the air raids, the cheap coal they use and the lack of hygiene – it can be quite overpowering at times. You know...' Otto paused while two women walked briskly past them, as if trying to keep in step with each other, 'I was here just before the war started in 1939, and even then there was an odour about the city. I was told it was because the place was built on a swamp. I asked one of the Nazis who'd been made a manager at the factory about it and he told me it was the smell of Jews.'

They walked on. 'There were over a hundred and fifty thousand Jews in Berlin in the early 1930s, you know. Half of them left the city, and since the war started, they've been sending the others away, a thousand at a time, by train – many of them from Anhalter station, near the hotel.'

'Where are they being sent to?'

'Keep your voice down, Peter. Here's the park, let's go down this path. Where are they being sent to? Who knows? I never ask, I just hear things. There are terrible rumours about them being transported to special camps in the east, where many of them are killed. I don't know how true it is, but it wouldn't surprise me; after all, the Nazis have always said they want to annihilate the Jews. When you asked me in Copenhagen why I'm helping the British — well, perhaps that helps answer your question.'

They were inside the park now, and Otto pointed to an isolated bench.

'Anyone following us will hate this. They'll have to keep their distance; they're not going to be able to get near us without looking ridiculous. At least we can now talk properly. The irony of that Nazi telling me the smell was due to the Jews is that the city smells even worse now that they've almost all gone!'

'Perhaps it's the smell of Nazis?'

'Exactly, Peter, exactly.'

'What's happened to all the trees? So many appear to be missing.'

'I think some must have been destroyed in the bombing raids, but others would have been chopped down for fuel. That will really hurt the Berliners, having to cut down trees in their beloved Tiergarten. Now, let me tell you about Bruno, my contact here.' Knudsen removed his hat and placed it on his knee, turning it round to find the right position. 'I'll tell you what, why don't we speak in German? If it's too difficult to follow, just tell me, but it will be useful for me to have an idea how fluent you are.'

Prince nodded and unbuttoned his raincoat, also removing his hat. Despite the time of year, it wasn't cold.

'Feuchtwanger and Wolff was an engineering company founded in the 1890s. They were originally based in Potsdam but moved to Spandau around the turn of the century. Do you know where Spandau is?'

'I'm afraid not.'

'It's a suburb of Berlin, not too far from here. In fact, it's right across the Tiergarten — that way. So, Feuchtwanger and Wolff

– they soon became universally known as F&W – developed a very fine reputation for the quality of their work. They started off by making all kinds of engines, but after the Great War, they specialised in locomotives: my company's relationship with them goes back to that time. Both Harald Feuchtwanger and Fritz Wolff were Jewish, and in 1936 the company was taken from them and nationalised. Hitler's laws meant Jews weren't able to own businesses. Fritz Wolff had died in the 1920s and his son was involved in the company. Harald Feuchtwanger was still alive in 1936, though in his eighties. He was still active in the business, but after it was taken over, he went to live in Switzerland. As I understand it, the Wolff family also emigrated, possibly to Holland, I'm not sure. Most of the management at the time were sacked and Nazi Party members put in their place. You seem to be following me, Peter. Your German must be good.'

'I understand it well enough, much better than I speak it.'

'Don't worry, that could be important. So they nationalised the company and kicked out the senior managers. They even renamed it, calling it Spandau Locomotive Engineering, though I still hear people refer to it as F&W. Now, Bruno Bergmann was a very bright young engineer at F&W when Mortensen Machinery Parts started supplying them. By the time the Nazis took it over, he was director of engineering, and of course he was sacked. But nationalising the company and getting rid of the senior managers turned out to be a disaster. The Nazi Party officials who took it over had no idea what they were doing. Their main customer was DRG, the German state railway company. Because of the need to move heavy armour by rail, they demanded more powerful locomotives, but there was no longer the expertise at F&W, and their engines kept failing.

'Eventually they realised they had to bring back some of the senior managers they'd sacked, and Bruno was one of them. He technically has a director of engineering above him, but he effectively runs that side of the company. Since he returned

– which would have been around two years ago now – the loco-motive engines they're building have significantly improved. He's very good at identifying and specifying the parts he needs and we're very good at manufacturing them. It's an effective relationship.'

'What about him as a person? He's obviously not a Nazi.'

'Well, I wouldn't know. He wasn't a Nazi Party member in 1936, otherwise they wouldn't have sacked him, but you'll understand that I've never discussed politics with him. You simply don't do that here. However, I always got the impression – and it's only an impression, Peter – that he's not a Nazi. The phrase he constantly uses is "I'm only an engineer", but over the past couple of years there has been the odd remark. He may refer to food shortages, or a neighbour's son missing in the east, or having to be careful when he speaks in front of the children. But you must realise, I do nothing to embarrass him: I don't ask questions or discuss the war. It's a cordial relationship certainly, but a guarded one, and more than anything else, it's business.'

'So how did the meeting with the Luftwaffe officer come about?'

Otto frowned, thinking about his answer. He waited while a woman walked past with her dog, the first person to have been near them in a while.

'I've no idea, and to be honest, I still don't know quite what the meeting was about. I don't usually socialise with Bruno outside of work: they're long days and he wants to get back to his family. I'm usually tired and I prefer to stay around the hotel, eating there. I have been to dinner with him once or twice, though, so it was not so unusual when… hang on, Peter…'

A shabbily dressed man shuffled past them, doffing his hat as he did so. His stained raincoat was tied up with a length of rope and his shoes were filthy.

'*Guten Nachmittag.*'

They wished him a good afternoon in return, but he'd paused – more or less stopped, in fact – when he'd greeted them and looked as if he wanted to linger. When he eventually walked on, he turned round a couple of times, checking they were still there.

'Gestapo?'

'I'm not sure, Peter. How old would you say he was... mid-thirties? Quite young not to be in uniform. Where was I? Ah yes, so on the trip in August, Bruno suggested we go out to a restaurant one night for dinner. Outside of the hotels, it's hard to get a good meal in Berlin, and it's always complicated by the fact that you need food stamps too. Those restaurants that are decent and have a good supply of food are very hard to get into. But Bruno said he had a special voucher for a place on Donhoff Strasse and suggested we went there. It was a Bavarian restaurant, I don't remember the name, and the voucher meant we didn't need to present food stamps.'

'Is the restaurant near the factory?'

'Not at all: it's actually not too far from the hotel, near Friedrichstrasse. It turned out to be a very small restaurant, and rather cramped. Not long after we'd sat down, the manager asked if we'd be more comfortable upstairs, as our table was very narrow. It was a bit annoying, to be frank, because we'd just settled down. But we went upstairs and the room he showed us into had just the one table, quite large – you could have got eight people round it. It was a private dining room, apparently just for us. Even before we'd sat down, a man in uniform entered, not through the door we'd come in but through another entrance, one I hadn't even noticed. He joined us at the table and Bruno introduced him. He said something like "This is my friend Kurt: he's a Luftwaffe officer. He's very interested to meet you" – words to that effect, anyway.'

'And what happened then?'

'We ordered our meal; it was a Bavarian pork stew, I recall. I've eaten better, but the beer was good – that was Bavarian too. Kurt asked me a lot of questions about the challenges of fabricating parts for engines that can withstand very high temperatures. Then he started to talk about how he had some understanding of the problem because he was involved in a programme to develop a pilotless aircraft – he never called it a rocket. I was quite unsure of how to react. He was certainly telling me things he shouldn't have – you know all the detail, Peter, I gave it to you when we first met in Copenhagen. He left before us and said something about hoping we'd meet again. I know London have a lot of questions they want you to ask him, but I can't guarantee we will get to meet him. Whatever happens, I can't be seen to be pushing matters. We'll go to the factory tomorrow and at some stage I'll ask Bruno if he'll have dinner with us. If it feels right, I'll ask him if Kurt wants to join us.'

'London will not be happy if I come all the way here and don't get to see Kurt.'

'I shouldn't imagine they will be, but we're very exposed here. We have to be careful. And you know what I was saying about your German?'

Prince nodded.

'Don't speak it at all and don't let on you understand any. The fact that people will think you have no knowledge of the language may work to our advantage, you never know.'

–

Richard Prince slept fitfully that night. The heating was on constantly and the window only opened an inch or two at the top, making the room quite unbearably stuffy. Despite the curfew, there was a surprising amount of traffic on Saarland Strasse, mostly, as far as he could tell, army trucks. The bathroom was further down the corridor, but he did have a small sink in his room, and every hour or so he got up to run cold water over his face. The carpet was uncomfortable to walk on in his bare feet; it had an almost wiry texture to it.

But it was not just the noise and discomfort that kept him awake. As he lay in bed, he reflected incredulously on the developments of the past few weeks. As a police officer in Lincolnshire, his work had been interesting enough; not without some degree of excitement and certainly professionally fulfilling. He had an impressive degree of seniority for his age, and his strong reputation enabled him to be the master of his own fate. He could choose what cases to work on and he decided how to run them and who worked with him.

On the few occasions he allowed himself to indulge in fleeting personal reflection, he would think with satisfaction about how he was managing to bring his son up so well. If anyone had asked, which they didn't, he'd have assured them he'd recovered well enough from the death of his wife and daughter and both he and Henry were doing fine, thank you.

In Copenhagen, though, he'd had plenty of time to reflect, and it had become obvious that neither of them was doing quite as well as he'd liked to imagine. The reason he so rarely indulged in thinking about how he felt was because he missed Jane and Grace so much that anything more than a passing thought was far too painful. The fact that Henry was so young didn't mean he was immune from grief either: life would be a constant reminder to him of what had happened.

But as much as Prince loved and missed his son, he had to admit that his secondment to Copenhagen, and now this trip to Berlin, had brought him a surprisingly enjoyable degree of excitement. It was a familiar excitement, the kind he experienced at the start of a serious case and at the moment of solving it. It was the thrill of the chase and the personal challenge involved. And he had come to realise that despite the uncertainty and the constant threat of discovery, he wouldn't swap it for the world.

There was another unexpected emotion too: the way he found himself thinking about Hanne. It was a feeling of fondness; he realised he was missing her. He wished he was sitting next to her on the sofa, edging closer to her.

He and Otto met in reception at seven o'clock. His colleague had already had breakfast and looked as if he'd slept well. He was sitting on a chair reading *Völkischer Beobachter*, which he folded up as soon as Prince arrived, though not before Prince spotted the words 'Heroes' and 'Stalingrad' on the front page.

As they walked towards the entrance, a woman swept past them, her long coat brushing Prince and the scent of a powerful perfume following in her wake. As she turned to say something to a porter, he realised it was the same woman he'd seen the previous afternoon: the gentle accent, the remarkable eyes. This time she was wearing a fawn bonnet-style hat with a wide dark ribbon round it, tied into a large bow at the back. For a brief moment she glanced at Prince. It was not a look of recognition or communication, nothing like that. But she was clearly looking at him rather than his companion. Then she turned again, said something to the porter and disappeared down the steps.

Bruno Bergmann had sent a car to collect them: the journey across the city took forty minutes. They were stopped at two checkpoints, there was another delay when they were halted for a military convoy to pass, and Prince noticed that at least two roads on their route were closed due to what appeared to be bomb damage.

Otto leaned over, the coffee warm on his breath. 'Before the war, this journey would take twenty minutes!'

The Spandau Locomotive Engineering works were vast, taking up three blocks in an area that seemed to be an uncomfortable mix of industrial and residential. Bruno Bergmann was much as Otto had described him: not unfriendly, but no small talk, and very much the engineer. He wore a stained light brown work coat over a shirt and tie.

The first hour was taken up with a tour of the factory, with Otto translating everything from German into Danish for Prince's benefit. Then it was up an iron ladder attached to the wall onto a large gantry overlooking the main assembly plant.

'What did you think of the factory, Herr Rasmussen?' Bruno asked.

'Very impressive; every bit as impressive as Otto said it would be.'

'You're a maritime engineer then? I am sure we have much to learn from our seafaring colleagues!'

Worried that he was about to be asked technical questions, Prince replied hurriedly, 'That was some time ago, I'm afraid. Now I'm as rusty as some of the old boilers I worked on. I—'

'Peter's role,' said Otto reassuringly, 'is more commercial. He's shadowing me on the sales side of our business so that if for some reason I'm unable to visit you, he could take my place. He is even due to start German language lessons soon. The truth is, Bruno, your drawing and specifications are so good that our draughtsmen and engineers need to do little with them. You could always find a job with us.'

For the next few hours, Bruno brought a series of drawings to the large table in the middle of the meeting room. They were intricate diagrams of machine parts. The idea was that Otto would then estimate a price and the following day negotiations would continue.

'It is difficult to raise this, Bruno, but after my last visit the price we had to agree on... it barely covered our costs.'

'Our instructions are...' Bruno paused and glanced at Prince, who'd adopted a mildly dazed look suggesting he didn't understand what they were talking about. 'Your colleague, Peter – are you sure he won't understand this part of the conversation?'

'Of course I'm sure. To be honest, I told them it's not much use him not speaking German, but they insisted. He has family connections with one of our directors, you know how it goes. He is bright, though, and reliable.'

'Very well then: our instructions are to impose the lowest price possible on suppliers from the occupied countries. I know that sounds blunt and unpleasant, but it is what I've been told. If it is of any comfort, I could have pushed you even harder. The bosses here think we can get everything on the cheap. I tell them that if we do that, our locomotives will break down again. It's not as if that hasn't happened before.'

Another hour of talks, some translated into Danish, and then Bruno suggested they go to the canteen before they visited one of the specialist workshops.

'Tonight, Otto, I was going to suggest we had dinner at the same restaurant we went to in August. Would you like that?'

'That would be most pleasant, Bruno, thank you very much. Will your friend be joining us again?'

Bruno looked around before nodding.

'And I presume the invitation extends to Peter?'

He raised his eyebrows, an unspoken question.

'Don't worry,' Otto said. 'He's most trustworthy. I can absolutely assure you of that.'

A long period of silence, during which Bruno drummed the eraser end of his pencil on one of his diagrams. He had a slightly worried look about him. He shot a glance at Prince, who was staring out of the window into the main assembly plant below. An enormous hoist was travelling across the ceiling, a huge boiler suspended from it by chains, and he was following its progress, clearly fascinated.

'I think I understand, Otto. That's why you brought him to Berlin, isn't it?'

—

'Ah, here we are – Das Bayerischer Haus.'

The restaurant was on Donhoff Strasse, close to where it joined Kommandantenstrasse. It had been a ten-minute stroll from the hotel, one that would have been quite pleasant had Otto not spent much of it glancing ominously up to the sky.

'There's no moon and no clouds tonight; your RAF like to bomb Berlin without those distractions. If a raid starts before we reach the restaurant, I think it would be better to head back to the hotel. Make sure you keep your pass safe.'

The passes had been issued to them by the hotel, confirming they were registered guests, giving their names and the dates of their stay and declaring they were allowed to be out and about in the *Mitte* district until nine thirty – 'precisely' – that evening. They had an impressive array of stamps, including one at the top with a large swastika.

At the entrance, Otto stepped back and gestured for Prince to enter first. Once he was inside, he turned round. Otto was still holding the door open, this time for a woman on her own. It was unquestionably the woman from the hotel, now wearing a beret with a single feather set at an angle on the side of it. She glanced in Prince's direction, her darting eyes connecting with his for the briefest of moments, and had it not been so dim in the restaurant, he'd have sworn she smiled.

As they were shown to their table, he wondered whether he should mention her to Otto but thought better of it. Otto would probably wonder if he was deluded. *An agent in enemy territory overcome by paranoia. Not unheard of.*

In any case, it was almost certainly a coincidence: a guest at the same hotel who he'd bumped into a couple of times, now in the same restaurant as them. Nothing unusual.

What happened next was very much as Otto had described from his first visit to the restaurant. The ground floor was busy and the tables were packed closely together. With the windows covered by blackout material, the interior was quite gloomy, making it hard to see much around them. A tall waiter with a nervous tic showed them to a table for two by the stairs and provided them with a menu. Prince look round and noticed that the woman was sitting on her own at a small table by the door, her back to them, facing the window. He had barely had a moment to study her when the harassed-looking *maître d'* appeared. He was terribly sorry, but there had been some confusion over bookings, for which he could only apologise: it was his fault. He would need their table to join to another one to accommodate a booking of four people. But he did have a room upstairs. Perhaps they'd find it more comfortable up there anyway?

The private room too was as Otto had described it: certainly large enough for eight people, the table with four place settings on it. The room was wood-panelled, stained rather inexpertly in dark brown. They sat down and waited for five minutes, neither saying a word. Eventually one of the panels opened – Prince had had no idea it was a door – and Bruno entered, followed by a taller man in his twenties wearing a long greatcoat and a peaked cap. Without speaking, he removed his hat and coat, revealing the grey uniform of a Luftwaffe officer. He sat down next to Bruno, opposite Otto and Prince.

Bruno made the introductions. 'You already know my friend from Denmark... this is his colleague; I believe he has some questions for you. I am assured he is to be trusted absolutely. Unfortunately, he doesn't speak German, but my friend will translate.'

Before either Otto or Prince could say anything, Kurt spoke, his voice sounding younger than he looked.

'Let me anticipate your first question: why am I sharing all this information with you?'

Prince found himself inadvertently nodding even before Otto had translated. Kurt paused and looked at him slightly suspiciously.

'You will have to be satisfied with this brief explanation. You know me as Kurt, which is of course not my real name, though I am an *Oberst* in the Luftwaffe. For the past eighteen months I've been attached to our scientific division. Over the last year almost all of our resources – money, equipment, people – have been diverted to the V-1 pilotless aircraft I was telling you about last time we met.'

He had a distinctive accent: as far as Prince could tell, it was a form of High German, possibly indicating he was from Bavaria or Austria.

Kurt nodded to Otto and paused for him to translate.

'I'm going to be frank with you: many of us are frustrated beyond words about this. We have to devote everything to developing the V-1 when we have reservations about it; these are professional reservations, you understand. If I thought for a moment the V-1 could be developed quickly and at a low cost and could make a significant contribution to our war effort, I wouldn't be sitting here now, I can assure you of that. But the technology is complex and at every stage of the development programme we're facing major problems. It could take years to get this right. Your friend really speaks no German? He gives the impression of following what I say.'

'He understands the odd word, really no more than,' said Otto, before translating.

'One of our many problems has been sourcing components that can withstand very high temperatures, and this led to my meeting Bruno. To be honest, my initial approach was a perfectly proper one, part of my job – hoping our friend here from Copenhagen might be able to provide those components and this would help the V-1 development. But before that meeting I began to think about matters in a more reflective manner. Say we did solve the problem – what would happen then? There would still be dozens of other problems with the V-1 programme.

'I began to see that the issue was a wider one: by solving one problem I'd be helping to keep the bigger problem on track, whereas in fact the best service I could do for the Luftwaffe and for the German people would be to bring about the abandoning of the V-1 programme. It's distracting the Luftwaffe from doing its real job. Stalingrad has been a disaster: we've already lost hundreds of aircraft and we have to send in Junker 52s and Focke-Wulf Condors to break the siege, and they're simply not up to those conditions. Throughout Europe our planes are outperformed by the RAF. We'd stand a chance of reversing that if all our efforts weren't going into the V-1 programme.'

He waited for Otto to translate, pouring himself a beer and drinking most of it in one go.

'But giving us all this information, it could be seen as treason.' Prince spoke in Danish. He noticed that Bruno looked shocked when it was translated, startled at what he'd found himself mixed up with.

'Depends on what you mean by treason. I'm trying to stop something I think is bad for Germany, so that can't be treason. And in any case, there's something else... the SS have now started showing interest in both our V-1 programme and the army's V-2 rocket. There's talk of them wanting to take both over. That would be an utter disaster. It would amount to the SS taking control of the Luftwaffe. I'm not a Nazi Party member, but I am a patriotic German and a professional Luftwaffe officer. I can't sit by and do nothing while Germany's future is compromised by these crazy programmes. What you do with the information I give you... well, I don't want to know, just so long as it helps stop these ridiculous so-called miracle weapons. Anyway, you had some questions for me?'

Prince had, of course, not written anything down, but he'd memorised the questions London had sent via Stockholm.

Can Kurt give more information on the speed of the V-1?

How long does it take to reach that speed?

Can he give more detailed information on how any test flights have gone?

Have they managed yet to launch a V-1 with a one-ton warhead?

Can he say anything about the fuel systems?

Can he give any information on how the V-2 programme is going?

Kurt did his best to answer the questions, though Prince had the impression there was some information he was holding back.

'May I ask you a question?' He'd lit a cigarette when he'd finished answering and was leaning back in his chair. 'I don't

166

need to know who you work for – in fact I don't want to know – but what will they do with this information I give you?'

Prince shrugged. 'I'm little more than a messenger, but I imagine they'd want to stop the programmes.'

Bruno shifted nervously in his seat. 'We have possibly been here long enough. I propose we leave in no more than five minutes. We haven't even eaten yet!'

'I have one last question for Kurt: are the V-1 and V-2 projects being developed in different places?'

Kurt looked at him suspiciously and spoke to Otto. 'Tell me, where is he really from, this friend of yours?'

'He's Danish.'

'I don't believe that. I think he's working for the British. I wouldn't be surprised if he's understood every word I've said; I've seen the way his eyes follow the conversation.'

No one spoke. The silence was eventually broken by Prince, now speaking in German.

'Let's be honest, eh? If you were that concerned about what happens with the information you're passing on, you wouldn't have come here tonight in the first place and answered my questions. As far as the V-1 and the V-2 are concerned, we may have different reasons, but we both want them stopped. So maybe you can tell me the places they're being developed?'

Kurt thought for a while, drumming the fingers of both hands on the table. He had a resigned look about him when he spoke.

'Very well. Peenemünde – it's a massive site on the Baltic coast, not too far from the Danish coast. I'm surprised you've not heard of it.'

'And that's the site for the V-1?'

'Both the V-1 and the V-2: separately but on the same site, if you see what I mean. In fact—'

They were interrupted by an urgent rapping at the door. Bruno went over to open it. It was the woman in the beret with a single feather, the one from the hotel with the dark, darting eyes. She leaned into the room, speaking with an urgency that shocked them all.

'You'd better leave now, all of you. Quickly. The Gestapo are on their way.'

Chapter 12

Berlin, December 1942

There was no panic in the private dining room of Das Bayerischer Haus. Once the woman in the beret had disappeared, Kurt pointed to the hidden door in the panelled wall and they filed towards it. It opened onto a steep stone stairway, lit from the top by a bright bulb, which revealed an iron rail running down the wall. They gathered together at the top of the steps as Kurt closed the door behind them, quietly sliding three sets of bolts into place. No one had said a word, though everyone was breathing hard.

'It will be safer to turn out this light,' said Kurt, his voice little more than a whisper. 'Walk down slowly, one step at a time. Just make sure you don't let go of the rail. Are any of you armed?'

They all shook their heads.

'I've got my Mauser; I'll go first. What's that?'

They listened in silence: the muffled noise seemed to be coming from the room they'd been in.

'We'd better hurry. When we reach the bottom of the steps, I'll open the door. You'll find we're in a back yard. It's not the yard to the restaurant, which will be to your left, on the other side of a high brick wall. Once we're all out, I'll lock that door – you'd better give me the key, Bruno – and then we'll go our separate ways. Come on, let's move.'

The descent was a perilous one in the pitch dark; the steps, as well as being damp and slippery, were also of varying heights, making their progress slower than they would have liked. Behind them they could hear some kind of commotion. Kurt was at the front, Prince behind him, followed by Otto, with Bruno at the rear. Kurt waited until they were all at the bottom before sliding open the single bolt.

The yard was empty, and although it was dark, it was possible to make out their surroundings: two large dustbins ahead of them and the high wall Kurt had mentioned to their left, behind which was the rear entrance to the restaurant. They could hear voices coming from that yard. To their right was a tiny passageway that led to the street.

They closed the door and Kurt locked it, placing the key in one of the dustbins. Somewhere in the distance they could hear shouting, and a dog barking. He gathered them in a huddle and pointed to the passageway.

'That opens on to Lindenstrasse,' he whispered. 'I'll turn left, which will take me back towards Donhoff Strasse. Bruno, you turn right and then into Kommandantenstrasse. You two carry on down Lindenstrasse. You're at the Excelsior, correct? Well, keep going until you see Koch Strasse: that will lead you back towards Askanischer Platz. We'd better hurry now.'

They moved as a group down the passageway and waited behind Kurt as he peered up and down the street. At last he turned and nodded, as if to indicate all was clear. He buttoned up his greatcoat, checked his cap was at the correct angle and put his semi-automatic pistol into his side pocket. Then, without saying a word, he stepped confidently into the street.

Bruno followed a few seconds later; he looked terrified, the sweat pouring from his forehead and his hands trembling violently as he put his hat on.

'We'll be at the factory as planned tomorrow morning,' Otto whispered. 'We'll see you then.' Bruno looked at him as if he was mad: tomorrow morning was a country so far away he had no expectation of ever getting anywhere near it.

Otto made to move out of the passageway almost immediately after Bruno had left it, but Prince put his hand on the other man's arm to stop him. 'Give it a minute.'

He was back in Matlock now, being trained for what they called 'out and about', which made it sound like a nature ramble rather than the deadly serious matter of how to operate in a town: how to avoid being followed and what to do if you were stopped.

Don't walk too fast.

Don't walk too slowly.

Don't keep looking behind you: avoid doing so where possible.

At a junction is the best time to look around you.

Resist the temptation to stop and look in shop windows, especially at night. It can appear too obvious.

If you're stopped, make sure you can explain where you've come from and where you're going.

If you're with someone else, they will most likely split you up before questioning you, so make sure you have the same story.

Keep your hands out of your pockets, otherwise they may think you're armed.

Don't argue when you're stopped, but do appear slightly annoyed: if people are too compliant, that can look suspicious too.

He had felt much of it was obvious, but they'd made him memorise it: they called these the Nine Steps, and a couple of times he'd been woken up in the middle of the night and forced to recite them. Now he was going through them in his mind.

By the time they left the passageway, there was no sign of either Kurt to their left or Bruno to their right.

'Walk a bit slower, Otto.'

'You sound as if you've done this before.'

'A bit quicker than that, though – just normal speed, that's it. If we're stopped, tell them we've been looking for a restaurant and walked up to Unter den Linden but decided to return to the hotel instead. Tell them we're Danish businessmen and I don't speak a word of German. Act confused as to why we've been stopped, but don't be rude.'

They paused at the junction with Kommandantenstrasse. As they looked up and down it, they could just make out the figure of Bruno, walking faster than Prince would have liked, though he was at least heading away from the restaurant rather than back towards it.

No sooner had they crossed Kommandantenstrasse than they heard the sound of a car speeding towards them from behind and screeching to a halt.

'Oh my God,' said Otto.

'Be calm. Remember what I told you to say.'

A long black Mercedes sedan had pulled alongside them, its front wheels mounting the kerb in case they were disinclined to stop. Three men, clearly Gestapo, climbed out.

'Halt: stand still and keep your hands by your sides. When I tell you, give us your papers, but do so slowly.'

Prince glanced at Otto.

'Don't look at each other! You – move away from him, over here! Don't you hear what I'm saying?'

'My colleague does not understand or speak German, I'm afraid.'

'I don't care. Papers.'

They each handed their papers over to a different officer, who studied them for a while and then consulted the man behind them. As he moved forward, Prince realised he recognised him: it was the shabbily dressed man who'd wished them good afternoon in the Tiergarten the previous afternoon.

He spoke with a sharp working-class Berlin accent. 'Where have you been?'

Otto cleared his throat and shifted anxiously from foot to foot. 'You can see from our papers that we are staying at the Excelsior on Askanischer Platz. We decided to see if we could find a restaurant to eat at tonight because we fancied a walk too, and the concierge kindly gave us passes. We went up

Friedrichstrasse to Unter den Linden but couldn't see anything we liked or that had a table, so we decided we may as well eat at the hotel after all. That's where we're heading now.'

'Why have you come this way? You've gone round in a circle: why didn't you go down Friedrichstrasse or Wilhelm Strasse or even Jerusalemer Strasse?'

'You'll have to excuse us, sir, but we're guests in your city. We are not terribly familiar with it, and with it being so dark… I'm afraid we must have become disorientated.'

'Enough. You come over here with me.' It was one of the other Gestapo men, gesturing for Prince to join him a bit further down the pavement, away from Otto.

'But my colleague doesn't speak German!'

'Shut up, unless you fancy spending the night as our guest in Prinz Albrecht Strasse. I can assure you it's not nearly as comfortable as the Excelsior.'

The Gestapo man fired questions at him. 'What brings you to Berlin? Who have you met with? Where exactly have you been tonight? Did you visit any restaurant on Donhoff Strasse?'

But Prince smiled apologetically, shaking his head. '*Ich spreche nicht Deutsch… Dansk… Dänisch…*'

The man who'd followed them to the Tiergarten strolled over, speaking to the other man as if Prince wasn't there.

'I tell you, it's a waste of time. They're just two fucking Danish businessmen. The other one is well known to us: his company supplies the Reich. He's never been any trouble. We're wasting our time, come on.'

'But they were coming from that direction, weren't they? Donhoff Strasse is just up there. Weren't we supposed to be looking for more than one person?'

'Maybe, but it's obviously not one of these bastards, is it?'

Prince's sense of relief was short-lived. In the distance, there was the sound of shouting, loud voices, one of them possibly that of the young Luftwaffe officer. It was too far away to make out the words, but they were followed by pistol shots, four or five in very quick succession, fast enough to have come from a semi-automatic. Almost immediately there was a retort of gunfire. It sounded like a machine gun, and was followed by a brief scream, then more shouting and dogs barking.

'Quick, we need to get up there. I told you we were wasting our time here. You two: go straight back to your hotel – now, move!'

Otto and Prince walked as fast as they felt they could get away with. Just before they crossed Wilhelm Strasse, Otto turned into a shop doorway and threw up.

'You need to pull yourself together, Otto. We can't afford to draw attention to ourselves. You look like a bag of nerves.'

'Not without good reason! We were stopped by the Gestapo, for Christ's sake!'

'That happens all the time in Berlin, I imagine. We must regard it as routine. The important point is they don't suspect us.'

'How the hell do you know that?'

'Because they were talking freely in front of me, remember? They assumed I didn't understand. The one we spotted in the Tiergarten yesterday described us as two fucking Danish businessmen and said they were wasting their time on us. If they'd suspected us of anything, they wouldn't have let us go, would they?'

'But what if they've caught Kurt or Bruno and they've confessed? And that shooting – what was that about?'

Prince moved in front of Otto, grabbing him by the shoulders. 'Pull yourself together! There's nothing we can do about the others. We need to act normally: return to the hotel, go to the factory in Spandau in the morning and then fly back to Copenhagen in the evening as planned. If we do anything unusual, we'll just be drawing attention to ourselves.'

For the second night in a row, Prince hardly slept. This time it wasn't the heat or the noise but the events of that evening that kept him awake.

The meeting with Kurt had been very productive: he'd answered the questions London had passed on to him and the information about Peenemünde felt like gold dust. If that didn't satisfy London, then nothing would. Prince thought he could be home within a week, two at the most, and would finally see Henry.

But then the drama: the woman in the hat. He'd been right in assuming she was watching him, but it wasn't for the Gestapo. She must be on the same side as him, but who did she work for? Was she a companion of Kurt's, there to watch his back?

And then he wondered about Kurt: had he been followed to the restaurant? And how come they'd been able to escape with relative ease? Could it all be a web of deceit they'd been drawn into?

He knew there was little they could do other than stick to their routine for the day, which meant being at the hotel entrance at a quarter to eight for the car to take them to Spandau Locomotive Engineering.

—

Otto hardly said a word in the car. He'd been more or less silent since they'd met in reception that morning. He'd clearly not slept, and the smell of vomit was still on his breath. The tension in the car mounted as they passed through Charlottenburg. Neither of them had any idea what had happened to Bruno after they'd spotted him in Kommandantenstrasse, just before they were stopped by the Gestapo. The only straw they could cling to was that they both agreed the shooting appeared to have been further away, closer to the restaurant.

To their relief, as the car pulled through the factory gates, Bruno was standing on the steps of the office block, peering anxiously out to the car park. The friendly engineer was in a terrible state. He looked pale and gaunt; his red-rimmed eyes had a haunted look to them.

'Come this way,' was all he said before leading them down a long corridor into a noisy basement workshop, the smell of grease and diesel fumes almost overpowering.

'If anyone asks why we're here, I want you to look at this.' They were in front of a workbench with a long cylinder on it, not unlike an oxygen tank. Next to it were various springs and other small machinery parts, including a box of ball bearings with *Mortensen Machinery Parts – Copenhagen* on the lid. 'No one can hear us, it's too noisy here. Gather closer and keep looking at these parts as we talk. It must appear as if we're studying them. I have a family, you know. My wife is pregnant. Do you know what would happen to them if I was caught? My children would be taken away from us and my wife would be sent to a concentration camp.' He pushed some of the parts around the table, appearing to be on the verge of tears. His hands were shaking so hard he managed to knock some of the parts onto the floor.

'What happened to you last night, Bruno?'

'Nothing, would you believe it. I went down Kommandan-tenstrasse as Kurt had said and then caught the U-Bahn home from Moritz Platz. No one followed me, I wasn't stopped, and there wasn't even a security check on the train like there often is at that time of night. When I arrived home, I was in such a state I told my wife I felt unwell and stayed downstairs. You two obviously got back all right.'

'The Gestapo stopped us, but they didn't suspect us. They were about to let us go anyway when we heard a commotion from the direction of the restaurant. There was an exchange of gunfire: it sounded like a machine gun and a semi-automatic, but I can't be sure.'

Bruno looked thoughtful. 'Kurt was carrying a Mauser, which is the semi-automatic pistol most Luftwaffe officers carry. If he fired his pistol and they fired back at him with machine guns, then he wouldn't have stood a chance. If he's been killed, I'm sorry, but at least no one will know about us.'

'Can he be traced to you? If he has been killed and for some reason he was already under suspicion, they'll be checking him out in detail now.'

'I thought about that all last night, Otto. I went over every minute of every contact I had with him, believe me. The first time we met was at a conference for military scientists and engineers in early July at Humboldt University. Afterwards there was a big reception, the kind where hundreds of people mingle together. We just got chatting and he asked me what I did. He said he'd be interested in talking to me in further detail about how to cope with machinery operating at very high temperatures; he said the Luftwaffe might want to know more. We had one meeting at a bar on Unter den Linden, which was when I told him about your company and the high quality of your parts. He said he'd like to meet you when you were next here, which is how that dinner in August came about. I'd told him when you were going to be here, and he said he'd be in touch. Two days before you arrived, he bumped into me in the street and we agreed to meet at the restaurant. He never phoned me, and I can't imagine there'd be anything in writing.'

'But we don't know for sure that he's not been captured, do we? He could still be alive.'

They left the factory at two o'clock. The car was to take them back to the hotel to collect their cases and then on to Tempelhof. As they pulled out of the factory, Otto slumped in his seat, mopping his brow. 'I'm never coming back here again, never. When I get back to Copenhagen – if I get back to Copenhagen – I'm going to tell my boss I've had enough of travelling. I have no intention of ever leaving Denmark again; in fact, the way I feel now, I never want to leave my apartment again. If he doesn't let me give it up, I'll resign.'

'Won't that draw attention, though?'

Otto turned to Prince, a slightly manic look on his face. 'I don't care, Peter, I really don't care. I'm never coming back here again, ever.'

–

They both knew that if there was the slightest hint of suspicion over them, they'd be stopped at the airport, but it was an incident-free departure, though not without the inevitable tension.

Their papers were fine, their visas were checked, their cases gone over and Otto was able to satisfy the Gestapo officers that the purpose of their visit had been to help the Reich. Their flight was at five past six, and they entered the departure lounge an hour before that. Otto went to the bar to buy them each a beer and came back with a copy of *Der Angriff*, the Nazis' afternoon newspaper. Its front page was dominated by a head-and-shoulders photo of Kurt, under a stark headline: *Luftwaffe officer killed in Mitte shooting.*

Oberst Albert Kampmann was killed following a shooting incident in the Mitte district of central Berlin last night. Der Angriff understands that Oberst Kampmann was taken to the Charité hospital, where he died of his wounds in the early hours of the morning. The 26-year-old officer had been in the service of the Führer since 1939 and was based at the headquarters of the Air Ministry on Wilhelm Strasse. The circumstances of the shooting are still unclear and are being investigated by the Gestapo special investigations unit at Prinz Albrecht Strasse. Anyone with any information regarding Oberst Kampmann are required to contact this unit or their nearest Gestapo office as a matter of extreme urgency. Citizens of Berlin are reminded that ultimate victory is a common cause and their vigilance in helping to inform on and root out enemies of the Reich is both a legal and a moral obligation.

'It's not very subtle, is it?'

'That's the way the Nazis work. But it's worrying, isn't it?'

Prince nodded. 'Of course it is. He seems to have been alive at some stage. They could have got something out of him before he died. But then again, if they had, we wouldn't be sitting here now, would we?'

'They were on to him, though, weren't they? Those last two sentences: it's a clear message that they regard him as a criminal. There'll be a thorough investigation. They could link him to Bruno and then us. They'll know where we are in Copenhagen.'

Both men sat in silence, their heads bowed, their beer untouched.

'I tend to agree with what you said earlier, Otto.'

'What was that?'

'About never wanting to come back to this country again. Still, at least my job is done.'

—

At ten to six, they were led out of the departure lounge and along the front of the building to where their plane to Copenhagen was waiting. The group of passengers paused in front of another glass-plated lounge, waiting to be escorted across the apron to the plane.

Prince looked through the window. She was standing there, this time wearing an elegant trilby-style hat with a neat floral arrangement on one side. The jet-black eyes darted around before settling on him, and the briefest of smiles crossed her lips. As the passengers were moved on, she raised her hand as if to adjust her hat, allowing it to form a fleeting farewell wave.

Chapter 13

London, December 1942

'I say, Roly, would you believe it? There's the most dreadful row going on at our local church – about this year's Christmas carol service of all things. Most of the choir are vehemently opposed to "Silent Night" being included in the service. They claim it's a German hymn and—'

'Well it is, Tom – "Stille Nacht". Don't you remember we were made to sing it in German lessons?'

'Don't you start. Poor old Elizabeth has stuck her neck out by insisting it doesn't matter. People are falling out with each other – her friend Marjorie refuses to speak to her and the vicar's close to having a nervous breakdown. And now they've asked me to come along to the parish council to give my opinion – as if I have one!'

'They know what you do?'

'Not as such, but most of the people in the village like to think they have an idea. I'd love to sit there and explain how I have to consider matters of life and death every day. I'd like to think that would give them some sense of perspective, but I very much doubt it. You know what village life is like, eh? Now then, talking of life and death...'

They were walking slowly along a corridor somewhere underneath Downing Street. Gilbey had a sense they were passing under the Cabinet Office, perhaps even under White-hall. They were going to use one of the new secure meeting rooms, which apparently had fresh air pumped into it.

'You've seen Agent Laertes' report, no doubt, Roly. Terribly helpful.'

Pearson held out an arm to stop his companion. He needed to catch his breath. 'Wait for the meeting, Tom, eh?'

—

The secure meeting room was less cramped and stuffy than the one they'd met in the previous month, but the air of tension was the same, as was Lord Swalcliffe's evident irritation. Churchill's principal scientific adviser sat on his own on one side of the table, files and pencils arrayed in front of him, fingers tapping impatiently and a generally unhappy demeanour about him.

Air Vice Marshal Frank Hamilton and his colleague from the RAF intelligence branch sat at one end of the table, the wall behind them covered with charts and photographs. Long from the Ministry sat at the other end, while Pearson and Gilbey sat next to each other, opposite Lord Swalcliffe.

'The lighting in here is far too bright.'

'I think you may find, Lord Swalcliffe, that the lighting in the previous room we used was too dim.'

'You don't need to lecture me of all people on the difference between bright and dim, Pearson, I'm the scientist here. Now, this report – I'm not sure it's anywhere as reassuring as you evidently think it is, Gilbey.'

'On the contrary, Lord Swalcliffe, based on what we received from Agent Laertes on his return to Copenhagen, it is clear that the German called Kurt answered all the questions we sent over. Isn't that correct, Frank?'

Hamilton leaned forward to answer but was interrupted by Lord Swalcliffe.

'But isn't this the point, though, what this Kurt chap said in his answers? Let me quote. Here we are. Agent Laertes – do you employ classics scholars to come up with these ridiculous code names, Gilbey? – Agent Laertes says Kurt told him: "The technology is complex and at every stage of the development programme we're facing major problems. It could take years to get this right." And then he went on to say… where am I… ah, yes, here: "One of our many problems has been sourcing components that can withstand very high temperatures. Say we did solve the problem – what would happen then? There would still be dozens of other problems with the programme."

'So we either believe Kurt or we don't. If we choose not to believe him, then what he says about the V-1 and V-2 programmes can be dismissed anyway as either nonsense or disinformation. If we choose to believe him, then we have to give weight to what I have just quoted, namely that the programme is not working and they're facing major problems – dozens of them, as he says. Very much as I predicted, in fact. I simply do not believe they can develop the right fuel systems to launch a one-ton warhead and keep it in the air.'

'But these problems can be overcome. We can't afford to ignore them.'

'Come on, Gilbey: you can't have your cake and eat it. When we last met, we wondered, did we not, about Kurt's motivations. Well, we have them here in black and white, courtesy of the resourceful Agent Laertes. The *Oberst* is a loyal Luftwaffe officer and his motivation for passing the intelligence on to us is presumably for us to do our part in helping to stop the V-1 and V-2 programmes so the Luftwaffe benefits. Here's what he says: "The best service I could do for the Luftwaffe and for the German people would be to help bring about the abandoning of the V-1 programme. It's distracting the Luftwaffe from doing its real job." Then he goes on to say what a disaster Stalingrad is, and continues: "Throughout Europe our planes are outperformed by the RAF. We'd stand a chance of reversing that if all of our efforts weren't going into the V-1 programme."'

Lord Swalcliffe closed his file and placed it neatly on top of the others in front of him. 'In my opinion, Pearson, we'd be doing the country a disservice if we did anything about this. My opinion that both the V-1 and the V-2 are doomed to failure has been vindicated. Let the Germans carry on wasting their time and resources on the programmes. Surely the last thing we want is to be complicit in bringing about their cancellation, thereby aiding the Luftwaffe, eh, Hamilton?'

The air vice marshal paused before replying, as if wanting to be certain Swalcliffe really had finished. 'I hear what you say, Lord Swalcliffe, and it is not without some merit, but on balance I'm inclined to the same view as Tom: namely that we cannot afford to ignore the V-1 and V-2 programmes. Tim has done some analysis of the detailed answers Kurt gave to the questions we sent.'

The young wing commander opened a notebook. 'There's no question that the intelligence we've received from Kurt has added significantly to what we know about the weapons. For instance, we now know that the V-1 is to be launched from a special ramp and that it has a maximum flying time of one hour, after which the missile drops to earth and its warhead explodes on impact. He was also able to provide more detail on the V-2: the fuel is a mixture of liquid oxygen and alcohol, and after a minute it can reach a height of around twenty-three miles. It's probably more accurate than the V-1 and its warhead weighs one ton.' He spoke for another ten minutes, and as he came to an end, he closed his notebook. 'Our conclusion is that there are clearly a number of problems facing the programmes, but we do not think this necessarily means they're insurmountable ones. We think it is possible they can be solved, and therefore both programmes represent a real threat to this country and cannot be ignored.'

'And may I add,' Hamilton stood up as he spoke, and moved to the side of the maps and photographs behind him on the wall, 'that from our point of view, the information Kurt gave on Peenemünde being the single site where both the V-1 and V-2 are being developed and manufactured is of enormous importance: if that was the only intelligence that resulted from Laertes' trip to Berlin I'd have been delighted. We were simply not aware of this hitherto.'

He picked up a cane and pointed to a map of northern Europe. 'This is Peenemünde, part of Germany even before the war, on an island called Usedom, south of the island of Rügen, on the Baltic coast. It is about seventy miles due east of Rostock, and the same distance south-west of the Danish island of Bornholm. To the south-east – about sixty-five miles away – is the Polish city of Stettin.'

'Kurt described it as a massive site, did he not?'

'He did indeed, Sir Roland.'

'So I presume reconnaissance has been relatively easy?'

'Tim?'

The wing commander stood up by a series of enlarged photographs. 'Actually, reconnaissance has been a major problem, sir. The distance to Peenemünde makes it very hard, for a start. Our best option has been one of the special Spitfires used by the photographic reconnaissance unit at RAF Benson. But these are very obvious: they're quite exposed and a long way from home, if you get my meaning. Just sending them over the site carries the risk of alerting the Germans that we know something's going on there. Nevertheless, we've had two runs over the site. The results,' he pointed to the photographs, 'are disappointing. They do show there is indeed a very large site, but we can't get much detail at all. Large areas of it are covered by camouflage netting or are under trees.'

'I should add,' said Hamilton, 'that we persuaded Bomber Command to lay on a raid over Rostock, the idea being that a couple of specially adapted Blenheims could detach from the main group and fly over Peenemünde on their way back. But I'm afraid one of the planes was shot down before it even reached Rostock, while the other came back with next-to-useless pictures – you can see them here. They also said there was an enormous amount of flak over the site.'

'We need to decide what to do pretty quickly. Winston keeps asking.' Pearson looked worried.

'I'm prepared to be persuaded if can get some better intelligence about the site than those ridiculous photographs. Frankly,

Chapter 14

'Stay in here, keep quiet and if you need to, use that bucket. I'm sorry it's going to be so uncomfortable, but the Germans don't usually come down here, so at least it ought to be safe. You have some food?'

Prince nodded and patted his backpack.

'Remember it will be very cold. I'd better find you a couple more blankets.'

He said he'd appreciate that. It was already five o'clock in the afternoon and the ferry wasn't due to sail from Gedser until nine the following morning. That meant sixteen hours in a windowless storage room, no more than three foot by seven, with much of the room taken up by piles of lifejackets and a large coil of foul-smelling rope. They were on the lowest deck, and the noise of the engine and the pumps reverberated around him.

'I'll get you the blankets and then I'll lock the door. I'll unlock it when we're in Warnmünde.'

'When will that be?'

Peder shrugged. He was the chief engineer on the ferry and a contact of someone recommended by someone Hanne knew. A friend of a friend of a friend: it all felt a bit tenuous, but Peder seemed pleasant enough and Prince had no alternative but to trust him.

'Depends on whether we get away from here on time, what the conditions are like on the crossing and how long the

Germans take to search the boat in Warnmünde. Sometimes they have two or three men taking less than half an hour; other times it can take a lot longer and be quite thorough. It's a three-hour crossing, so if all goes well you could be off the boat by one o'clock, but it may be later.'

Peder brought the extra blankets and then locked the door. He assured Prince there'd be no one on the boat overnight other than a nightwatchman on the top deck. He had also brought a small lamp but told him to use it sparingly. It gave Prince enough light to arrange some of the lifejackets into a bed of sorts. He'd hesitate to describe it as comfortable, but with the blankets wrapped around him it was not quite as bleak as it could have been.

As for his mood, though, that could not have been bleaker. He'd had every reason to expect he'd be back in England by now. He'd hoped he'd be spending Christmas with his son, but now it was the first Monday in January and he was heading into the German Reich once again.

—

It was only when he and Otto were in the taxi from Kastrup airport to Copenhagen after their flight from Berlin that Prince finally felt he could relax. He realised he was still a British agent in Nazi-occupied Denmark, with all that entailed, but the end of his mission was in sight. Within days he'd be back in England, with his son. Despite signs everywhere of the German occupation, Copenhagen felt considerably less menacing than Berlin.

All that remained was to compile his report and arrange his journey back to England. The taxi dropped him in Vesterbro, about ten minutes' walk from the apartment. As he got closer, he realised quite how excited he was to see Hanne. He'd no doubts now about either the nature or the extent of his feelings for her. It was the same feeling he had had in the early years of his marriage to Jane, before Grace was born. But he had to caution himself. He must assume these feelings were unrequited. It was all well and good him feeling so carefree: within days he'd be back in England. In a few weeks he'd probably be back as a detective in Lincolnshire and most important of all, with his son. Prince realised he was assuming Hanne felt the same way about him and he had to admit he had no real evidence for that. It was true Hanne had been warmer and friendlier than when they first met, but he'd have expected that anyway. He also knew that even if she did happen to share his feelings, her situation was very different to his. He could afford to relax; he would soon be out of danger. She could not contemplate either of those.

These uncertainties soon disappeared. Less than twenty minutes after he entered the apartment, Hanne arrived. Within seconds they had fallen into each other's arms and they remained like that as they staggered into the bedroom.

For the next hour, not a word was spoken, and when they paused for the first time, an exhausted Prince spoke, aware that what he said was likely to change the mood.

'I need to write my report and you've got to encode it. I presume you'll drop it off on your way to work in the morning? If so, we really haven't got long.'

She hauled herself up and brushed the hair away from her face, looking slightly disappointed. 'I suppose you're right. You write it while I get some sleep. Wake me up when it's done. I'll encode it before going to work.'

It took Prince three hours to write the report, constantly editing it to be as succinct as possible, but ensuring he quoted Kurt's key answers as directly as possible. He decided to leave out what had happened when they left the restaurant. He didn't think there'd be sufficient time and space, but he also felt – not entirely logically, he realised – its inclusion might disappoint London and somehow delay his return home. He did, however, allow the indulgence at the end of the report of a question about the arrangements for his journey back to England.

The report was placed in the dead letter box on the Friday morning: by the Sunday lunchtime it had been collected.

'It won't get to London before late Monday at the earliest, more likely Tuesday or Wednesday,' Hanne told him. 'By the time they get back to us, it could be another week. You'll just have to stay here. I'm sure I can find plenty of ways to amuse you!'

The response from London took longer than expected, and it was the weekend before Christmas before they finally heard back.

> London very much appreciates Agent Laertes' report.
>
> Agent Laertes will understand that a number of issues remain unresolved: there are still questions to be answered.
>
> Therefore, he is to travel covertly to Germany and gain entry to the Peenemünde site.
>
> Because of the uncertainty of travel over Christmas and the New Year, he is to leave Copenhagen on 4 January.
>
> He is to assume the identity of a French slave labourer.
>
> He is to supply detailed information on what is going on at Peenemünde and provide a detailed diagram of the site.
>
> He is to remain at Peenemünde until otherwise instructed.
>
> En route to Peenemünde he is to meet an agent in Greifswald: this agent will facilitate his entry to the camp and receive his communications when he is there. Further instructions to follow.
>
> On his return to Copenhagen, London will be very happy to arrange his return to England.

It took Prince a few days to get over the shock of this message: instead of spending Christmas with his son, he would be remaining in Copenhagen. That was bad enough, but the prospect of travelling back into Germany – a journey London had helpfully described as covert – was hard to contemplate. And as for gaining access to Peenemünde… just the thought of it terrified him. Even if he got in, he doubted he'd ever get out. He felt none of the excitement he'd experienced in anticipation of the Berlin trip.

Hanne was adamant he should remain in the apartment until he started his journey. They could never be certain that his Peter Rasmussen identity hadn't been compromised. No one knew where he was staying: Otto Knudsen was unaware of it, and the address on his *legitimationskort* was that of an apartment that didn't exist in a large and mostly deserted complex on the other side of Vesterbro.

Hanne spent much of the Christmas period at work, covering for colleagues who wanted to celebrate with their families. On Christmas Day, she visited her father. As much as she wanted to be with Prince, they both realised that if she spent too long in his apartment rather than her own, it could arouse suspicion.

Nonetheless they did have a good deal of time together, the physical passion unabated and bringing with it a genuine love, one they clearly shared.

But the sheer tedium of staying in the flat for a month took its toll. Prince would count the hours until Hanne's next visit and worry if he thought she was late. Henry was never out of his thoughts: a love for his son that became more painful by the day, along with a growing sense of guilt that he'd abandoned him.

There were no fireworks in Copenhagen that New Year's Eve. There was some optimism in the city, as people read between the lines and realised Stalingrad was turning into a disaster for the Nazis. The more astute said this was the turning point of the war. *Not long now – maybe this time next year!*

New Year's Day was a Friday, and Hanne appeared at the apartment that afternoon. She pushed away his advances: they had serious matters to talk about.

She'd heard from London and had made arrangements for his journey. She'd called in a number of favours. A friend of hers – someone she absolutely trusted – would drive him down to the island of Falster tomorrow. They would take him to the port of Gedser. There he would be handed over to a friend of this friend. The following day – Sunday – the second friend would get him into the docks, where an engineer called Peder would smuggle him onto the ferry. There he'd be hidden and would spend the night. On Monday the ferry would sail to Warnmünde, which was the port area of Rostock. When Peder told him it was safe, he'd leave the ferry and make his way to Rostock railway station, where he'd catch a train to Greifswald. Once there, he'd meet an agent called Blackbird.

'Are these people you trust?'

'The person taking you to Gedser I know well, I absolutely trust them.'

'And the others – the friend in Gedser and this Peder?'

Hanne shrugged. 'What can I say? I trust my friend and I have to assume the other two are trustworthy. But as I've said before, we can't pretend this isn't a dangerous game.'

'And when I get to Germany, what identity do I use?'

'You have plenty of Reichsmarks, that's something.'

'I wasn't talking about money; I was talking about my identity.'

'Take your Peter Rasmussen *legitimationskort* with you but keep it concealed – you'll need it for when you get back. If you're challenged, use this.'

It was an identity card for a German national: Ulrich Leuschner.

'Seriously, Hanne? You think he looks like me?'

'He has a beard.'

'That's about it.'

'And the age is similar. It only needs to last one journey. It will have to do.'

'Where did you get it from?'

'It was one of a dozen identity cards stolen by the resistance from German engineers who'd be sent here to work on the Gestapo headquarters. They came into the hands of the police and we've kept them safe, so to speak.'

'Won't they be looking out for the names if the cards were stolen?'

'They were stolen over a year ago. Hopefully they'll have forgotten about them.'

Prince shook his head. 'It's crazy. My German's not good enough.'

'Don't say much; you're an engineer after all. Just mutter.'

Chapter 15

Berlin; Rostov-on-Don, December 1942–January 1943

Charlottenburg, Berlin
26 December 1942

My dearest Karl-Heinrich,

Not a moment of the day or night passes when you are not foremost in my thoughts. Yesterday was so difficult: Christmas is a time for joy and families and I have neither. Christine persuaded me, against my better judgement I have to say, to join her family for dinner on Christmas Eve. It was like entering a different world. They were so happy and I so sad. Christine is a dear friend and one of the few people I am able to talk to, but her life is so different to mine. She has her parents and her four wonderful children, while my dear parents are no longer and I have failed the Führer and you through my inability to have children.

I am of course blessed with you, my wonderful husband, though your absence pains me deeply. Christine is so fortunate Friedrich is now based in Berlin. I don't want to sound bitter, but I didn't see any sign of his injury impairing him: for someone whose knee was apparently so badly injured, he certainly managed to dance very well!

But then I was racked with guilt. Here I am in our beautiful apartment, with wonderful furniture and a full-time maid. I don't want for food, warmth or other comforts. Being the wife of a senior SS officer brings so many privileges, for which I must be grateful. And where you are it must be so difficult. I feel terrible about feeling sorry for myself.

I understand how you will not be able to talk about your circumstances: from what I read, the situation in Stalingrad is difficult and the weather must be dreadful. But I have no doubt whatsoever that right will prevail and the communists will be defeated. I hope that when you finally capture the city there will be a few communists and Jews still alive so you can ensure justice is served upon them.

Spending yesterday on my own has made me resolve to do more in the new year to help other people. Before Christmas there was a talk at the Frauenschaft about a wonderful home the organisation runs in Mecklenburg, where it takes care of the children whose parents have died in the service of the Fatherland.

I have decided to travel there tomorrow and spend a few weeks helping to run the home, which is in the city of Greifswald. You should still write to me at this address: Maria will arrange for any letters to be forwarded to me.

I hope you do not disapprove of my doing this, Karl-Heinrich. I do know your view that a woman should remain at home, but I feel I must do my part in helping to bring about the Ultimate Victory!

With all my fondest love,
Heil Hitler!

Your loving wife,
Sophia

Headquarters of the 6th Army
Rostov-on-Don
8 January 1943

Darling Sophia,

Your letter warmed my heart more than all the fuel we dream of!

You must promise me not to feel guilty about the fact that I am here on the front line and you are enjoying comforts in Berlin. That you are safe and cared for is a source of great joy to me, one of the few things that sustains me at this difficult time.

I wish I was able to say otherwise, but life here is very hard and the military situation does not improve — in fact, it gets worse. The Soviets launched a major attack on our armies in November and we have found it hard to recover. Now we are being encircled and our thoughts are of survival rather than the capture of Stalingrad.

If you wonder why I am able to be so frank with you it is because I am sending this letter by hand with Konrad, whom I trust implicitly. Poor Konrad's injuries are very bad and he is no longer resisting his repatriation to the Fatherland. I think it would be prudent if you burnt this letter once you have read it.

I am sorry to sound so miserable, but I have to be honest with you. However, my belief in the ideals of national socialism and my absolute conviction in Ultimate Victory are as strong and resolute as ever!

Whatever you may hear about the outcome of the Stalingrad campaign, do not lose heart. One setback will not prevent us winning the war. The blame for the situation we find ourselves in must not be placed on the Führer! If this campaign had been handled by the SS, I have no doubt we'd have been in control of Stalingrad by now. However, one always doubts the ability and the loyalty of the Wehrmacht. Colonel General Paulus is proving to be an inept commander. If he is replaced, there is still hope.

I would be surprised if any Jews (or indeed anyone else) remain in Stalingrad by the time we capture the wretched place, but if they do, rest assured that I will personally make sure we dispatch them in the usual manner!

I know you are a good and loyal National Socialist, and your typically selfless act in going to Greifswald to help those less fortunate than yourself is a wonderful inspiration and comfort to me. Be assured your work there will be a contribution to victory and it is something I heartily approve of!

There is a very large barracks in Greifswald and I do know that a few months ago Oberführer Hausser commanded the SS detachment there. Should you ever need his help, just mention my name!

I have to go now. My adjutant tells me there's a staff meeting I have to attend. When will they learn that meetings don't win wars!

With my eternal love,
Heil Hitler!

Your devoted husband,
Karl-Heinrich

Chapter 16

To his surprise, Prince managed to grab some sleep on the ferry, especially after the engines were turned off for the night. The pumps continued to hum in the background, a sound he found reassuring. Less so the intermittent clanking sound of metal moving, which came across as if the hull of the ship was bending one way then the other.

He woke a few times, the cold eating through him despite the blankets. He sipped water and ate the sandwich from his backpack, but otherwise just sat there in the darkness, occasionally switching on the lamp to check the time. The ferry pulled away from its moorings at nine o'clock, and he certainly felt every minute of the crossing to Warnmünde, most of the journey making sure he wasn't pitched against the side of the cupboard he was in.

It docked a few minutes after noon. He knew the port police would come on board and search the ship, so he pulled a pile of the lifejackets over him in the hope that that was all anyone would see. After an hour, he began to worry. He had to get from Warnmünde to Rostock station to catch a train to Greifswald, and this was a journey he'd rather do in daylight. Security checks seemed to be more demanding in the dark, and he didn't think his Ulrich Leuschner identity would withstand much scrutiny.

Just before one thirty, he heard people walking past his hiding space, and then silence. A few minutes later, the cupboard was unlocked, and through a gap in the lifejackets he could see Peder.

'Everything is fine, you may come out now.'

Prince gave himself a minute or two to straighten up and get used to the light. Peder handed him a mug of black coffee.

'There were no problems today, but still be careful when you leave the ship. The railway station is about ten minutes' walk from here, maybe a bit less – you can't miss it. From there it's about a fifteen-minute journey into Rostock central station. You don't need to tell me where you're going from there, but it is possible to buy a ticket from Warnmünde straight through to your destination – as long as that's on a direct line from Rostock.'

At Warnmünde station, a train was already waiting, due to depart in five minutes. The woman in the tiny ticket office didn't bother to ask for his identity card and was happy to sell him a ticket straight through to Greifswald as long as he had the correct change: 'Don't make me mess around with lots of coins, you understand? I'm doing this job on my own today. That's fine, sir, have a good journey. My sister-in-law lived in Greifswald. Heil Hitler!'

By two thirty, he was on the main concourse of Rostock central railway station. Much of the roof was missing and the inside of the station showed extensive evidence of bomb damage. As far as Prince could tell, only two platforms were operating, and the board over one of them showed that the next train departing was at a quarter to three, stopping at Stralsund and arriving in Greifswald at a quarter past five.

Only now did he realise quite how hungry he was. Overnight he'd eaten the sandwich and apple he'd packed, and he'd had his last biscuit as the ferry crossed the Baltic. There was a station café, which looked inviting as long as one ignored the broken windows, but he decided not to push his luck. The sooner he boarded the train, the more likely he was to get a window seat in the centre of a carriage: in one session at

Matlock, Hendrie had mentioned how police on a train seemed to be more bothered with people sitting in aisle seats by the doors, since they were likely to be looking for a quick getaway.

He found a seat by a window in the centre of a carriage towards the front of the train: he was counting on any police checks starting from the guard's wagon at the back. He helped an elderly lady with her case and listened to her talk about her son for a few minutes. She introduced herself as Frau Henlein, and told him that she was going to Greifswald too. Would he be kind enough to help with her case when they arrived?

Prince assured her that of course he would and – through a bout of coughing – asked her to excuse him but he was not feeling too good and perhaps she'd understand if he rested for a while?

Not only did she understand, she also had a perfect remedy for him. From an apparently bottomless handbag she produced a bottle of schnapps.

'It's homemade,' she told him. 'My mother's recipe: made with plums from my own garden. Please have some, it will make you feel better... and you must have some of this cake, too, made with my own cherries. You look so hungry...'

Prince dozed off, the schnapps warming him up inside. He dreamt of Frau Henlein's garden, a veritable Garden of Eden, and somewhere in the dream he and Henry were helping the old woman to collect plums, of which there were more than they could handle.

He was woken by shouting in the carriage: 'Tickets! Identity cards! Make sure they're ready!'

He was still slumped in his window seat when they arrived alongside. He peered up, apparently having just woken up.

There are two types of police checks on trains: bad and not so bad. The not so bad are the Bahnschutzpolizei – that's the railway police. Here are some pictures of their uniforms, please have a good look. And then there's the bad: the Gestapo.

There were two men working the carriage, and with their distinctive gunmetal-grey tunic with black trim and black trousers, he could tell they were both Bahnschutzpolizei.

'Tickets! Identity cards!'

The passengers either side of him took their time, and by the time the *Bahnschutzpolizei* officer had finished with the old woman, he looked irritated. Further down the carriage, his colleague called out to him: 'Hurry up, Franz, we'll be in Stralsund soon.'

'By the time this lot find their tickets, we'll be on the return leg to Rostock. You, come on!'

Prince handed over his ticket and identity card. The Bahnschutzpolizei officer studied the ticket carefully. 'Where are you going to?'

'Greifswald.'

Then the identity card: the familiar and dreaded head movement, looking down at the photo on the card and up again at his face. Up and down. Repeat.

'Name?'

'Ulrich Leuschner.'

'Speak up, man!'

'Ulrich Leuschner.'

'The purpose of your journey?'

He was saved by two people. First by Frau Henlein, who told the Bahnschutzpolizei officer the man was unwell and he should leave him alone, and then by the officer's colleague shouting again: they really needed to get a move on. He handed the papers back to Prince and carried on.

'Perhaps you'd like some more schnapps?' asked Frau Henlein. 'You really don't look so good.'

–

'So those are my instructions – seriously? I arrive at Greifswald and do nothing?'

'You've not been listening Peter: I didn't say do nothing, did I? You leave the train…'

'Obviously.'

They were in the apartment in Copenhagen and Hanne was giving him his final briefing. She'd received instructions from London.

'…then you walk out of the station. Blackbird will greet you soon after that. They will say, "You look so well after such a long journey," and your response is… go on, Peter, your response?'

'I'm to say, "But I could do with a good meal and a proper sleep."'

'Correct.'

'Which is all well and good, but what is my fallback story?'

'What do you mean?'

'It's supposed to be rule number one when in enemy territory: know where you're going and have a story to tell in case you're stopped. If I'm stopped before I leave the station, what am I to say? With this identity I won't last a minute.'

She looked at him as if she knew he was right. 'Hopefully it won't come to that.'

–

By the time the train arrived in Greifswald at a quarter past five, he'd drunk the best part of Frau Henlein's bottle of schnapps. He wouldn't say he was beyond caring, or even that his guard was down, but he was certainly more relaxed than he ought to have been in the circumstances. He insisted on carrying her cases to the ticket barrier – where he was waved through – and was introduced to her daughter.

'He's such a nice man – but so unwell!'

Greifswald station was small: just two platforms as far as he could make out, and a large number of troops lined up along one of them. He bid farewell to his travelling companion, more grateful for her company than she'd ever realise, then followed the other passengers out of the station onto the Bahnhofstrasse.

He paused to tie his shoelaces, which he'd been advised not to do (*too obvious, old chap*), and set off along the road.

By the time he saw her and recognised her, she'd already embraced him.

'You look so well after such a long journey!'

It was the woman from Berlin: the woman with the distinctive hats. She was wearing the turban-style one now and she looked genuinely pleased to see him.

'But I could do with a good meal and a proper sleep.'

She nodded. All was in order. 'It's good to see you, though you actually look terrible. I have a car just along here, and some papers for you. You're my cousin from Dortmund, by the way.'

'You'd better tell me your name.'

'Of course. I'm Sophia. Sophia von Naundorf.'

–

Agent Blackbird – Sophia von Naundorf – had rented a small villa on the outskirts of the town overlooking the mouth of the River Ryck. It was in an ideal location: set at the end of a single-track road, the closest neighbours the other side of a field and the villa itself surrounded by a high wall, with an iron gate of similar height separating the drive from the road.

The house and the area around it were bathed in darkness, the moon blurred by clouds. She led Prince into the villa and he waited in the hall while she turned on the lights.

'They take the blackout very seriously around here: the British don't seem to know much about the area, but it's near Rostock so there's always a danger they could hit the town. You look like you could do with a bath. I've laid some things out for you in that bedroom. When you're ready, I'll make you a meal, then we can talk.'

It was an incongruous setting for their first proper meeting. They sat opposite each other in a small but elegant dining room, the French-polished table replete with what Sophia apologetically described as a modest meal.

They said nothing for the first five minutes. Prince ate, occasionally glancing up at Sophia. She was the kind of woman people in England would tend to refer to as refined, and was younger than he'd thought. While he'd been in the bath, she had changed into a smart dress and had put on more make-up, most noticeably dark red lipstick.

She waited until he'd finished his soup before she spoke.

'You must have so many questions.'

'I'm not sure how much you can tell me – and I'm certainly not sure how much I can tell you.'

'You don't need to tell me anything. I know as much as I need to know, and I'll tell you what you need to know. Can you pass me the potato salad, please? I don't know if you like wine, but my husband got that bottle from France. Apparently it is excellent, I brought it with me from Berlin.'

She filled her plate with potato salad and cold meats and poured wine into two crystal glasses.

'I could have brought my maid with me from Berlin too but decided it would be prudent not to. So for the first time in many years I'm looking after myself, and to be honest, I quite enjoy the solitude. A local girl comes in most mornings to clean, but I've told her not to bother tomorrow or Wednesday. By Thursday, you should be gone. You realise I work for the British, don't you? In Berlin my job was to keep an eye on you and ensure you were safe. I spotted the Gestapo following the Luftwaffe officer. My job here is to get you to into Peenemünde and then to pass on any messages you can get out of the place. When your mission is finished, I'll do my best to help you return to Denmark, then I can go home to Berlin.'

'What is your excuse for being in Greifswald?'

'Have you heard of the Frauenschaft? It's a Nazi women's organisation. Dutiful wives like me are expected to attend its dreadful meetings where we blame the Jews for everything and then decide what good we can do. They run an orphanage here in Greifswald and I volunteered to come up for a few weeks to help out. Everyone thinks I'm wonderful. Take some more herring: it's really rather good, a local speciality. Those pickled cucumbers are good too.' She pushed some more plates in his direction. 'My husband is a senior officer in the SS. He's a *Brigadeführer*, which is equivalent to a general, apparently. He's currently taking part in the Battle of Stalingrad, hopefully suffering like the rest of them and awaiting defeat. With luck, I'll never see him again. You look confused?'

'You wish that on your husband?'

'I was born in 1910; my mother died when I was five. A year later, my father went to fight in the Great War. I don't recall him even saying goodbye to me. I was looked after by nannies and always felt abandoned by him. He returned in 1918 but remained a distant figure. We were very comfortably off: not rich, but with a nice house in Berlin and holidays in Switzerland. We certainly wanted for nothing. Father was in manufacturing, household equipment, that kind of thing. But as the German economy crashed, he lost everything. The business closed, he had to sell the house and we ended up in a rented apartment in Wedding, a less pleasant part of Berlin.

'I found work in an office and Father became obsessed with the idea that I should marry well. When I was twenty, I met Karl-Heinz. I was working in a legal office on Fasanenstrasse and he was one of the high-flying lawyers there. He's ten years older than me and an attractive man, not handsome in the conventional sense but very smart and athletic, and he did have a charm about him, along with ambition and drive. When Karl-Heinz wants something, he invariably gets it. Not long after we met, he decided he wanted me. I wasn't at all sure; I felt I wanted someone who was maybe more cultured and sensitive and possibly closer to my own age, but he was very determined and he had an ally in my father, who not only thought Karl-Heinz was wonderful but also saw him as a route out of the hardship we found ourselves in.

'So against my better judgement – though I say that with hindsight, of course – we married. That was in 1932. Until then we'd never really discussed politics; it wasn't something that Karl-Heinz seemed interested in. But all that changed after the Nazis came to power in 1933. He joined them and became a passionate Nazi, giving up his law job and becoming an officer in the SS. I cannot describe how terrible he became, though I have to tell you he's always been very proper with me. I have no doubt he loves me and cares about me. Unfortunately, we've been unable to have children, and unlike many men in his position he has never held this against me: he's paid for the best medical treatment and has always been sympathetic.

'A couple of years after we married, we moved to a beautiful apartment in Charlottenburg. I became very friendly with a Jewish family in an apartment below us – the Goldmanns. I was especially close to their daughter Esther, who was the same age as me. It was around this time that life became intolerable for Jews in Berlin. The laws being passed made their lives unbearable in almost every respect. Esther's father was a doctor and lost his job at the Charité hospital, and would you believe it, their beloved dog was taken from them because a law was passed forbidding Jews from owning pets. They could only shop at certain times, they couldn't own a radio, so many petty things – it was awful. Karl-Heinz thought this was hilarious. He was always rude to them, and when he was around, Esther kept out of the way.

'Eventually the Goldmanns fled Germany – they went to Belgium as far as I know; I've never heard from Esther since they left. Because they left so quickly, most of their possessions remained in their apartment. Karl-Heinz arranged to have the pick of what they owned, so our apartment is stuffed with their silverware, their dinner service, a beautiful dining table and chairs – even paintings. I'm ashamed of this, of course, but I've decided to take the view that I'm looking after everything until the family return after the war.

'As time has gone on, Karl-Heinz has given me every reason to hate him. He boasts about the role he's played in murdering

Jews. I can't say too much, but I even have evidence of the dreadful things he's done. He actually seems to believe this impresses me. It has had the opposite effect. I thought about escaping, but where could I go? Then in late 1940 I met an American journalist in Berlin. He was someone I could instinctively trust. I told him I was opposed to the Nazis and wished to help the British. Through him I made contact with the right people in London, and here we are.

'As far as Karl-Heinz is concerned, I'm a loyal wife and a devoted Nazi and I play up to that role. It's the perfect cover. Being married to an SS general is like being a member of the aristocracy. Finish the potato salad, there's only a little left.'

She began to clear the plates and Prince helped her carry them into the kitchen. She made a pot of coffee and they went into the lounge.

'It's real coffee, none of that ersatz rubbish: this is what happens when you marry into the SS. Now then, you haven't come here just to drink decent coffee, have you?'

'My instructions are to get into Peenemünde, provide a detailed diagram of the site and remain there to await further instructions. They want me to assume the identity of a French labourer. I have no idea how...'

'You speak French?'

'A little: my accent is passable enough, but I'm not sure many people will believe I'm French.'

'Don't worry. I've been thinking about this, and I have a plan. I have to work tomorrow at the orphanage but I'm free on Wednesday. In the meantime, you need to get as much rest as possible while you can.'

–

'What do you think? I know it's a ridiculously big car, but the important thing is the size of its boot. We could fit two of you in there quite easily.'

Richard Prince climbed out of the boot of the Mercedes-Benz 770, which Sophia had reversed with some difficulty into the garage alongside the villa. There was no question he would fit into the space under the boot with room to spare. She had even placed a rug and some blankets in there to make it more comfortable.

'It's around twenty-five miles to the island. I could do it in an hour, but the roads aren't too good and the checkpoint at Wolgast to get onto Usedom island can take another hour to get through. This will be the fourth time I've crossed over, so hopefully they know me by now.'

'But surely they'll search the car?'

'Of course, but they won't think of looking in that space, and remember, I'll have various odds and ends on top of it. Before I forget, you'd better give me your identity cards – the Danish and German ones. It will blow your cover if you're caught with them. I'll keep them safe for you, don't worry.'

They left at ten o'clock on the Wednesday morning, having spent twenty minutes ensuring Prince was safely stowed in the space under the lining of the boot. It was more comfortable than he'd expected, though still claustrophobic: he knew he'd be in there for at least two hours, and possibly considerably longer.

An hour after leaving Greifswald, the car stopped. For the first time he could make out sounds around him other than that of the car's considerable eight-litre engine.

'Heil Hitler! Good afternoon, my lady: my very warm greetings to you. I didn't expect to see you again so soon.'

'Heil Hitler! I had today off, Oberleutnant, and I found my visit to the island on Sunday so peaceful that I felt pulled towards it once again.'

'And do you have papers, my lady?'

'Of course, Oberleutnant! I wouldn't want to embarrass you like last time, would I? You were so kind to me then. My husband's colleague Oberführer Hausser – he's the senior SS officer in Greifswald, you know – has given me these travel papers.'

There was a pause.

'These are general travel papers covering Mecklenburg, my lady. They are not for Usedom.'

'But Usedom is in Mecklenburg.'

'I know, my lady, but as I told you before, because of the sensitive nature of some of the activities in this area, we have to be very strict.'

'I understand. I suppose I could always turn round. My husband the SS *Brigadeführer* will—'

'My lady, please don't misunderstand me. Where is it you're proposing to visit on the island?'

'Zempin.'

'Very well: I can issue you papers for today only and on the very strict condition you don't travel further north than Zempin. Do you understand that?'

'Of course. I'm so grateful. Perhaps you would allow me to give you these cigarettes as a token of my gratitude.'

'Juno? Thank you so much, my lady. Three packets, are you sure? I'll just quickly check the car; it won't take long.'

Prince became aware of the boot opening, but it was for no more than a few seconds. He recalled what she'd told him back at the villa.

I've checked it out three times now.

I'll drive into Zempin and get as close as I can to the coast. Each time I've been there, groups of foreign workers have been moving up and down the coast road. They don't seem to be guarded very closely. It's not as if they've got anywhere to escape to.

If it seems safe, I'll approach them.

Fifteen minutes after leaving the checkpoint and crossing onto the island, the car stopped again. He heard the door open and close. It was another few minutes before the boot opened and he heard Sophia's voice. 'We're by the coast now. There are two groups of slave labourers nearby: one group seem to be Russians or Ukrainians and there are two guards with them. The group slightly nearer to us are French, and as far as I can see, they're on their own at the moment.'

'What are they doing?'

'Repairing the defences on the beach, I think. You can come out from under there now, but stay inside the boot for the time being. You see this?'

She was standing in front of a large white-painted wooden post. A weather-beaten life belt was attached to it below a sign warning people not to go anywhere near the beach. Behind the post was an area covered in shale. She beckoned him forward and he crawled to the edge of the boot.

'When you've finished the map of the camp, put it in this.' She handed him a black waterproof pouch. 'Then bury it under the shale directly behind the post. When you've done that, scratch a mark underneath the life belt using a piece of shale. You know the Russian cross? That's the sign you should use. I'll look out for it and know to search for the pouch. Wait here, the group is coming closer.'

She returned a few minutes later. 'They think I'm mad, but I've given them sausages and cigarettes. I don't think they've ever heard of anyone wanting to break into a camp.'

'Nor have I.'

'They're all wearing dark grey, so you'll fit in. Quick now, good luck.'

-

It had been as easy as that. Prince had rolled out of the back of the Mercedes-Benz and scrambled over to the beach, where a group of bemused Frenchmen were standing as if they were looking at a ghost. As far as he could tell, there were around half a dozen guards on the beach, scattered around and mostly with their backs to the group. The two closest to them were huddled together, trying to light cigarettes. Summoning his best French, Prince wished the Frenchmen a good afternoon and said he'd like to come with them into the camp. Would they be able to help?

They gathered around him so he was now enclosed in the centre of their group. He suspected it was because they distrusted him rather than for protection. An older man moved close to him.

'Where are you from?'

He'd known he'd be asked this and had decided he had no option other than to tell the truth. It was a risk he had to take. 'I'm English. I'm here to find out about the camp.'

All the men looked at him through narrowed eyes. Despite the wind howling across the beach, he could hear the breathing of every one of them, and his own heartbeat. After what seemed like an eternity, the older man spoke, nodding his head approvingly as he did so.

'Very well, we'll help you, Mister Churchill. Stay in the middle of us.' Then, in French: 'Jean-Claude, give our friend your hat; Alain, swap jackets with him. It won't do if he walks into Peenemünde looking like Mister Churchill, eh?'

They went back to repairing the sea defences, and after a while, the guards called them: they were to return to the camp. The older man walked close to Prince. He introduced himself as Émile.

'You're lucky, Mister Churchill: you can't trust all the slave labourers here, especially the Ukrainians, and I'm ashamed to say, not even us French. But my little group, most of us worked together in Tours: we're socialists to a man. Just look tired as you go in. They're so lazy, they only worry if there are people missing.'

Prince was astonished by the security around the camp. As they approached it, the ground around them was a sea of barbed wire, their route in a narrow path with the machine guns from the watchtower trained on it. Entering the camp itself was a lengthy process: he reckoned they went through half a dozen gates, each leading into a more secure area, but Émile had been right: all the guards were interested in was counting them and ensuring their group wasn't smaller than when it had left the camp that morning.

'Here, Mister Churchill – wake up! You're now Pierre Breton. You even look a bit like him.' It was the early hours of the morning and Émile was leaning over his bunk. 'I knew they had a spare prisoner identity card in the next block; they got it from a prisoner who died. I had to give them two packets of cigarettes and my sausage. They'll make sure Pierre Breton's name is entered on the work list.'

So Richard Prince became Pierre Breton, a slave labourer. His first day at the camp was unusual, the others told him, because that night they were given what they considered to be a better meal than they'd had for a while. It was a strange stew, watery and oily at the same time, and the most identifiable ingredients were chunks of potato, more raw than cooked. Prince thought it was one of the most disgusting meals he'd ever tasted, but the others made him eat it. 'We only get something like this a couple of times a week.'

They were right. The rest of the time it was a mug of soup, a hunk of stale bread and sometimes some jam. Within two days Prince felt the hunger gnawing away at his body and strange chilling sensations attacking his limbs. Food became his main obsession, so much so that he had to force himself to concentrate on what he was there for: to find out as much as he could about Peenemünde, and especially its layout.

The French group was regarded as one of the most useful as far as the Germans were concerned. Most of them were mechanics or electricians, and they knew how to play the system. They cooperated with the Germans just enough to ensure their work was usually less physically onerous than that of other slave labourers. That wasn't to say the Germans trusted them. They had an inherent dislike for the French, but they also regarded them as being intellectually smarter than the Russians and the Ukrainians and more able than the Poles.

It was rare for a group to work in the same area for more than a day at a time. 'Don't ask me why,' said Émile. 'Maybe it's something to do with minimising the chances of sabotage, or it could be because they don't want people to gather too much detailed information about what's going on here.'

It was common knowledge in the camp that this was where the V-1 and V-2 rockets were being developed and manufactured. The slave labourers talked about them openly.

'The Germans know there's only one way we'll leave this camp alive.'

'What's that, Émile?' They were in their hut after what passed as the evening meal and the final roll call. It was bitterly cold, the wind whistling through gaps in the wood, a single layer of which was all that stood between them and the Baltic.

'If they win the war – which they think they will do with these rockets. If they don't win, they'll kill us.' The other men nodded in a matter-of-fact manner.

'Even if they do win the war,' said Alain, 'we'll be dead by then. How much longer do you think we can survive in these conditions?'

Prince asked a few more questions while they were gathered together: he needed to get on with his map of the camp. Where did they think the power station was and the main rocket test fire area?

They all joined in with their advice. He was now building up a good picture of the layout.

'We're helping to sign our own death warrant.' It was Alain again, one of the few men not from Tours.

'In what way?'

'What do you think they're going to use your map for, Mister Churchill? To put on Christmas cards? No, they'll use it to bomb this place.'

'Good,' said Émile. 'Just make sure you clearly mark where we are – and maybe ask them not to bomb that part!'

By 24 January, Prince believed he had as much information about the camp as he was going to get. He took out a sheet of paper he'd been hiding under his straw mattress and managed to sharpen his pencil using a stone. He'd been drawing for ten minutes when Alain came over.

'That's shit. You can't draw. Give it to me, I'll do it.'

'Hang on, why would you—'

'I'm a draughtsman, Mister Churchill. Are you a draughtsman?'

'No.'

'What do you do?'

'I work in an office, actually.'

'Ha! Your map will look like a child's drawing of a bus. Mine will look like a map of Peenemünde: I'll even be able to give it a sense of scale.'

Two days later, Alain had finished his map. To Prince it looked like a masterpiece: accurate and clear. The northern tip of Usedom, where Peenemünde was located, was shaped like a thick cucumber. Alain had drawn the airfield in its north-western corner, with the power station below it on the banks of the River Peene. Just inland from there was the liquid oxygen plant, and then on the north-eastern tip of the island the main rocket test-firing area. Below that, on the Baltic coast, was the experimental works, just above the V-2 production works. South of the V-2 production area and closer to the Baltic coast was the housing estate and the army barracks. 'Make sure you mark that properly,' Émile instructed Alain. 'We want as many of those bastards killed as possible.' At the southern end of the camp, less than two miles from Zempin, was Trassenheide, the camp where the foreign slave labourers were housed: the camp where they were now.

When it was complete, they all gathered round to admire it. Émile pointed to Trassenheide. 'If your RAF bomb us, Mister Churchill, I'll kill you!'

Chapter 17

Berlin; Copenhagen, January 1943

It was a complete bloody mess.

There was no other way Kriminaldirektor Frank could describe the situation, with the possible exception of saying it was a complete fucking mess, but the president of the police in Berlin, Gruppenführer von Helldorf, had quite a Lutheran streak, and there was a limit to what kind of language he'd tolerate.

It was the middle of January: Oberst Albert Kampmann had been shot on Wednesday 2 December – six weeks previously – and died in the early hours of the following morning. Since then, the Gestapo had insisted that this was their case. They'd assured everyone they'd solve it very soon: this was a sensitive political issue, almost certainly involving matters of espionage and state security. No other organisation had the ability to investigate the *Oberst*'s case or could be trusted to do so.

But as December turned into January and the irritation of those who mattered increased, it became evident that the Gestapo had no idea what they were doing. So von Helldorf was instructed to put his best man on the case. These were the circumstances that had led to Gunther Frank of the Kripo – the criminal police – sitting in von Helldorf's office on a bitterly cold Tuesday morning. Von Helldorf's secretary had attempted to light a fire, but after a few failed attempts he told her not to bother.

'You're not too cold, are you, Frank?'

'I'm fine, thank you, sir.' Frank was pleased he'd not yet removed his coat. He'd been warmer when he'd taken his dog for a walk just after dawn. He slipped his hands into his pockets, hoping von Helldorf wouldn't notice.

'The Kripo should have had this case from the beginning in my opinion.'

'I agree, sir.'

'You'd have solved it by now.'

'One would hope so, sir.'

'This is the file – getting it from them was like prising sweets from a spoilt child. Go away and study it, then get on with the case. How long do you think you'll need – three, four days?'

'To read the file, sir?'

'No, Frank, to solve the case.'

–

It had already been dark for five hours when Frank finally finished reading the file marked *Oberst Albert Kampmann*. The only light in his office came from the Anglepoise lamp illuminating his desk and the glowing end of what must have been his thirtieth cigarette of the day.

He closed the file and looked at his notebook. He read through what he'd written, then turned to a fresh page and started writing again: just a few salient points, the most important ones. This was his method: to make notes as he went along, edit them, refine them and extract no more than a dozen key facts or questions to work through. It was a system that rarely failed, but he had a nagging feeling in his stomach that this case might prove to be the exception.

It was indeed a bloody mess.

Sometime in November – incredibly, they hadn't even made a note of the date – the Gestapo had received an anonymous tip-off that an *Oberst* in the Luftwaffe's scientific division based in the Air Ministry on Wilhelm Strasse was passing on secrets to the enemy: first name either Alfred or Albert. They soon established that there was only one *Oberst* in that division with the first name Alfred or Albert. Even the Gestapo could manage that: Oberst Albert Kampmann.

Their incompetence did not stop there. They failed to contact the security division of the Luftwaffe; they didn't speak with anyone at the Air Ministry, not even any of their own people there. They simply put a tail on Kampmann, and according to the notebooks of the half-dozen or so idiots responsible for following him, they somehow managed to lose him for a crucial few minutes here, a few minutes there.

Not that their notes suggested the *Oberst* was up to anything. He lived in the officers' quarters at the Luftwaffe base next to Tempelhof, from where he travelled to work before seven thirty most mornings, returning some twelve hours later. Outside of work he swam two or three times a week (*mostly front crawl*) or drank with colleagues in a bar near the Air Ministry. He was not a member of the Nazi Party and like so many Luftwaffe officers was not known to be political. His family were from Augsburg and contact with them appeared to be limited to a letter each way once a month, the language in them polite and formal, the subject matter inconsequential.

On the evening of Wednesday 2nd December, Oberst Albert Kampmann was followed after leaving work on Wilhelm Strasse. He didn't go into one of his regular bars, nor did he catch a tram or the U-Bahn back to the airbase. Instead he took a particularly circuitous route, one that aroused the suspicions of even the Gestapo: north on Wilhelm Strasse to Unter den Linden, up and down Unter den Linden before picking up his pace quite considerably and hurrying down Friedrichstrasse, where they lost him for a few minutes, before eventually picking him up turning left into Leipziger Strasse. He was followed across Jerusalemer Strasse into Donhoff Strasse, where he disappeared again. They looked everywhere for him: the notebooks weren't terribly explicit, but from as far as Frank could ascertain, it was a good ten minutes before they decided to look in a restaurant on Donhoff Strasse called Das Bayerischer Haus. One of the Gestapo offers had noted: *We have reason to believe this could be a Bavarian restaurant*.

They couldn't see him downstairs, but a waiter told them there was a group of men in the private dining room upstairs. When they went up there, the room was empty. Unbelievably – though Kriminaldirektor Frank could actually believe it – it took them another five minutes to work out that there was a door concealed in the panelling, behind which was a staircase leading to the yard of a neighbouring building.

They searched the area and through what Frank reckoned was probably luck more than anything else, came across Oberst Kampmann further down Donhoff Strasse. They challenged him to stop; he refused and opened fire with his Mauser semi-automatic, hitting one of the Gestapo officers in the leg. Two of them returned fire with their sub-machine guns and Kampmann was mortally wounded. He was taken to the Charité hospital but never regained consciousness.

Idiots on every count, not least for using sub-machine guns: the idea surely was to capture Kampmann alive. But worst of all – the kind of basic error Frank wouldn't have expected of a police cadet in their first week – was their failure to secure the restaurant and stop potential witnesses from leaving. The catalogue of errors continued: the Gestapo left it a day before they examined Kampmann's quarters at the Luftwaffe base, and a further day before they asked permission to search his office. They had floundered around like this until Christmas, seemed to do nothing for a week, and when they resumed their investigation in the new year, it was to no effect. And now Kriminaldirektor Gunther Frank had to pick up the pieces.

The following morning, he called in the Gestapo case officer, a shabbily dressed man called Manfred Lange with filthy shoes and a dirty raincoat that he kept on throughout their meeting. Frank realised Lange was out of his depth: as far as he could tell, he was really no more than a Gestapo 'watcher', someone whose job was to follow people. He'd no doubt been over-promoted as a result of being a particularly zealous Nazi. But Frank knew he needed to be careful. Whenever there was a conflict between a state body like the Kripo and the Nazi Party, the party always won. If he put a foot wrong, he'd be in trouble.

'So no one thought to keep all the other diners in the restaurant so they could be questioned?'

'Of course we did!' As he spoke, Lange revealed a mouthful of misshapen teeth, all of them an unpleasant shade of dark yellow.

'But you have none of their details.'

'By the time we returned to the restaurant after the shooting, they'd all gone.'

'How long did you leave it?'

'Half an hour.'

'What about the manager, this... Hoffmann?'

'He's a good party member, a loyal and—'

'Maybe so, but was he able to give you any helpful information?'

The Gestapo man shook his head, aware that he wasn't coming out of this well. 'The only other person in the restaurant whose details we have is the waiter, a man called Hinkler. H-I-N—'

'I can spell Hinkler, thank you.'

-

Following an unpromising start, Hans Hinkler turned out to be very helpful indeed. A tall, stooped man with a nervous tic and a distrusting air about him, he was monosyllabic for about five minutes, until Franks gave him a cigarette, told him to take off his coat and called him Hans. He wasn't in trouble, he said, and the Kripo was most certainly not to be confused with the Gestapo, if he could see what he meant.

'Are you in the party, Hans?'

'No, sir, but I—'

'Don't worry, Hans, nor am I. So perhaps we can be honest with each other, eh?'

Hans Hinkler smoked most of his cigarette, staring at the Kripo officer as he did so, as if weighing up whether to trust him. 'That evening, my boss, Herr Hoffmann, told me two Scandinavian gentlemen would be coming in. May I trouble you for another cigarette?'

He used the pause to think of what to say next. 'He said I was to place them at a small table by the stairs and give them a menu. Then I was to inform him that they had arrived. I wasn't to do any more than that. To be honest, I wouldn't have thought any more of it but for the fact that Herr Hoffmann told me if all went well, he'd give me a bonus that evening. That was unusual, to say the least, because he's tight with his money.'

'Carry on, Hans.'

'So that was what happened: the two men came in, I seated them and then Herr Hoffmann came over and said something to them about needing the table but there was a room upstairs where perhaps they'd be more comfortable, and they went up. After perhaps… I'm really not sure, maybe a bit over half an hour, I noticed a woman who'd been sitting by the window rush up the stairs. She came down a minute later and then hurried out, leaving payment for her meal on the table. Moments after she left, three or four men burst into the restaurant shouting, "Gestapo!" looked around and then ran upstairs. There was a commotion: one of them came down and ran out, and there was shouting and everything. All the customers left the restaurant as this was going on. There were probably around a dozen of them and no one likes to hang around when the Gestapo are getting busy.

'Herr Hoffmann seemed to be very nervous. He told me to lock the doors and tidy up. Soon after that we heard shooting further down Donhoff Strasse, but we didn't look out. About thirty minutes later, the Gestapo came in and took our details. They asked if either of us knew the names of the people upstairs, and we said no. That was it. When they left, Herr Hoffmann gave me a very generous bonus and said I mustn't say a word about what happened, but I'm sure he knew something… he must have known they were coming in.'

'Just a few more questions, Hans. You mentioned the woman who rushed upstairs and then left the restaurant.'

'Yes, sir.'

'Do you know who she was?'

'No, sir, I'd not seen her there before.'

'Can you describe her?'

'Not really: a very elegant lady, spoke with a good Berlin accent.'

'Anything else?'

'Ah, yes!' Hinkler looked pleased with himself; he'd obviously thought of something helpful. 'She wore a hat – with a feather in it!'

–

Rudolf Hoffmann struck Gunther Frank as a typical Bavarian: the accent of course and well-built, with a certain sense of arrogance, which he reckoned would not last too long.

'I told the Gestapo I have no idea who these men were. It was busy downstairs so I moved them to the dining room upstairs, that's all there is to it. If anyone else broke in using the back staircase, I know nothing about that. I never use that door myself.'

The interrogation continued, Frank probing the other man with a series of questions, all very similar, all intended to expose inconsistencies. After an hour, he told Hoffmann he was to wait in another room and they'd resume later.

'Do I have to stay?'

'What do you mean Hoffmann?'

'Well, am I under arrest? If not, you can't keep me here. I—'

'If it helps your sense of propriety, Herr Hoffmann, I can certainly arrest you…'

He left the Bavarian waiting in a cell for four hours; by the time he returned, Hoffmann was a different man. The arrogance had gone; now he was frightened.

'The problem is, Herr Hoffmann, I'm not sure I believe you.'

'In what way, sir?' It was the first time he'd shown such deference.

'Hans Hinkler made it very clear you'd told him to seat the two men downstairs. I think you knew full well what would happen. Saying the restaurant was busy was a ruse to get them upstairs. I also think you knew about another man – or maybe more – letting himself in through the back staircase. I think you were bribed. I don't think you're mixed up in espionage, I—'

'Espionage! What?' All the colour – there'd not been a lot to start with – drained from Hoffman's face. He clutched the sides of his chair. 'What the fuck do you mean? I thought it was a business deal and they needed a quiet—'

'Ah, so you did know about it?' Frank said nothing for a while, allowing Hoffmann to fully savour his considerable predicament. 'Two things can happen now, Herr Hoffman. One is you can tell me everything you know, including names. Without names I won't be satisfied. You look like you could do with another cigarette.'

The Bavarian's hand was trembling as he guided the cigarette to his lips. 'What was the other thing, sir?'

'I could hand you over to the Gestapo. They tend to adopt a different approach to interrogations than the Kripo. You could describe it as a more physical one.'

Hoffman needed no persuasion. One of the men was called Bruno, he told Kriminaldirektor Frank; he was a fairly regular diner at Das Bayerischer Haus. In fact, he'd held a dinner there for his fortieth birthday and used the private dining room, which was how he was aware of it. Hoffmann remembered showing him the room and pointing out the door concealed in the panelling and the staircase down to the yard. In August, Bruno had come to him with a favour to ask: could he use that room for a meeting, and would Herr Hoffmann mind leaving the door from the yard and the one in the panelling unlocked? He'd thought no more of it. Bruno was most generous, and when he'd asked him again in early December for the same favour, he was happy to oblige. He'd had absolutely no idea he was doing anything wrong and he—

'Do you know his surname?'

'Whose surname?'

'You've been doing so well, Hoffmann, please don't spoil it now. Bruno's surname!'

'Bergmann, sir: Bruno Bergmann. And if it's of any help, I even know where he works.'

-

'You have done very well, Kriminaldirektor Frank: your work is as thorough as I have come to expect. You will certainly receive a commendation for this.'

'But it's not complete, sir. I need to arrest this Bruno Bergmann.'

Gruppenführer von Helldorf avoided looking at him and shifted uncomfortably behind his large desk, moving a bottle of ink from one side of it to the other and carefully straightening his blotting pad. 'I'm afraid your role in this investigation has come to an end, Gunther. My instructions are that the Gestapo will handle matters from now on. I am told that as they began this investigation, they should be allowed to complete it.'

-

Manfred Lange wasted no time. Within minutes of Gruppen-führer von Helldorf passing on Bruno Bergmann's name, he headed for Spandau Locomotive Engineering along with a dozen of his men: he didn't want to leave anything to chance. He sent another team to Bergmann's house to search it and arrest his wife.

Within an hour – Lange was proud he'd been so quick – they were back at 8 Prinz Albrecht Strasse. Normal practice was to beat the suspect up and then leave him in a dark cell for a couple of hours: received wisdom was that after that they were much easier to interrogate.

But Lange was impatient. He didn't want that patronising bastard from the Kripo getting any credit whatsoever. He ordered his men to take Bergmann down to the lower basement. 'You know where I mean, and you know what to do.'

When he arrived there a few minutes later, Bruno Bergmann was strapped to a rack on the wall, his arms and legs splayed and pulled hard so he formed an X shape. His arms supported his body weight and Lange knew it was only a matter of time before his shoulders dislocated. A spotlight had been trained on his face. He looked as terrified as Lange had hoped he would.

Lange pulled up a chair in front of him and lit a cigarette, a feeling of excitement and power sweeping through him. For as long as he could manage it, he said nothing. The only sound was that of Bergmann whimpering. After a while, he nodded to one of the two men standing on either side of him.

He was enormous, a former heavyweight boxer. He stepped forward and took up a classic southpaw stance: right foot slightly forward of the left, right hand up in a defensive position. Then he swayed forward and with his left hand punched Bergmann so hard in the stomach Lange was worried he might have killed him with one blow.

'Leave him now,' he instructed. 'Bergmann, let me inform you of two things. We have your wife and children in custody. If you cooperate, their lives may be spared – certainly those of the children. We know you have a connection with Oberst Albert Kampmann. You can save your family...' He paused here so that Bergmann could absorb the word 'family'. Also, he didn't look too good: his eyes were closing and blood trickled from his mouth. 'You can save your family if you confess to everything.'

Which Bergmann did, telling Lange how he'd met Kamp-mann — whom he knew as Kurt — at a conference when he'd enquired about a series of technical issues. All along, he told Lange, he thought he was helping the Reich: that was his only motivation. By the time Kampmann had asked to meet his contact from Denmark, it was all too late. He bitterly regretted that—

'Who is this contact from Denmark?'

Bergmann hesitated, but the boxer moved forward again.

'Otto Knudsen, from Mortensen Machinery Parts, sir. We do an awful lot of work with them. They're based in Copen-hagen.' Lange was smiling now, and Bergmann had obviously noticed and decided that this was a good sign. If he was cooper-ative, he was bound to be spared. 'If it's any help, sir, he stays at the Hotel Excelsior on Askanischer Platz. And on his last visit he was accompanied by another man from Copenhagen called Peter Rasmussen, whom I did not like one bit.'

Lange was delighted at how successful his interrogation had been. There was no question but that this would be looked on favourably by his superiors. He ordered Bergmann to be cut down and taken to one of the dungeons. He'd need to remain alive until the trial.

'That will be in a couple of weeks,' he told one of his colleagues. 'It shouldn't last more than a day.'

—

Manfred Lange had rather hoped he'd be allowed to go to Copenhagen to arrest this Otto Knudsen. He'd never been to Denmark and he fancied a trip there. He'd heard wonderful stories about Scandinavian women, and he was sure his Gestapo colleagues in Copenhagen would happily accommodate him in that respect: 'blonde and very young' would be his request.

He was also sure he'd be treated with a good deal of respect. He'd get to fly on a plane for the first time, would probably be picked up in a Horch, put up at the best hotel in the city and no doubt have an opportunity to impart his wisdom and advice to an appreciative local Gestapo, honoured by a visit from one of their colleagues from Berlin. Maybe he'd end up with a posting to somewhere agreeable.

To his disappointment, Lange remained in Germany. He had to pass on all the details of Otto Knudsen and Peter Rasmussen to the Gestapo in Copenhagen. At least he'd have the fun of dealing with them once they'd been sent back to Berlin.

–

In the Gestapo headquarters on Kampmannsgade in Copenhagen, there was some concern. When a job came from Berlin, it had top priority; they didn't like to get it wrong. Otto Knudsen was no problem: they quickly identified where he lived on Nyhavn. But Peter Rasmussen was an altogether different matter. They could find no trace of him. They had his *legitimationskort* details from his travel documents, but the address in Vesterbro turned out to be a false one. They decided that the best way to find him was to keep an eye on Otto Knudsen, which they did for two days, following him to and from work, even searching his flat while he was out.

By then, the pressure from Berlin was becoming intolerable, and there was even talk of sending a team to take over from them, so they decided to give it one last chance in the hope that they'd also net Rasmussen. The plan was to follow Knudsen on his way to work one morning. If Rasmussen didn't approach him en route, they'd arrest him at his office.

–

It was a wet Wednesday morning when Otto Knudsen entered the head office of Mortensen Machinery Parts and climbed to the top floor and along the corridor towards his office. As he did so, he saw his managing director coming towards him. As they drew close, his colleague – whom Otto thought looked quite unwell – muttered, 'I'm so sorry, Otto,' and then hurried on.

Before he could react, he spotted two men following in his boss's wake. They were unmistakably Gestapo. When he turned round, there was no sign of his colleague, but two more Gestapo were now behind him.

Otto's shock was so profound, he was aware of little for the next hour or so. He was taken to the Gestapo headquarters on Kampmannsgade and interrogated. They told him he was being sent to Berlin 'to be dealt with', but in the meantime he was to tell them all he knew about Peter Rasmussen.

He said he didn't know a Peter Rasmussen, but when they insisted he must do because he'd travelled to Berlin with him the previous month, he knew the game was up. He could feel tears welling in his eyes. It had been a good life, not as fulfilled in some ways as he'd hoped, but it had been interesting, and he'd been comfortable and had enjoyed good health, which now felt somewhat ironic. But since meeting the Englishman, he'd feared it could end like this, and he'd resolved what to do. He was prepared.

'I'll tell you everything: it's all down to Rasmussen. I know where he is.' They all nodded, evidently pleased that it had been so easy. 'Perhaps if I could use the toilet first?'

He was searched, but they seemed to be looking for weapons. Nonetheless, he didn't have long. One of them stood just outside the cubicle, the door open. From inside his collar he removed the pill he'd obtained just before the trip to Berlin. His pharmacist friend told him he'd supplied dozens of them. *The Nazis are good for the poison industry. This will take up to twenty seconds to work, Otto, and I'm afraid it won't be a very pleasant twenty seconds. Whatever you do, make sure you swallow it quickly. Don't keep it in your mouth or they could pull it out. Once you've swallowed it, you'll have passed the point of no return.*

'Hurry up!'

He couldn't wait any longer. He didn't regret helping the Allies, but then again… he slipped the pill into his mouth. It felt much larger than he'd imagined, and he had to cough to gather enough saliva to swallow it. He heard shouting – maybe they suspected something – but by the time someone grabbed him by the shoulder, his body had begun to tighten from the inside and a dizziness swept over him, followed by darkness, and then it was too late.

–

It was a sign of failure for the Gestapo to seek the help of the Danish police. That they barely trusted them went without saying. What bothered them more was how it showed them up: the Gestapo were meant to be the elite, the representatives of the master race, the occupiers. Asking for assistance was not part of the image they sought to encourage.

They'd gone to the police headquarters on Polititorvet, but no one in the registration and records department could help them: there were quite a few Peter Rasmussens in Copenhagen, but none matched the description of the man they were looking for.

'And you've tried that address?'

'Of course we've tried that address, you fool! What do you take us for?'

None of the Danish officers answered.

'Has anyone in here come across a Peter Rasmussen?' one of them called out across the room.

'Peter Rasmussen, you say?' It was an older officer, who'd just entered the room, glasses perched on top of his head, reading a document. He hadn't spotted the two Gestapo officers sitting with their backs to him. 'Hanne Jakobsen from the Major Robbery Unit at Nørrebro asked us to issue a *legitimationskort* for a Peter Rasmussen back in November. She signed the authorisation herself.'

By the time the two Gestapo men stood up and turned round, it was too late. The temperature in the room turned ice cold.

'Hanne Jakobsen, you say?' A thin smile was spreading across the Gestapo officer's face.

The room had been quiet up to that point, but now a sudden and chilling silence descended on it. It felt as if the air had been sucked out of the place.

And from that moment on, those who knew Hanne Jakobsen began to speak of her in the past tense.

Chapter 18

'Remarkable Tom, absolutely remarkable.'

'What is Roly?'

'Oh do come on Tom. This Agent Blackbird – saves Agent Laertes' life in Berlin, keeps the whole mission on track and now manages to get him inside Peenemünde. I call that remarkable.'

Tom Gilbey remained impassive. 'And brave.'

'Goes without saying. And you totally trust them?'

Tom Gilbey nodded. They were sitting in the meeting room deep under Downing Street, waiting for the others to arrive. Sir Roland Pearson had suggested he and Tom Gilbey meet a bit earlier ('make sure we're singing from the same hymn sheet, Tom, you know the score…')

'And is there anything else you can tell me about this Agent Blackbird?'

'Come on, Roly, you understand how this works. The fewer people who know, the better and in any case, she's Barney Allen's agent, I told you. I'm not in a position to divulge anything about Agent Blackbird and frankly I'm surprised you…'

'Naturally one understands that Tom, but of course I only ask in case Winston asks and if…'

'…in my experience Roly, Winston rarely does ask. He's got a very good appreciation of how intelligence works. They'll be here any time now, remember, and I don't want this meeting to end without a commitment to bombing the bloody place. Don't let Swalcliffe talk you out of it, Roly. You're supposed to have Winston's ear just as much as he does.'

-

The meeting had the feel of a family gathering with tensions bubbling just beneath the surface, the participants obliged to meet, the occasion made all the more awkward by the links that had brought them together in the first place.

As usual, Lord Swalcliffe sat on his own opposite Sir Roland Pearson and Tom Gilbey, his face barely concealing a look of resentment. Air Vice Marshal Hamilton and Wing Commander Carter were at one end of the table, in front of a wall covered in charts and photographs, and Long from the Ministry was opposite them, as ever his presence somewhat enigmatic: unexplained, largely silent but nevertheless apparently important.

'I think you will have to concede, Edward, that the map we received from Agent Laertes does rather substantiate Kurt's intelligence: Peenemünde is where the V-1 and the V-2 are being developed.'

Lord Swalcliffe huffed and puffed and shifted around in his chair, clearly unhappy at the suggestion that he might concede anything.

'None of this so-called intelligence proves these bloody things can fly, though, does it? My concern remains that this could all be part of a very sophisticated deception operation by the enemy. Even if it's not, there's no guarantee their technology works. It could simply be something to indulge Hitler. The war in Europe is beginning to turn against him – by all accounts the Nazis have been defeated at Stalingrad just this week, and lost the whole of their 6th Army in the process – and he needs to convince the German people everything will be fine because they're developing secret weapons to defeat us. If we go ahead and bomb Peenemünde and turn the site into rubble, as I dare say you're going to propose, we'll be shooting ourselves in the foot. I say let them carry on with this nonsense. If we bomb some common sense into them, it will rebound on us: mark my words, the Luftwaffe will end up as the main beneficiaries.'

'What do you chaps make of it, Frank?'

Air Vice Marshal Hamilton stood up, positioning himself between two large charts.

'There can be no doubt that the map we received from Agent Laertes is consistent with what we were able to ascertain from our aerial reconnaissance photographs. It's terribly good by the way, quite the professional touch to it. As we said before, our photographs were poor quality. With the help of the map, they now make considerably more sense. The intelligence from your agent not only corroborates what we knew about Peenemünde, but actually adds significantly to it.

'For instance, we've been able to identify what the different structures and locations are. We now know that this – here – is the power plant; we had no idea that this was the experimental works; and here, at the southern end, this complex of buildings is actually where the slave labourers live. Had we not known that, we might well have destroyed it. So put together,' his cane tapped the blow-up of the map and a panel of photographs, 'we now have a pretty damn good idea of what will be below our boys when we come to bomb the place.'

'If that is what this meeting decides.'

'Of course, Lord Swalcliffe. Tim, why don't you take us through some of the plans we have for a possible bombing mission?'

The young wing commander moved one of the large charts to the centre of the wall and removed a cover sheet to reveal a map of northern Europe, including the United Kingdom.

'We've discussed this in detail with Bomber Command, and this is essentially their plan, based on our reconnaissance and the intelligence from Agent Laertes.'

'Hang on, hang on… you say this is Bomber Command's plan. Is Arthur aware of it?'

'Yes, Lord Swalcliffe,' said Hamilton. 'Not only is Air Marshal Harris aware of it, but he has personally approved it. I was with him at a meeting of the air staff yesterday and he—'

'Arthur is committed to the campaign of bombing German cities, Hamilton. He and I and Winston all see eye to eye on this – that is our priority. Operations like this are a distraction from what we see as the primary purpose of Bomber Command.'

'But surely, Lord Swalcliffe, being committed to a campaign of bombing German cities does not preclude us from also having select strategic bombing operations like this one? Carry on, Tim.'

'This is the plan: the aircraft take off at different times from bases along the east coast. They fly in small groups in an east-north-east direction over the North Sea. There will be three separate attack waves: each will rendezvous at an agreed point over German Bight, off the west coast of Denmark – round about here. They will then fly in a south-easterly direction across Denmark, over the islands of Jutland, Funen and Lolland – some may also fly over Falster, here. They will avoid going anywhere near the island of Zealand – as you know, that is where Copenhagen is and it's therefore much more heavily defended.

'Once they've cleared Lolland – approximately here – they'll be over the Baltic. They'll keep north of Rostock and Stralsund and head for the island of Rügen. Let me turn to this map – you can see the area in more detail here. They'll aim for a point in the north-east of Rügen, over Cape Arkona. From there they'll head due south to Peenemünde, which is approximately thirty-five miles from this point.

'This map here is based on the one supplied by Agent Laertes and also on our own reconnaissance. It shows the various targets within the Peenemünde site. The plan is for the first wave to be over Peenemünde at midnight; their role will be primarily as pathfinders, to drop the markers in the correct positions to enable the second and third waves to hit their allocated targets with more accuracy. That first wave will mainly comprise Halifax and Stirling bombers. The second wave is due over the site at twenty minutes past midnight, by which time the first wave will have cleared the area. The second wave will mainly be Lancasters, and their targets will hopefully have been nicely lit up for them by the pathfinders. Twenty minutes later, at twenty to one, the third wave comes in: more Lancasters and Halifaxes. They should be out of there before one o'clock.

'If we turn to this chart, gentlemen, you can see their route away from the site. They'll all drop their bombs while heading south, and when they finish, they'll turn west-north-west and head back towards the North Sea on a route just south of the one they flew in on – this is to ensure that each wave of aircraft avoids hitting an incoming wave. It's a more perilous route because it takes them closer to Rostock, which is very well defended, and also of course because by then the Luftwaffe will know what we're up to and will be out looking for the returning aircraft.'

'Won't they be all over us by the time the second wave passes over Denmark?'

'Possibly, Sir Roland, but we are organising a series of decoy bombing raids to coincide with the one over Peenemünde. Specifically, here and here: Berlin and Hamburg. These raids will start at eleven thirty, so with some luck they'll have drawn most of the German night fighters away from the Peenemünde area.'

'When will the raid take place?' It was a rare question from the normally silent Long from the Ministry.

'Bomber Command say it should be on the night of a full moon, or as close to it as possible. The next full moon over that area is around the twentieth of February, and for various operational reasons they feel Thursday the eighteenth would be the best day.'

'So two weeks today, eh?'

'Indeed, Sir Roland.'

The young wing commander sat down as Air Vice Marshal Hamilton stood up again. 'The objectives of this operation are threefold: to destroy as many of the identified structures as possible; to cause maximum loss of life in the areas where we believe the Germans are – most importantly their scientists; and to avoid hitting the slave labour accommodation at Trassenheide.'

'Well that's vital, obviously,' said Sir Roland. 'Can't have Tom's agent blown up by his own side, can we? Though presumably we'll be pulling him out of the area well before Bomber Command go in?'

There was a sudden silence in the room; then gentle coughing as people looked around to see who was going to speak first.

'I think one has to accept,' said Tom Gilbey, 'that Agent Laertes needs to remain in Peenemünde for the duration of the bombing.'

'The reason being,' added Hamilton, 'that we need someone on the ground to evaluate the damage and tell us how accurate our bombing was. Post-operation aerial photo reconnaissance will give us some indication, but that won't be anything as valuable as an eyewitness.'

'Once Agent Laertes has done that, we can pull him out. Agent Blackbird will help get him back to Denmark, and then we can bring him home.'

'Assuming,' said Lord Swalcliffe, 'Arthur's chaps haven't blown him up.'

–

'What's this Agent Laertes really like, Tom?'

'He's already proven to be pretty resourceful, I'd say, Roly. He's operated in Denmark and Berlin and managed to get into Peenemünde.' They were in Pearson's office after the meeting, the bombing raid now approved and a bottle of sherry on the desk.

'Once the bombs start falling, that'll be the real test, eh? So far he's been in danger, but he's had plausible enough cover stories. Once the place is destroyed, he'll be completely exposed. Assuming he survives, that is. What was the name of that chap in the year above me at school? Big bully, captain of his house... you remember, he had three surnames...'

'Furneaux-something-something-or-other?'

'That's right, filthy rich. What was it his father owned?'

'Northamptonshire, I believe, Roly.'

'Ah, was it? Well, I'm told he went to pieces on the Western Front. Never in much danger, managed to get himself a sinecure behind the lines, but was close to them one day when a shell exploded nearby. Wept like a baby apparently, had to be sent back to England; hasn't dared show his face at old boys' events since. Now for him, that shell was what truly tested him. Let's hope your chap is made of stronger stuff. How about we open the sherry?'

'I'll pass, Roly, but there is something I want to make you aware of that I thought it better not to raise at the meeting.'

'For Winston's ears?'

'Only if he asks.'

'Pour me a sherry first if you don't mind, Tom. Sounds as if I'm going to need it.'

Gilbey reached for the bottle. 'We heard from Weston yesterday...'

'Remind me, Tom, so many bloody names...'

'George Weston, our head of station in Stockholm: he runs Agent Osric and is the go-between between her and us.'

'Of course, carry on. And make it a large one.'

'He thinks something's gone wrong in Copenhagen. He hasn't heard from Agent Osric for over a fortnight and his messages aren't being collected. He sent another courier in at the weekend to retrieve the messages; didn't want to risk anything. It's most uncharacteristic of Osric: no warning signs at any of the dead letter boxes, nothing. As far as he can tell, she's disappeared. He fears she's been arrested by the Gestapo. The chap's only a courier; George doesn't feel he's up to looking into it further.'

'Oh dear. Perhaps a splash more sherry, Tom. Are you sure you won't join me?'

'Maybe a small one then, Roly. I'm afraid it gets worse. George has copies of *Politken* sent over to Stockholm; it's one of the more reliable Danish papers. They carried a brief obituary last Thursday for Otto Knudsen: Agent Horatio. According to *Politken*, he died in police custody.'

There was silence in the room as Pearson sipped his sherry, his hands trembling slightly as he did so. 'I don't know, Tom, sometimes I worry we take these agents too much for granted, asking them to do things we know could result in their deaths. The poor woman. One shudders to think what has happened to her.'

–

It was a Saturday in the middle of February before Prince – now Pierre Breton – managed to get on a work detail to the beach near Zempin where his dead letter box was. There were three groups of prisoners that day: Ukrainians, Poles and French, and the latter just had the one guard, who as soon as they arrived went to join his comrades for a cigarette. Prince had come to realise that because there was so much security around the camp and on the island, the guards felt able to relax a bit in some of the areas where the men were put to work. It wasn't as if they could escape anywhere.

While he had the chance, he hurried to the white-painted wooden post with the life belt attached to it. The short walk was up a steep incline, and he quickly found himself out of breath. He was constantly shocked at how easily exhausted he was now, sapped of energy, his body persistently cold, often wet and desperate for food. He used his boot to loosen the shale and sure enough there was a black waterproof pouch. He slipped it down the front of his trousers. He would read the contents later.

–

He lay on his bunk that night, staring up at the rotting board above him and unable to sleep. He'd read Sophia's message a dozen times, memorised it and destroyed it. Now he was going over what it said again and again in his mind. It was hardly ambiguous.

> *Be prepared for visit 16–20 February: it will be on a night when there's a full moon.*
>
> *Essential you remain in the camp.*
>
> *Trassenheide will be spared.*
>
> *Afterwards you will gather as much information as possible on impact of visit: regard this as a priority and an instruction!*
>
> *When this task complete, you may leave the camp.*
>
> *I will be where I dropped you every Sunday, Tuesday and Friday starting 48 hours after the raid between 2–4 p.m. Meet me there.*

There was little to reassure him in the message, not least its lack of subtlety. Peenemünde was to be bombed, which came as no surprise. But he'd somehow assumed he'd be given ample warning and would be able to escape before the raid. That Trassenheide was to be spared was of little consolation. Even if it was, gathering intelligence on what damage had been done was going to be perilous in the extreme – and Sophia's escape plan sounded more fanciful than anything else.

He wondered whether to mention anything to Émile, but realised it was too risky. Although he'd grown close to the group of French workers in his hut and they knew what he was up to, he couldn't be sure he'd trust them enough once they became aware of the raid.

The 16th was a Tuesday and it didn't look like a full moon, so he decided to remain in the hut that night. But on Wednesday, the moon certainly seemed rounder and brighter. He feigned a bad stomach that evening, which was feasible enough given the pitiful food they received: all the prisoners in the hut next to theirs had a type of dysentery, and they'd been told that some of the Russians further up the camp had died from malnutrition. He kept his work clothes on and stayed in the toilet block behind their hut all night. He did the same thing the following night, and it was then that the raid happened.

Many of Prince's childhood Sundays had been spent on long, bracing walks across fields that went on for ever in the Lincolnshire countryside. Apart from the mud, the silence and the vast skies, his enduring memory was of enormous murmurations of starlings flocking above them, twisting and turning in an intricately choreographed display. They'd bumped into a farmer one day who, like them, was watching the display with awe.

'Now then, lad, how many birds do you think there are up there?'

'A thousand… two thousand?'

The farmer shook his head and bent down to let him into a secret no one else should hear. 'Over one hundred thousand: there're more starlings above us now than there are people in the whole of Lincoln!'

That was his abiding thought once the raid began: the bombers like a flock of starlings, dark shapes merging as one mass, twisting and turning in the moonlit sky, menacing and fascinating at the same time.

The first planes appeared from the north just after midnight. Once the alarm sounded, he left the toilet block and ran into the woods, where he climbed a tree to get a better view.

He had no idea how many planes there were, but it must have been hundreds. At first there hardly seemed to be any bombs, but the area to the north of them was illuminated by hundreds of lights.

The second wave of bombers came around twenty past midnight. This time the target was further to the north, possibly the V-2 works. As soon as this attack finished, a third wave appeared, bombing targets even further north, maybe the experimental area. The anti-aircraft fire was in full operation now, and Prince spotted at least a dozen aircraft being hit.

Now the Trassenheide camp itself seemed to be the target, and he was terrified that stray bombs could land in the woods, so he jumped down from the tree and ran into the fields beyond, making sure not to get too close to the barbed-wire perimeter. As far as he could tell, the camp was ablaze.

The RAF bombers had been flying low, and as the final wave left, they seemed to descend before their final turn out towards the west, giving him a much clearer view. They appeared to be mostly Lancasters, and he was overcome by emotion. They'd have flown here from the bases in Lincolnshire he knew so well: Scampton, Wickenby, Woodhall Spa and Binbrook.

Just the year before, there'd been the thousand-bomber raids over Germany, and the planes had gathered in the skies above Lincolnshire before forming and heading out across the sea. They'd made so much noise that Henry had woken up, and father and son had stood in front of the blackout curtains watching them, Henry trying to count them.

Would Henry have been watching these aircraft as they'd left their bases earlier that evening? Would he see these same planes when they returned in a few hours' time? And would he still try to count them?

–

His memory of the next twelve hours was a mixture of brutal clarity and blurred confusion. His main problem, as he looked back on it, was to recreate in his mind the correct sequence of events.

He remembered running from the woods towards the perimeter wire fence and then hearing a guard shout and running back to the huts. His own hut had taken a direct hit, as had the ones on either side of it. All three were so well ablaze it was impossible that anyone in them could have survived. A hut housing Ukrainians had also been hit, but there were some survivors there, all badly burnt.

For a while those labourers who had escaped the fires were corralled in their own area by a small number of very nervous guards, but they were then marshalled into groups to go into the main part of the camp to help fight the blazes.

Prince tried to make a note of where they were and what damage he could see, but it was near impossible to make much out in the darkness and the confusion. They'd spend a few minutes fighting one fire before being hurried to another then waiting to be given another task. They spent several hours carrying bodies to a makeshift morgue near the airfield, and as dawn broke, the extent of the damage began to become apparent.

It was hard to know what kind of detail London wanted. The majority of buildings did appear to have been hit, but only a few had been completely destroyed. There was even evidence in the experimental area of work continuing as normal, and he saw a large rocket – apparently unscathed – being mounted on what looked like a railway wagon.

Later that morning, he was allocated to a small work detail in the main barracks area, where the Germans lived. One housing block had taken a direct hit and two others were damaged, but the destruction was not as extensive as he'd hoped. As they were helping to clear a roadway, a young SS officer came over to them. His face was ghostly white and he was trembling as he lit a cigarette. Prince smiled and held the match for him. He was amazed when the officer offered him one.

'Where are you from?' He sounded grateful to have someone to pass a few moments with.

'France, sir.'

The officer nodded, as if to confirm that he'd heard of France.

'Which part?'

'Lyon, sir.'

'My cousin is based there. You speak good German.'

Prince couldn't quite believe how uncharacteristically placid the SS officer was. This was the perfect opportunity to find out what he knew.

'How many people were killed last night, sir?'

The German shrugged. 'How the hell would I know? Hundreds, certainly.' He nodded in the direction of the destroyed housing block. 'All of them in there, for a start.'

'Were there soldiers or scientists in there?'

Now the officer looked a bit more suspicious. 'Why are you asking?'

'I was just wondering. The airfield looked intact, but the V-2 works seemed to have taken a few direct hits...'

He'd misjudged the situation: the officer was no longer placid. 'Why the hell are you asking all these questions?'

'I know why he's asking all these questions.'

Prince turned round to see who'd spoken. It was another French prisoner, one from a hut a little way away from theirs. They were a group from Blois whom Émile insisted were not to be trusted: Pétainists.

'Why's that then?' The SS officer had walked over to the man.

'Because he's not who he says he is. I don't even think he's French. He turned up in the camp a few weeks ago...'

Prince told the SS officer he'd never heard anything quite so ridiculous. He'd been here for over a year, he said, and was as French as the next man.

At first the SS officer looked inclined to believe him, or at least to let the matter go: frankly, there were much more important things to worry about than two French prisoners bickering. But the other man from Blois wouldn't give up.

Go on then, find out if he's French!

I'm telling you he was smuggled into the camp a few weeks ago.

a willing volunteer, she had acquired an impressive-looking nurse's uniform, which, along with a sheaf of documentation from Oberführer Hausser in Greifswald and the Mercedes stuffed with provisions for the sentries at Wolgast, would hopefully ensure she'd get to Zempin with little difficulty.

When there was no sign of the Englishman, she imagined he was still gathering information, or needed another few days before he could get on the right work detail, so she returned on the Tuesday and again on the Friday. There was still no sign of him. On the Friday, she managed to speak with a guard by the beach, who was grateful for the cigarettes she slipped into the pocket of his greatcoat. It must have been terrible, she said. Were many people killed?

'Quite a number, my lady, but not as many as you'd expect, not given the number of planes that flew over us and the amount of bombs they dropped.'

She told him how brave he was, and he must take this sausage, please... no, I insist. Was it mostly good Germans killed, or slave labourers?

'A surprising number of slave labourers, my lady – hundreds of them actually: you'd have thought they'd have avoided that area, but maybe the RAF aren't as smart as the Luftwaffe! Ah well...'

But still she didn't give up. She returned the next Sunday and the following Tuesday and Friday. On Friday she was questioned by a Gestapo officer at the checkpoint. He was respectful enough, but quite twitchy and not entirely trusting of her answers.

It was now more than two weeks after the raid. She had to conclude that Agent Laertes had been killed, which was very sad, but now she had to think of herself.

Her visits to Usedom appeared to be arousing suspicion.

She must return to Berlin.

–

Back in Greifswald, she explained to the orphanage that she had received distressing news about her husband and was going home. She used the weekend to pack up the villa and prevail upon Oberführer Hausser to allow her enough fuel to get back to Berlin. On Sunday night, she retrieved the Englishman's Danish and German identity cards from their hiding place and burnt them.

She left Greifswald at first light on the Monday and was in Berlin that afternoon. A letter from Karl-Heinrich had arrived that morning and was waiting on the beautifully polished hall table with ivory inlays that he'd stolen from the Goldmanns. She managed to send a detailed message to London: the raid appeared to have had limited success; many slave labourers had been killed; she feared the Englishman was one of them. They were not to expect to hear from her for a long while.

On Tuesday morning, she went to visit Konrad, her husband's closest friend and fellow SS *Brigadeführer*. He'd been sent back from Stalingrad because of his injuries and was now working at SS headquarters.

'We must regard no news as good news, Sophia. Karl-Heinrich is so smart, I'm sure if anyone can get out of there it's him. You mark my words.'

'But it sounds so unlikely, Konrad. Paulus surrendered over a month ago. Surely I'd have heard something by now.'

'Don't be defeatist, Sophia. But tell me, is there anything I can do for you?'

'There is one small favour, Konrad. Karl-Heinrich told me that if anything ever happened to him – or even if it looked as if he might be in danger – I was to go to Zurich to collect some gold he has in a bank there and bring it back here. I think I should do that now, but I'll need papers to allow me to leave the Reich and get into Switzerland.'

'That's not a small favour, Sophia, it's—'

'He also said what a good friend you've been, so loyal and trustworthy. There is a lot of gold, Konrad; he got it from Jews before he sent them on their holidays in the east. I know he would wish you to have some of it, as a small token of his respect for you.'

The SS *Brigadeführer* told her that he needed a few days to work on this: perhaps by Friday?

She said Thursday would be better, as then she'd be able to take the train on the Friday. 'With luck, Konrad, I'll be back here this time next week, with a certain something weighing down my bags. If it is possible also to have papers to show I'm on state business – for the SS perhaps – that would be so helpful.'

He told her to come back on Thursday, and she returned to the apartment in Charlottenburg. She had so much to do and so little time in which to do it. She knew it would arouse suspicion if she took more than one suitcase, and it was hard to know what to leave behind. She'd wear her furs and jewellery, and she packed more jewellery along with the silver candlesticks belonging to the Goldmanns. She knew how important they were to the family and hoped one day to be able to return them. The final item to go into the case was perhaps the most important one: her husband's diary.

She took care to ensure her maid was not aware of what was going on. She gave her a few days off and told her she'd be back by Monday.

When the maid had left, she took out Karl-Heinrich's letter and read it a few times, savouring it the way one does a compelling novel. Then she opened one of the bottles of what he had assured her was an excellent vintage champagne: Mumm, his favourite.

She ran a bath and stayed in it for an hour, then put on her silk dressing gown before pouring her fourth glass of champagne and reading the letter once again.

Chapter 19

Stalingrad; Switzerland, January–February 1943

Headquarters of the 6th Army
Gumrak Airbase
20 January 1943

My darling, darling Sophia,

I write this letter with a heavy heart because I fear it is possible this may be the last time you hear from me, your devoted and loving husband.

I cannot describe how difficult the circumstances are in which I write. The cold is unimaginable; we no longer have fuel for any form of heating or for cooking, though there is hardly any food left to cook anyway.

We are now completely encircled by the Soviets and it can only be a matter of days if not hours before they capture Gumrak. I should have taken the opportunity to get out of here last week when I actually had the chance to do so on a Heinkel. However, Colonel General Paulus has made this his headquarters and I decided to remain. In truth, it is some weeks now since there was any need for the SS, since our role was to help in the capture of Stalingrad and then deal with those who'd remained in it.

The Heinkel and Junkers pilots have been quite heroic, flying through the most atrocious conditions to deliver a few supplies and along with those our mail.

There is a Junkers preparing to depart here in a few minutes and I will make sure this letter gets on it. I have no doubt this will be the final Luftwaffe flight out of Gumrak.

The last letter I received from you was dated 26 December, when you told me you were going to volunteer at the Frauenschaft orphanage in Greifswald. I had hoped to hear from you since then, but I imagine you have been too busy doing your bit to help our noble cause. That you have been so selfless and think only of others comes as little surprise to me.

There is much defeatist talk here of surrender: it seems Paulus is inclined in that direction. There are rumours that the Führer is about to promote him to field marshal, as no German field marshal has ever surrendered, but I doubt even this will persuade him. Although this is shameful, I have to take my lead from the commanding officer. If I remain alive after the fall of Gumrak, then I will no doubt be taken prisoner. The rumours are that the Soviets treat German prisoners properly, but that does not apply to the SS. I have therefore obtained a Wehrmacht uniform and have given myself a junior rank. Imagine – your husband has demoted himself! At least this should ensure I survive, albeit in captivity. Please continue to write to me, and hopefully your letters will reach me through the usual channels. Ensure you use my new identity, Oberleutnant Karl Naundorf.

There is so much I could say to you, about my love for you and how you have been a loyal wife and a proud National Socialist. However, I have to hurry: I can see the Junkers is getting ready to leave and I must ensure this letter gets on board.

Until we meet again, have utter faith in Ultimate Victory!

With my eternal love,

Heil Hitler!

Your devoted husband,
Karl-Heinrich

–

Bern, Switzerland
23 March 1943

Dear Karl-Heinrich,

I have so much to say I hardly know where to begin. I think perhaps the best thing to do would be for me to recount everything in the order it happened.

However, first I need to acknowledge that if you are reading this letter then I hope you will already be aware of the part I have played in whatever fate awaits you, a fate you fully deserve.

I should also acknowledge that to an extent, I am to blame for the predicament I have found myself in. When you gave up being a lawyer and joined the SS, I should have left you, or at the very least objected. When you started to espouse the most appalling views, I should have divorced you. When you treated the Goldmanns so dreadfully, I should have done something about it. That I didn't is a source of considerable regret and shame.

Then the war started and you were in your element. When you started boasting of your part in the massacres of Jews and others, I decided I'd had enough, but by then it was very difficult for me to do much about it. I had no means of my own and divorcing an SS officer would have had serious consequences for me.

I was ashamed of myself for doing nothing, and then, in late 1940, two things happened. The first was when you were in Poland, not long after you'd been home on *leave. I was getting ready for bed one night when I heard the maid scream. I went into the corridor to see what was happening and she was in a real state: she'd seen a mouse in her room. She'd chased it out and it had gone under the door of your study. We went in to look for it, and saw something dart under the desk. We managed to move the desk and pulled away the carpet to reveal the floorboards, one of which had a hole in it large enough to get two fingers in. I did this and was surprised at how easily I could pull the board up. I spotted a package wrapped in cloth hidden beneath it and realised it could be important, but told the maid I couldn't see anything and we'd better put everything back. The following day when she was out shopping, I took the package out.*

You know of course what was in it: the details of a Swiss bank account in your name, held at Bank Leu on Paradeplatz in Zurich. The other item was a diary you had kept from August 1939 to October 1940. Over the next few days I read every word of that diary. The events you wrote about, the casual way you recorded them, the detailed descriptions – they were so shocking I could only manage a few pages at a time. But when I finished reading, I determined I would do something with that diary. If nothing else, it was proof that you had committed terrible and unforgivable crimes against innocent civilians. I decided I must use it to help ensure you were held to account for these crimes.

Of course, there was always the possibility that when you were home on leave you could remove the diary, so I decided to copy every word of it, to transcribe all of its contents.

We'll come back to the diary soon, but just think, Karl-Heinrich – you were undone by a mouse!

I mentioned two events in late 1940. The second one – and you'll understand if I'm somewhat vague here –

was that I met a person from a neutral country who had links with Allied intelligence. To cut a long story short, I became an Allied agent. Again, I do not propose to go into detail, but I want you to know I've been an active and effective agent for them. I have done what I can to undermine the Nazis. My trip to Greifswald, of which you were so proud, was simply to provide me with cover to assist the Allies in their spying on the nearby Peenemünde rocket base. The base was destroyed in February and I'd like to think I played no small part in that.

But after that happened, I decided that now was the time to leave Germany. I'd been an agent for over two years and I felt my luck could run out soon.

So I returned to Berlin, and with the help of your dear friend Konrad, I was able to obtain papers to allow me to travel to Switzerland. I told him it was to collect gold you had there and bring it back, promising him his cut. His greed ensured I received an excellent set of papers.

I took the train to Zurich, where, thanks to your paperwork and the fact that I was able to prove I was your wife, I was able to access your account. It is now empty, Karl-Heinrich, and I have used the funds to open an account of my own that will ensure I never want for money. I used some of it to pay for a new identity as a Swiss citizen. It was expensive, but the identity is excellent: no one will ever be able to link me with Sophia von Naundorf.

From Zurich I travelled to Geneva, which is where the International Red Cross is based. You see, the diary was still under the floorboards when it was time for me to leave Berlin, so I was able to take the original with me as well as the copy I made. My idea was to hand the diary over to them along with this letter for you, as I understood they delivered letters for prisoners. But this *did not work out. The Red Cross could not have been less interested — they said they couldn't deliver letters to German prisoners in the Soviet Union, and as for the diary, either they didn't understand or more likely they didn't care.*

But when I left, a secretary followed me out. She said she'd overheard what had happened: why didn't I take the matter to the Soviet Embassy in Bern?

So I took her advice and travelled to Bern — I have to tell you, Karl-Heinrich, Switzerland is the most peaceful country, with wonderful scenery, and travelling through it by train (first class, thanks to your generosity!) is a most satisfying experience.

At first the Soviet Embassy was rather sceptical. I saw a junior diplomat to begin with, but he referred the matter to someone more senior, and then someone else investigated it in detail. It seems they were able to check out some of the facts in your diary, and especially the entry from January 1940 regarding Kielce. I am sure you remember it, but just in case, I am enclosing in this letter another copy I have made of that entry.

You may wish to read it, Karl-Heinrich. It has helped seal your fate.

The Soviet officials have been most helpful, even enthusiastic. The diary will help them identify a number of war criminals, including you. You said in your last letter that you were going to disguise yourself as a junior Wehrmacht officer. They have been able to check with their comrades responsible for the prisoners captured at Gumrak, and they now know that Oberleutnant Karl Naundorf is actually SS Brigadeführer Karl-Heinrich von Naundorf. You really ought to have been more imaginative in adopting another identity, but then I guess your arrogance got the better of you.

So there we are, Karl-Heinrich. The Soviets assure me that for security reasons they will only show you this letter in the moments before your execution, so that you will not be able to divulge its contents to anyone.

My new life starts now, as yours comes to an end.

Sophia

—

Wednesday 24 January 1940
Kielce, Radom district, General Government of Poland

I thought nothing could be more fun than conquering Poland in less than a month last September, but these days life is even more amusing. I've not made an entry for a couple of days because we've been so busy, though it's not been exactly hard work! Last night, after our 'exertions', Karl, Gerd, Georg and I 'borrowed' a crate of excellent vodka from a merchant's house in one of the better districts of this miserable city. I don't remember much of what happened, but let's say that this morning there wasn't much vodka left. Gerd had also managed to get hold of six girls: four of them Polish and two Jewish, and not one of them over the age of eighteen! I do remember we had an argument about which of us would have two girls, and in the end, it was Gerd and me: Gerd because he'd found them, me because I pulled rank!

Because I felt so 'guilty' this morning, I wrote a long letter to Sophia pledging my undying love as always. She writes such sweet letters to me I feel I must reply in kind.

So the fun we're having at the moment is all to do with the Jews. This place is full of the bastards! Fritz Katzmann, who is now looking after the policing of the district, told me the other day that before the war there were only around 15,000 Jews in the city. Now there are over 20,000, because they're bringing them in from other places. I guess sooner or later they'll have to put them in one area so they can be controlled while we come up with other plans for what to do with them.

Yesterday morning I was in Katzmann's office and he told me about a house on Pocieszka where a bunch of radical Jews were hanging out. Apparently they came from a small town called Chmielnik, which is just south of Kielce. According to Katzmann, these Jews were political radicals; they belonged to a secular socialist party called the Bund. He said he had his eye on them because he was concerned they might cause trouble. I said to him, 'Katzmann, what the hell's the point of keeping your eye on them? What are you waiting for – you want them to start taking shots at our boys?'

He didn't look too happy at me talking to him like that. He's the same rank as me – an Oberführer – though I'd be surprised if I'm not ranking him in a matter of months if my promotion to Brigadeführer comes through as I'm sure it will. He said, 'All right, von Naundorf, you deal with it,' and I said I happily would. Karl, Gerd and Georg were free, so we took a unit of Stormtroopers with us and went to the house on Pocieszka.

I decided we should treat the raid as a proper operation; after all, we didn't know if these people were armed. I commanded a unit going through the front of the house while Georg looked after the rear. Gerd and Karl took their men into the houses either side, because these Jews have been known to use the roof spaces as escape routes.

But there was no trouble. There were about a dozen of them, all in their late teens or early twenties – split equally between men and women – all sitting in the kitchen having some kind of meeting. There wasn't a weapon to be seen. They were obviously shocked when we burst in, but one of them, would you believe, had the cheek to ask us if we had permission to enter the house like that! I told him this was all the permission I needed, and pulled out my Luger pistol and hit him across the face with it. I'm sure I must have broken his jaw, but he didn't make a sound; he just stood there and smiled. I was so angry I shot him there and then, and the others started screaming.

Once we'd quietened them down, I ordered my men to search the house. One of the women stepped forward and said there was no one else there and they'd happily come to the police station. This seemed odd to me, to say the least. Until we'd shot the young man, they'd had a rather defiant air about them, and now they were volunteering to come along to the station. I reckoned it was because I'd ordered a search of the house. So then I said I wanted an extra-thorough search to be carried out. Sure enough, they discovered a trap door in the cellar, and through this a small underground room — more of a hole really — with half a dozen young children in it. Well, that was a bonus!

When we brought the children out to the street, where the others were waiting, there was quite a commotion, the gist of which was the adults pleading with us to take them but spare the children. Imagine, the sheer (and I have to say typical) arrogance of the Jews, thinking they could negotiate with us!

I was about to arrest them all, but Gerd said he had a much better idea. He herded them together and made them all march along. The adults were trying to comfort the children, who were terrified. My guess is they were all aged around five or six. Soon we came to the River Silnica, which isn't much of a river, to be honest, but it more than served our purpose, especially as the water was so cold. Gerd got his men to line the children up on the bank, and he personally pushed them in, one by one!

I can tell you, they didn't last long. I think the cold must have been too much for them. We noticed some *of the local Poles watching us from the other bank, and when the kids drowned, they cheered, as if we'd put on a show for them. I sometimes think the Poles in Kielce despise the Jews more than we do.*

After that, we took the adults to the SS headquarters, though to be honest, by then I was quite bored with everything. I'd rather hoped they'd have put up some resistance at the house on Pocieszka. I was all for handing them over to the Gestapo for questioning, but Oberführer Katzmann is more of a bureaucrat than a soldier and he insisted that we needed to process the prisoners and then they'd be sent off to a camp.

I couldn't be bothered with all this red-tape nonsense, so I told Georg just to shoot the prisoners there and then. He hesitated, I guess because two Oberführers had given conflicting orders, so I said, 'You know what? I'll do it myself!' I got the Stormtroopers to line the prisoners up against the wall and we machine-gunned them there and then.

They were remarkably calm, and when they realised their fate, they started singing a song, very quietly, but they sounded like a choir.

I have no idea what the song was, but I can't get it out of my head.

NKVD (The People's Commissariat for Internal Affairs)

Official memorandum: restricted and confidential

To: Commissar of State Security (First Class) A. I. Stepanov, NKVD Desk, Soviet Embassy, Bern, Switzerland

From: Commissar of State Security (Third Class) Semyon Mikhailovich Chernyakhovsky, NKVD office, Beketovka prisoner of war camp, Stalingrad Oblast

Date: 29 March 1943
Subject: SS Brigadeführer Karl-Heinrich von Naundorf

Comrade Stepanov,

Further to your communication dated 23 March. Your report was forwarded to my office.

The majority of Germans taken prisoner following the glorious victory in the Battle of Stalingrad are being held in either the Dubovka or Beketovka prisoner of war camps. All of the Germans who were found alive at Gumrak Airbase (liberated 21 March) have been brought here to Beketovka.

Upon receiving your report, we were able to establish that a Wehrmacht Oberleutnant by the name of Karl Naundorf was indeed captive at this camp.

He was subjected to intense interrogation by my officers. At first, he rigorously denied he was an SS Brigadeführer by the name of Karl-Heinrich von Naundorf. However, we were soon able to establish that this prisoner was indeed a member of the SS when upon examination we discovered the SS tattoo in his left armpit. Other German prisoners also identified him as an SS officer.

When confronted with the detail of your report and specifically the allegations of his crimes against the civilian population in Nazi-occupied Poland, he refused to comment.

The case was passed to me for review: I decided there was clear evidence of SS Brigadeführer Karl-Heinrich von Naundorf having committed war crimes and I ordered his execution.

The execution took place at 0600 this morning. As per your request, immediately prior to his execution the prisoner was shown the letter from his wife, dated 23 March, along with the section of his diary relating to Kielce. He read some of the letter but refused to read any more, so the remainder of the letter and the diary extract were read to him by a German-speaking comrade.

I can report that I have never seen a prisoner – either a German soldier or a Soviet citizen – so angry and distressed. Even though he was hand-cuffed, he nevertheless had to be restrained.

His fury continued unabated until the moment of his execution, so much so that he had to be strapped to a chair and carried to the gallows like that. As a result, death by hanging was not instan-taneous. The added weight of the chair and his struggle meant the rope snapped and the prisoner was writhing on the ground in considerable agony until he expired some ten minutes later.

Upon my instructions, he was not shown the mercy of a bullet to dispatch him.

Chapter 20

Neuengamme; Lübeck, April 1943

The journey to Neuengamme had taken all day, with a running commentary provided by August, the German communist, who'd somehow been aware of their destination when they'd left Peenemünde. They drove through Mecklenburg and into Saxony, dropping south before Hamburg, driving through the plains north of the mighty Elbe and eventually following the path of a smaller river towards an enormous complex surrounded by barbed wire and searchlights that pierced through the low cloud and mist.

'We're lucky,' said August, chewing on the stub of a cigarette he'd found on the floor of the lorry.

'It doesn't feel like we're particularly lucky.' Prince spoke German with August. His companion had been a modern languages teacher in Berlin: English and French. Prince was aware that August knew he wasn't French and may have even guessed he was British, but he didn't risk hinting at it.

'Look, Pierre, they suspect all of us in here of being involved in that air raid in some way or other. My psychoanalyst friends – assuming any of them are still alive, which I doubt – would say they're being paranoid. The air raid threw them into a panic, and they're being uncharacteristically irrational about it. They're looking for anyone and everyone to blame for it. But we should take some comfort that they allowed us to leave Peenemünde; if they'd wanted to finish us off, they could have done it there and then. And if they'd wanted to torture us, there're plenty of other camps they could have sent us to, even those terrible ones in Poland you hear all the dreadful rumours about. Neuengamme is bad enough, but they put the prisoners here to work. There are factories all over the area. If we keep our heads down and are very lucky, we may survive a few months, and who knows what will happen then? The war may well be over!'

August the Marxist, forever the optimist.

–

They'd ended up in one of the sub-camps of Neuengamme, this one on the banks of the Dove-Elbe river. It was a collection of badly built huts in a large and exposed field of mud arranged around a parade ground where the prisoners assembled at the beginning and end of each day for a head count. Nearby was a large brickworks to where they were marched at seven o'clock every morning, returning ten hours later if they were lucky. On occasions they were so busy they were kept there all night, allowed a few hours' sleep on the filthy floor.

That was a good sign, according to the ever-optimistic August. Prince replied he was struggling to see it.

'The foreman is from Bremen. My grandmother was from Bremen.'

'And that makes it a good sign?'

'No, it means I can speak his dialect and he sometimes tells me things. He told me the authorities are increasingly desperate for bricks the Allied bombing raids are having a devastating impact. Hamburg has been really badly hit, as have all the other ports in this area, plus the Ruhr cities and Berlin, of course. So the more bricks they need, and the harder we're having to work, the more it's a sign that the Nazis are being defeated!'

There were other benefits to having to work through the night at the brickworks. The enormous kilns meant it was warm inside in contrast to the icy conditions in the camp huts. And they received slightly better food. In the camp, their main meal of the day was brought to their hut in a large pot after the evening roll call and heated up on a gas stove. It was a gruel-like concoction made mostly from vegetable peel with the occasional chunk of rotten meat thrown in. It wasn't unknown for them to find bits of animal carcass floating in it, sometimes with fur still attached to the skin. But if they had their main meal in the factory, the foremen would make sure they each had a piece of bread with it, which was occasionally not stale. Sometimes they'd give them raw potatoes, and when the guards weren't looking, they'd bake the potatoes on the kilns. Prince couldn't recall ever eating anything more delicious.

There were forty men in their hut in the camp, the majority Dutch or Belgian, plus a handful of Germans, a few French and a couple of Norwegians. The Russians, Ukrainians and Poles tended to be grouped together in other huts, often with quite violent consequences.

The atmosphere in their hut was not as visceral as it could be in others. Some of the nationalities didn't particularly like each other, but nor was there any deep-seated hatred. The atmosphere was more one of quiet resignation: most of their time there was spent in a state of exhaustion and hunger. Just staying alive and out of trouble kept them occupied.

At the back of Prince's mind was a constant anxiety that the Nazis hadn't forgotten why he'd been sent to the camp in the first place. He was all too aware that he was here because another French prisoner had denounced him at Peenemünde, and he found it hard to believe that that was the end of the matter. He was convinced that sooner or later someone at Peenemünde or even here at Neuengamme would get round to looking at his file and decide to question him again.

When he'd been at the camp for what must have been a month, this sense that he'd be called in any day now by the SS began to become an obsession. He was convinced that anyone walking behind him was following him on behalf of the SS; he even started to wonder whether August had been planted there to spy on him. He knew that once he was questioned, he'd be finished. He wouldn't be able to pass himself off as a Frenchman for more than a minute in a serious interrogation. A sense of hopelessness began to envelop him, and he soon lost track of time as he sank into a pit of despair, beyond caring what day of the week it was, or even what month.

One afternoon, one of the Belgians from his hut, a man in his fifties called Frans, found him slumped in a corridor in the brick factory, doing nothing other than staring at the wall. 'Are you ill, my friend?'

Prince shook his head, not taking his eyes off the wall in front of him.

'Then why are you sitting like that? If the guards see you, you're in big trouble, you know that.'

'I don't care.'

'You don't care about being in trouble?'

He turned away, hoping the Belgian would get the message that he wanted to be left alone. At that moment, footsteps approached them and he heard Frans talking in Flemish to one of the Dutch prisoners. Together they hauled Prince up and helped him back into the area he was working in.

Back in the hut that evening, he didn't eat anything and just lay on his bunk, face down, staring at the ground, watching a mouse scurry beneath him. Something was dripping on his neck from the bunk above, but he lay still, not bothering to move even one inch.

August came over and sat next to him. 'Frans told me what happened in the factory. You've given up, haven't you?'

Prince didn't reply. He found it hard to disagree with the German. August grabbed him roughly by his shoulder and made him turn to face him.

'I've been in these camps since before the bloody war started, over five years now. You have to give me some credit for the fact I've got some experience. There are three things I know – are you listening to me?'

Prince couldn't ignore the fire in August's eyes and the passion with which he spoke.

'The first is that Nazism will be defeated and socialism will triumph. The second is this: there's a moment when some men just give up in the camps. They decide life is so terrible they couldn't care whether they live or not. I can see you're like that. The third thing, though, is that there is a way to survive, a way to get through even in the most appalling circumstances.'

August paused, looking for some kind of response. Prince sat up, his eyes showing the first signs of life for a few days.

'Look at Henk over there,' August continued. They both looked over at the Dutchman, a mild-mannered man in his late sixties, a university lecturer who'd been suffering from typhus since Prince had arrived at the camp but who stoically carried on, a gentle smile rarely absent from his face. 'Henk shouldn't be alive, should he? He's been a prisoner since the Nazis invaded the Netherlands; he was tortured by the Gestapo and has been here for years. He wasn't a well man even before the war. How come he's still alive, while younger, stronger men gave up and died?'

Prince shrugged: *you tell me*.

'It's because he has something he believes in. He has a goal to aim for. In his case it's his family. His wife is in hiding – he refused to betray her – and now he's holding on, convinced that one day they'll be reunited. That's what keeps him alive; it's more powerful than anything else. Those of us who've survived against the odds – it's because we've also got something to live for. For me, it's my politics; my belief that a better world will replace this one, that the triumph of revolutionary socialism is inevitable. The Frenchman over there, the one with no eyebrows... he has a restaurant in Paris, doesn't he? He spends all day planning new menus. He told me walking back here this evening that he knows the *plats du jour* for every day of the year after liberation, and now he's working on the following year. That's what has kept him going. You have to think of something to keep *you* going, your reason to survive. Are you married?'

For the first time in weeks, Prince felt emotion welling in him. His head dropped, and when he looked up again, there were tears in his eyes. 'I was. My wife and daughter were killed in a car crash.'

August looked at him for a while, unsure of how to respond. He placed his hand on Prince's shoulder. 'My friend, I'm so sorry... is there no one else? Do you have religious beliefs maybe?'

'No, but I do have a son. He's very young.' As he said those words, he suddenly felt stronger, as if the dead weight of despair had been lifted from him.

—

A fortnight later, around the end of March, some one hundred prisoners were ordered to remain standing at the end of morning roll call. It was one of those days when the wind begins to feel less harsh, more like spring than winter. In the fields beyond the barbed wire, they could even make out some flowers, a strange splash of colour in their grey world. They stayed standing for two hours, and although they were meant to be silent, the parade ground hummed with snatches of whispered conversations.

'They're going to shoot us.'

'They'll be taking us east.'

'Notice how they've not kept any Russians behind... or Poles.'

After two hours, a long black Daimler pulled into the parade ground and four men in SS uniforms climbed out. One of them walked to a microphone.

'That's Pauly, the bastard,' said August.

'Who's he?'

'SS Obersturmbannführer Max Pauly, the commandant of Neuengamme: as I said, a bastard.'

The loudspeakers threw out a series of screeches as the commandant moved the microphone around.

'In twelve minutes, trucks will arrive to transport you to Lübeck. I don't want you to think that because you're in a city and away from here somehow security will be less tight. In fact, it will be the opposite. My men who'll be accompanying you have orders to shoot anyone who causes problems. You should now go to your huts and pack whatever miserable possessions you may have.'

Lübeck had been bombed so heavily, it took Prince a while to realise that they were actually being driven through a city. Through the gaps in the tarpaulin it seemed at first as if they were in a quarry, and then an abandoned industrial area.

Eventually the trucks pulled into a port and came to a halt in front of an enormous building. They remained there for an hour while a series of arguments raged outside. The prisoners caught snatches of it, the gist being that the SS officer in charge of them thought it was too risky to keep them by the docks, while someone else said this was the only option: 'Otherwise you can turn round and drive them back to the Elbe!'

More arguing, then they were suddenly ordered to leave the trucks and hurried into the building, which seemed to be a deserted warehouse. They were marched up to the top floor, where a roll call was taken and they were ordered to remain standing. An hour later, they were taken down to the floor below, where in a vast room a pile of blankets waited at one end and two enormous vats of soup at another.

Eat.

Sleep.

They were woken at six the next morning and marched out of the building before being split into four groups. Prince's group walked for a mile into the town centre and stopped in front of the shell of what looked like an office block. They were ordered to take a shovel each and start clearing the rubble.

For the next two weeks, that was life in Lübeck: clearing rubble for ten or eleven hours at a time, the back-breaking work and sheer tedium occasionally broken by being sent on a detail to sort bricks and select ones that were considered to be more or less intact. All the time they had to watch out for the guards, an embittered bunch of thugs and sadists who'd look for any opportunity to abuse the prisoners.

One afternoon, Prince was part of a group sorting out a pile of bricks in a vast arched doorway, all that remained of a church. He was standing next to Henk, the Dutchman who'd been in his hut in Neuengamme and who'd survived because of his love for his wife. Henk had found an old rag, which he'd fashioned into a glove to protect his hand as he picked up the rough bricks. One of the guards swaggered over, a short man in his fifties with a red face.

'What the fuck are you doing?'

'Sorting bricks... sir.'

'I meant, what's that on your hand?'

'It's to protect it: it means I can work faster.'

'Take it off.'

'Why, so I work slower?' Henk smiled gently at the German, assuming he'd be grateful for the explanation.

'You think you're clever, eh? You insolent bastard...' The guard grabbed the brick from Henk's hand and smashed it into the Dutchman's temple. Henk staggered back, and Prince moved to support him, but the guard had pulled his pistol out.

'You, step back, leave him.' Henk was slumped on the ground now, blood pouring from his head, his eyes barely open. 'Get up!'

For a brief moment, Henk tried to rise, but the effort was too much and he collapsed to the ground again. The guard walked over, held the pistol close to his head and shot him. Then he turned and pointed his gun at the others. 'Who's next?' No one said a word.

At that moment, an SS officer walked over. He told them to carry on with their work, and Prince could hear him reminding the guard that they needed as many prisoners as possible.

A few days later, Prince was part of a smaller group sent to work in Travemünde, the busiest part of the port, the area closest to the Baltic. A particularly heavy bombing raid had destroyed the main road into the docks, and his group were helping to clear it. There were about twenty of them, and when they finished work, the guards announced that they'd be staying in Travemünde rather than travelling back to Lübeck each night.

On that first night, Prince realised that the guards – there were only three of them – hadn't taken a roll call. It was an uncharacteristic mistake, and he guessed the decision to send them to the docks had been a last-minute one, which meant there was probably no list of prisoners. They slept on the ground floor of the customs building, and the following morning were divided into smaller groups and sent back to work. Prince and August were ordered by a port police officer to help load a ship further along the quay.

'That's not what these prisoners are meant to be doing. They're supposed to be clearing the bomb damage; we can't allow them onto the boats.' It was the same guard who'd shot Henk.

'I don't care,' said the police officer, a tall, harassed-looking man who clearly outranked the guard. 'There are fifteen ships in Lübeck Bay waiting to come into port and another dozen waiting to leave. Unless we can get this mess sorted, we'll have the best part of thirty ships conveniently presented as sitting ducks for when the bastards return to bomb us.'

'That's defeatist talk, I'll—'

'Oh, is it? Well, how about I report you to the port commander for sabotaging trade, eh?'

A tense compromise of sorts was reached: Prince and August, together with a few other prisoners, would help to load the ship but wouldn't be allowed on it. Their job was to unload crates from a waiting lorry and carry them to the gangplank.

As they headed down the quay, they passed a number of other ships. One of them was clearly preparing to set sail, and as they walked past it, there was a loud blast from its horn. The vessel had been mostly obscured behind cranes; it was only as they came close to it that Prince looked at it properly. A shudder ran down his spine, his senses now heightened. He was so taken aback he stopped for a moment, and August had to prod him in the back to keep him moving.

When they reached the lorry they were meant to be unloading, the tense stand-off between the port police and the guards restarted, the guards arguing that it would take all morning to unload the lorry and their instructions were for the prisoners to repair the bomb damage.

Prince spotted his opportunity. As the argument continued, he moved round to the front of the lorry. Just ahead of the lorry was a wall running parallel to the quay, no more than three feet high.

He glanced round: the argument was still raging and the rest of the prisoners were grouped together on the quayside. He knew he couldn't hesitate. He moved quickly towards the wall in a crouching position and vaulted over it, dropping flat on the rubble. This would only take him a couple of minutes. He just needed to be careful.

'Hey – you! Stop!'

He froze. He wasn't sure where the shout had come from, or even if it was aimed at him. He pressed himself into the rubble.

'Put your hands up!'

Two rifle shots rang out. The first seemed to pass way over him, but the second thudded into the wall a foot or so ahead of him, a plume of red dust spraying out. He was aware of more shouting, and it quickly became apparent that it was directed at him. He'd been caught.

The guard who'd been in charge of his group – the trigger-happy one who'd shot Henk – marched over.

'Is this your prisoner?' A Wehrmacht soldier was standing by the wall, his rifle pointing at Prince.

'Yes, it's my prisoner, so you can fuck off now.'

'Perhaps you ought to watch your language and keep a closer eye on your prisoners, eh? Isn't that your job? It's not as if you lot have to worry about doing any fighting, is it?'

The guard hauled Prince back over the wall and kicked him in the back. He started to get up, but the guard pushed him down again.

'On your knees, French scum, and face the wall.'

He heard the safety catch being released on the machine gun and froze. For a fleeting moment he thought about diving over the wall again, or rushing at the guard, but he knew his situation was hopeless.

He opened his mouth to scream, but no sound came out.

Chapter 21

Lübeck; Copenhagen, April 1943

But then there *was* a sound.

This sound came from above, an indistinct, droning type of noise at first, which very quickly became louder and quite deafening and was replicated many times over, causing the ground to shudder. It wasn't just the noise, either; Prince was now aware of blackness and heat enveloping him.

He assumed he'd been shot.

But then he heard the guard behind him shout, 'What the fuck?' followed by an enormous explosion that threw Prince forward into the foot of the wall he'd been kneeling in front of.

He must have been knocked out for a moment or two: when he came round, he had no idea at first where he was or how long he'd been there. He was surrounded by explosions and choking dust, and covered in rubble. Although he was disorientated and confused, he gradually became aware of something heavy pressing on his leg. He realised that the Allies must be carrying out a bombing raid on the port, and it struck him how admirable it was that they felt able to do this in daytime: he must remember to tell Gilbey that. He would be pleased to hear it. The raid was still going on, and he decided to stay where he was. The rubble was acting as a form of protection.

After a few minutes, the noise abated: no more explosions, no more sound of aircraft above or anti-aircraft fire from the ground. There was a strange ringing in his ears. In the distance he could hear shouting, and nearer to him there were screams, but nothing else. He managed to free his leg and tentatively checked himself out. He could move all his limbs and couldn't feel any obvious pain. He pushed the rubble aside and looked around. The lorry they'd been supposed to unload must have taken a direct hit: little remained of it other than a tangled mess of metal. All around lay the bodies of the guards, the port policemen and the other prisoners, none of them moving, few of them in one piece. The ship they were loading had been hit too: black smoke billowed from it and it was listing heavily.

Prince clambered up, dusted himself down, then ran as fast as he could back along the quay towards the ship that had caught his attention earlier. It was still there and appeared to be unscathed, though there was frantic activity on deck: the crew were clearly in a hurry to leave port, and he could hardly blame them. He kept running, undecided whether to call out or just climb on board.

At that moment, the ship's horn sounded again and its bow swivelled away from the dock, pointing towards the port gates. Two sailors were frantically untying the ropes at the stern. Prince took a running jump, landing painfully on the deck, his fall cushioned by a pile of netting. He could feel the ship picking up speed as it headed out of the port.

The two sailors stood above him and between them he could make out the name of the ship on the bridge, picked out in white along with the name of its home port. It was this and the flag above it that had caught his attention, and it was the home port where he hoped the ship was heading to now.

Strand Stjerne. København.

'I'm Danish… I'm a prisoner. I've escaped, I need your help, please… I…' He was aware he was babbling as the two sailors stared down at him seemingly uncomprehending. Prince wondered whether they were Danish after all.

Then both glanced back at the quayside, peering as it faded in the distance.

'I don't think anyone saw him,' one of them said.

'In that case, we'd better take him to the captain,' the other replied.

Both spoke in Danish, and Prince felt warm tears stream down his face.

—

The captain looked at him as if he was a problem he could really do without. He fired questions at him.

How do I know you're Danish?

How did you escape?

How do I know this isn't a trap?

Prince told him there was little he could do to convince him other than begging him to believe he was telling the truth. He was a prisoner, he'd been in a concentration camp, he'd escaped…

Another officer had joined the captain now, an older man and altogether more sympathetic. He introduced himself as Otto and spoke with a Copenhagen accent. He sounded like Prince's grandfather. 'He doesn't look well, sir.'

'I was caught up in the bombing.'

'Obviously, but you look like you have a fever or something. You say you were in a camp?'

Prince nodded. He felt dizzy now, and for the life of him couldn't remember what to say if they asked for details of his Danish identity.

'Come on, we'd better get you into the sick bay. You can stay there until we get to Copenhagen. I'm afraid you're on your own after that.'

'When do we dock there?'

'Early tomorrow morning, with luck. Depends…'

'Depends on what?'

'On the bloody Germans.'

The voyage was straightforward, although he began to feel increasingly unwell during it. He was sure Otto was right, that he was developing a fever, and the rash that had appeared a few days earlier on his stomach was now spreading down his legs. They brought him blankets and food along with a change of clothing and told him they'd now cleared Lübeck Bay and that sea conditions were good for the time of year.

At six in the morning, Otto came into the sick bay with a mug of hot coffee. The *Strand Stjerne* was going to dock in Copenhagen within the hour, he said.

'We're going to have to hide you in the hold until we've been inspected and have unloaded. When it's over, I'll come and tell you. Wait five minutes, then go up to the deck and disappear. I don't know where you're going and I don't want to know, but we're docking in Holmen, near the city centre. Make sure you leave the docks through the south gates and you should be fine. Do you have money?'

Prince shook his head. He had nothing, not even any papers. Otto took out some notes and pressed them into his hand.

'The inspection will start when we dock. We'll start unloading after that.'

He managed to get off the boat just before eleven, and leaving the dock was straightforward enough. He kept walking, following the signs to Christianshavn. But it didn't take long for him to feel utterly exhausted, his fever rising and falling, every step now an effort. He crossed over on Langebro bridge, and just when he felt he could go no further, he spotted a tram to Vesterbro.

He knew he was ill and beyond exhausted, but the thought of a hot bath and a proper bed, and most of all of Hanne, kept him going.

'We need to think about some kind of warning system for when you return. This mission could take weeks, even longer, and it's always possible something could happen to me during that time.'

'Don't say that. I—'

'No, we need to be realistic.'

The conversation had taken place the day before he'd left Copenhagen at the beginning of January. Hanne said that when he returned, he should go first to the alley at the rear of her apartment.

'My bedroom window overlooks the alley. I have a tall porcelain statue of a black cat; you can't miss it, it's nearly two feet high. When I'm in my apartment and I consider there's no danger, I'll place the cat on the window ledge. When I'm out, I'll remove it. So you should only go to your apartment if you see the cat in my apartment. Understand?'

Prince nodded. 'Black cats for luck, eh?'

'Let's hope so. It may mean you waiting for quite a while – I could be at work and back late. There's an outhouse in the alley where the rubbish bins are kept. You can see the window quite easily from there. There are half a dozen bins there, big ones – you'll just have to hide there. If and when you see the cat, go to your apartment and the key will be taped to the top frame. Once you're in, put that blue vase over there – the one on the side table – in the window. Then I'll know you're back.'

'And what about if I wait and the black cat doesn't appear?'

She shrugged in a matter-of-fact manner. 'Then you must assume something has happened to me and it's not safe. We can't plan for every eventuality, Peter. I'm afraid you'll be on your own then. I'd suggest you try and make your way to Sweden.'

–

Now it was the middle of April, just over three months since he'd left Copenhagen, and he'd been hiding in the stinking outhouse in the alley behind Hanne's flat for nearly two days.

He'd arrived there at noon on a warm Wednesday, and now it was a few minutes past seven on the Friday morning, and in all that time no black cat had appeared in the window of Hanne's apartment.

As far as he could tell, there'd been no other sign of life from her home: not a flicker of light, no movement. He'd stayed awake all last night, propped just inside the doorway of the outhouse, the door positioned so it shielded him but allowed him a view of the window. At least that gave him some relief from the overpowering stench from the rubbish bins. On the first afternoon, he'd raided the bins for food of some kind and selected some stale slices of bread and a few discarded boiled potatoes. He thought that would be safe enough, but later he was violently sick. As darkness fell, it became apparent that he shared his outhouse with an extended family of rats, one of those families that kept themselves busy all the time and didn't believe in quiet nights in.

It was clear he couldn't go back to the apartment. She'd suggested he try to get to Sweden, but he was exhausted and had no money and no papers, and he had little doubt now that his fever was typhus, which was hardly surprising given that so many people around him for the past couple of months had been suffering from it. That he'd managed to get back to Copenhagen was little short of a miracle.

He crawled to the back of the outhouse, kicked a rat off the piece of flea-ridden carpet he'd retrieved from a bin and slumped down. At least he'd not vomited for a few hours now. Another rat peered at him with ill-disguised curiosity from under a bin. He recognised it as Adolf, so named because of a black patch under its nose.

As well as being ill and exhausted, he was also having to come to terms with the realisation that something awful must have happened to Hanne. It was a terrible shock, which had hit him like a sledgehammer. He'd regarded her as such a clever and resourceful person, he'd assumed she'd rise above any situation.

And now he realised quite how much he loved her.

–

He must have dozed off for a few hours, because he was woken with a start by someone opening the outhouse door and throwing something into one of the bins. When they left, he checked it: half a loaf of bread and two or three wrinkled apples. Nourished by this and rested after his nap, he could think more clearly, and as he did so, he remembered that last evening in Matlock, when he and Gilbey were alone in the dining room and Gilbey had assured him he was an agent he could trust implicitly.

We have a further source in Copenhagen, one so highly placed and so important to us that you are only to approach him in the most extreme of circumstances. His code name is Browning... I'm about to tell you how to contact him.

–

Prince left the outhouse later that morning, conscious that he smelt and looked just like someone who'd spent the last two days in the company of rats. Along with the absence of a *legitimationskort* or any other papers, he could be excused for feeling wary.

But he also felt distinctly unwell, the spreading rash now very painful and his temperature rising, and it was an effort to focus on what he had to do next. He recalled Gilbey's instructions.

Steal a bicycle. I'm told Copenhagen is full of them: annoying things. Do your best not to get caught.

He took a tram from Vesterbro to the Kongens Have park, where he'd previously noticed a large number of bicycles parked by Gothersgade. He took a seat on a bench in the shadow thrown by an avenue of trees and waited for prey to appear. Ten minutes later, it arrived: a man in his forties, perhaps, in a hurry and with a briefcase strapped behind the seat. He placed the bicycle against the railings and strode off, adjusting his hat and tie as he did so, heading north away from the park and from Prince's destination.

Prince waited another five minutes, and when he was sure no one was paying the slightest attention, he casually strolled up to the bicycle, mounted it and rode away.

The bike shop is in Indre By, in the centre of Copenhagen. It's down a narrow alley off Pilestræde. You won't be able to miss it; it's the only bike shop there. Even has a bloody bike over the entrance, I'm told.

It was only a short ride, but before he reached Pilestræde, Prince stopped, dismounted and fiddled with the front wheel. He walked along with the bike for the remainder of the journey.

The shop's called Jensen, that's all. Jensen's the name of the owner too.

The shop was just as Gilbey had described it. Prince pushed open the door, an action that set off a complicated sequence of movements and noises, culminating in a cord running down a wall pulling a bicycle bell.

Jensen is always there, otherwise it doesn't open. He has a beard.

He had a shock when the man he assumed was Jensen turned round at the sound of the bell. He was a doppelgänger for Leon Trotsky. Prince was familiar with the Russian's image from newspapers and magazines, and couldn't spot any differences between this Danish bike shop owner and the Russian revolutionary. Jensen had Trotsky's thick hair, greying and swept back; the round black-framed spectacles, the full moustache and goatee beard. He was even formally dressed as Prince recalled Trotsky always seemed to be, in a dark jacket and a tightly knotted tie.

'Can I help you?'

He was momentarily surprised at the man's unmistakable Danish accent. He'd somehow expected a Russian one.

'I appear to have broken a spoke on my front wheel.'

Jensen nodded, his face impassive. 'And have you come far?'

The correct response. 'Yes, from Skovshoved.'

Now Jensen would be sure too, and his dark eyebrows, so like Trotsky's, shot up a little. 'And your broken spoke – when did you notice it?'

'Fortunately not until the end of my journey.'

The man nodded and held the front of his counter, bowing slightly, concentrating on taking two or three deep breaths. It was a moment for him to gather his thoughts.

'You're certain no one has followed you?'

Prince nodded.

'Very well, you'd better come straight through to the workshop. I'll lock the door and put up a closed sign. Fortunately, it's almost lunchtime. You don't look too well – are you all right?'

–

'You're not Browning, are you?' Prince asked once they were in the workshop.

'No – I'm the contact for Browning. But I must ask you why you need to see him. I'm sure you've been told he can only be contacted as a last resort.'

You are only to approach him in the most extreme of circumstances... if your life is in danger, not if you've run out of milk.

Prince hesitated, unsure how much he could trust this man with.

'Don't worry – you need only tell me as much as you feel able to. It may be safer for you to leave out any names and addresses. That cuts down the risk. If it helps, I know Tom Gilbey. He recruited me, and I recruited Browning for him. I operate completely independently of any other British intelligence interests in Denmark; it's safer that way. Even Gilbey's people in Stockholm don't know about me. If Tom gave you this address, it shows he obviously trusts you. And by the look of you, you're going to have to trust me. Let me get you some water.'

Jensen had pulled two chairs up alongside a workbench, various bike parts scattered around them.

'I don't suppose you have any aspirin, do you?' Prince asked. 'I think I may have caught something.'

A few minutes later, he began to feel slightly better. 'Gilbey sent me over here in November. There's an agent here – a Danish woman – who's been looking after me. She provided me with somewhere to stay and a new identity, and she's passed messages and intelligence to and from London via the MI6 station in Stockholm. I've twice been on missions inside Germany. Could I trouble you for some more water?'

Jensen refilled his glass and told Prince to rest for a moment.

'On my last mission, I was arrested, although they didn't discover I was a British agent. Nevertheless, they sent me to a concentration camp near Hamburg. From there I was sent to Lübeck, and I managed to escape on a Danish ship that was sailing to Copenhagen.'

'What was the name of the ship?'

'The *Strand Stjerne*.'

'When and where did it arrive?'

'In Holmen, early on Wednesday morning. I'm losing track of time. Is it Friday today?'

Jensen nodded.

'Because I was going to be away for several weeks on this mission, the Danish woman and I had agreed to a safety signal, but it never appeared. I have no idea what to do. I have no papers, I'm unwell and I'm desperate. I know Gilbey said to approach Browning only in the most extreme of circumstances, but I think this must qualify.'

It was only when he'd finished speaking that Prince realised quite how unwell he suddenly felt. He had the sensation of the room spinning round, and his vision was blurred. His body felt as if it was tightly wrapped in a rough, very hot blanket, and a wave of nausea rode through him. He was aware of a person moving towards him and saying something, though he couldn't make out any words. After that, he sensed he was lying down, overcome by dizziness. He tried to say something but was unable to form any words. When he attempted to lift his head, there was a jarring pain and everything went black.

–

He lay very still for quite a few minutes. He had no idea where he was, other than in a room that resembled a cell, so he assumed he'd been arrested. He was covered by blankets and lying on a mattress on the floor taking up the width of the room and most of its length. The walls were white-painted stone, and high in the one behind him was a window sending a shaft of bright sunshine into the room. Above him was a light shade with a floral pattern, which didn't feel very cell-like, and the door in front of him was ajar.

He had the impression of having been asleep for a long while: he was soaked in perspiration, and when he raised his head, he felt dizzy but better than before. Slowly he began to piece together his last memories: the outhouse behind Hanne's apartment; the tram to the park; the bike ride and then finding the shop; the man who looked like Trotsky – he even recalled the name Jensen; a conversation in the back room, and then… nothing.

'So you're awake!' Trotsky had appeared in the room, smiling and carrying a wet flannel. 'How do you feel?'

'I'm not sure. Where am I?'

'In a room at the back of my workshop. I normally keep bicycles in here. I brought a mattress down from my rooms upstairs; I was unable to carry you up. Do you know how long you've been asleep?'

Prince shrugged.

'You arrived here late Friday morning. It's now early Sunday afternoon. You have typhus, you know.'

'I thought so.'

'After you collapsed, I called Dr Oppenheim. He came that afternoon and diagnosed it straight away. He gave you some injections, including one to help you sleep. He'll be in tomorrow and will talk to you then.'

'And Browning, were you able to contact him?'

'Not yet. It's a complicated business getting hold of him and I wanted to be sure you were well enough. Now I can set things in motion.'

Chapter 22

Copenhagen; Stockholm, April 1943

At precisely ten minutes to eight on the morning of Monday 19 April, the commercial attaché of the German Embassy to Denmark left the breakfast room of his generous residence in Lyngby, a genteel suburb to the north of Copenhagen.

He went into the hall, smoking his fourth cigarette of the morning and resolving – as he did every morning – not to smoke more than one packet that day. He stood by the mirror adjusting his tie and listened to his housekeeper, who'd followed him into the hall.

Yes, venison stew sounds very good – thank you.

Yes, I will be dining alone – as usual.

No, on Tuesday night there's a function at the embassy.

He took his coat and hat from the housekeeper and stopped by his study to pick up his briefcase. At five to eight, he opened the front door, where his driver was waiting. The two men exchanged Heil Hitlers, one with considerably more enthusiasm than the other.

Ferdinand Rudolf von Buhler settled into the back of his Horch for the twenty-minute drive to the embassy. It was going to be a trying week, even more so than usual. Tomorrow was Hitler's birthday, an event marked with a good deal of extravagance at the embassy. It was bad enough being required to indulge in this enthusiasm, but worse was the expectation that Danes would share it. Of his many Danish contacts, only two had no other engagements for that evening. German officers would have to be drafted in to ensure the reception had a respectable turnout.

But Ferdinand Rudolf von Buhler was about to find out that Hitler's birthday celebrations would be the least of his problems that week. The first sign of trouble came as the Horch entered Nørrebro. They were on the main road, which had been carefully selected because it was so busy in the morning that cars were obliged to drive slowly.

As he always did, von Buhler watched carefully as they drove past the pharmacy, a beautiful building with a Beaux Arts facade in pinkish-red brick. On a shelf high in the window were three enormous blue medicine jars. Except this morning the three blue jars had been joined by one red one. The message was clear and caused the commercial attaché of the German Embassy to Denmark to experience a sensation of fear and excitement.

'Georg, I've just realised I'm short of cigarettes. Stop at the tobacconist's, please.'

'The usual one, sir?'

'Of course, Georg.'

The tobacconist's was more a kiosk than a shop, so narrow there was room for only one customer inside it at a time, which von Buhler imagined was the reason it had been chosen for this purpose.

'Two packets of ten, please.'

The tobacconist took two packets from the shelf behind him. 'And I imagine you'd like matches today, sir?'

The message was confirmed. He was needed: urgently.

–

Before Ferdinand Rudolf von Buhler had even removed his coat in his office on the fifth floor of the German Embassy, he checked his appointments for the day with his secretary.

'There's the routine with the ambassador at ten, and at eleven you have the Dairy Industry Federation coming in. That is scheduled to finish by a quarter to one, and then your driver will take you to lunch, which is with Herr Lorenz of the shipping agency at the fish restaurant on Nyhavn.'

'Cancel that.'

'I beg your pardon, sir?'

'No, sorry, I mean don't cancel lunch, but cancel it at the fish restaurant.'

'I thought it was your favourite restaurant, sir?'

'It was, but I didn't enjoy it last time. I've come to dislike this Scandinavian passion for raw fish. I'll tell you what: book us a table at that Norwegian place Heinz took me to the other week, the one on Pilestræde. Make it for one thirty. And I'll walk there. I need the exercise.' He patted his stomach through his coat and winked at his secretary. 'And one other thing, make sure the dairy people are gone by twelve fifteen. There's only so long one can talk about cheese.'

That sorted, he went into his office and closed the door. With his coat still on, he unlocked his desk and opened one of the drawers. In an envelope under a pile of papers was a receipt, which he folded and placed in his wallet.

Only then did he remove his coat.

The receipt was for a bike. It gave him an excuse to be going to the bicycle shop off Pilestræde. He'd not yet collected a bike from there; each time he went, he was given a new receipt, so if anyone checked it would not seem too dated. He was a clever chap, that Jensen, the one who looked uncannily like Trotsky.

–

Dr Julius Oppenheim arrived at the bicycle shop after his morning surgery. He apologised profusely to Jensen.

'I'm sorry, I'd hoped to be here earlier, but there are patients... you'll understand, I hope... patients who only feel safe seeing me these days. There's a fear that's beginning to envelop us; people are becoming worried. So he's woken up then?'

'Finally, Dr Oppenheim, yes. Please come through.'

The doctor examined Prince carefully. He said little until Jensen left the room.

'You're lucky: this is early-stage typhus. Although it hit you quite hard, collapsing as you did was probably fortuitous. I've been able to treat you symptomatically, and I believe we've halted the progress of the disease. Had we not done so, it could soon have progressed to the next stage, with psychotic symptoms, and then you'd have been extremely unwell. I'd like to think the forty-eight-hour sleep stopped the illness in its tracks, and the important thing is that you're now in a typhus-free environment. This medication here,' he opened his case and took out a large brown bottle, 'will help. Where did you catch the disease?'

Prince said nothing at first. 'I was in Germany.'

'You were in a camp, weren't you? Jensen told me. Which one?'

'Neuengamme, it's near Hamburg.'

Dr Oppenheim leaned forward, a look of pain on his face. 'Were there many Jews there?'

'I'm not sure. I don't think so. We heard rumours that there'd been Jews there earlier in the war, but most of them had been sent to camps in the east. There are rumours about those places...'

'Believe me, we hear them too, my friend. There are maybe ten thousand of us in Denmark, possibly less, who knows for sure? We couldn't be treated better by the Danes – I mean, we *are* Danes. But the rumours we hear, the terrible rumours... we fear it's only a matter of time.'

—

Ferdinand Rudolf von Buhler conducted the meeting with the Dairy Industry Federation with a haste bordering on rude-ness. There were times when representing the occupying power had unintended benefits. The dairy men hadn't even got onto the vexed subject of butter when von Buhler announced the meeting had come to an end.

'But Herr von Buhler, you specifically asked at the last meeting for more time to discuss the issue of—'

'That can be for the next meeting, then – it gives us something to look forward to!'

He left the embassy via the rear entrance and hurried through the streets of central Copenhagen. Within ten minutes he was inside the bicycle shop off Pilestræde, breathless and anxious. He didn't think he'd been followed, but he hadn't had enough time to take the more circuitous route that would have allowed him to be certain.

Jensen was behind the counter as usual, a half-smile fixed on his face. The diplomat presented the receipt he'd removed from his desk earlier that morning.

'I was wondering if my bicycle is ready yet?'

'It is indeed, sir, though I wonder if you will require further adjustments?'

'I'll only know when I see it.'

'Perhaps you should come into the workshop then. Give me a moment while I close the shop for lunch.'

Jensen locked the door and put up the closed sign before taking von Buhler into the back of the shop, through the workshop and into the small room behind it. Prince was still on the mattress on the floor, but was now propped up against the wall. The doctor was beside him, taking his blood pressure. The diplomat stepped away from the room and called Jensen over.

'There's someone else in there.'

'Yes, Dr Oppenheim. He's trustworthy, totally.'

'And I take it he's Jewish?'

Jensen nodded. 'I hope that's not a problem for you.'

'Not at all; the opposite, in fact. It means I can trust him.'

Dr Oppenheim moved aside to allow the German into the small room. The diplomat asked him to wait in the workshop.

'You speak German?' Von Buhler was kneeling down beside Prince.

'Some, yes.'

'Do you want to give me a name?'

'Are you Browning?'

The German nodded.

'I'm known as Peter Rasmussen here in Denmark, but I've lost all my papers. I was based here, then sent into Germany. I was at the camp in Neuengamme, but I managed to escape. My contact here has disappeared and I need to get back to England. Gilbey told me I should contact you in an emergency.'

'And you think this is an emergency?'

'It certainly feels like one.'

'Very well then – and you work for Gilbey?'

Prince nodded.

'I take it you're British?' Von Buhler spoke the words in English, perfectly pronounced.

'Yes, I am.'

'Were you given an escape route?'

'No. I think it was assumed my contact here in Copenhagen would handle that.'

The German said nothing, but lowered his head, thinking matters through. 'The only feasible way out is through Sweden. Do you have any contacts there?'

Prince shook his head.

'I understand the MI6 officer at the British Embassy in Stockholm is a man called George Weston. I have no links with him, obviously, but I will endeavour to get you over to Sweden. Once you're there, you're on your own: you must make your way to Stockholm, then to the British Embassy, and contact Weston. It will take me a few days to sort this. In the meantime, you remain here.'

'I wasn't planning on going anywhere.'

'Good. Is there anything else you need?'

'There is, actually… the agent who was looking after me: I fear something has happened to her. Would you be able to find out?'

'I can't promise. What is her name?'

'Hanne Jakobsen. She's a police officer here in Copenhagen.'

On the way out, von Buhler approached Dr Oppenheim, who was still waiting in the workshop. 'Tell me, Doctor, how long before he's well enough to travel?'

'It depends how far and what kind of journey.'

'It's important he looks well. We can't have him appearing so ill he draws attention to himself.'

'In that case, I'd say not before the weekend, certainly.'

'A week tomorrow – next Tuesday?'

'Yes, I think that sounds reasonable. I must leave now. I have a clinic this afternoon and—'

'One moment, Doctor. This is my card: have a look at it, please.'

Ferdinand Rudolf von Buhler

Commercial Attaché, German Embassy, Copenhagen

It would have been hard for the doctor to look more shocked and unsettled. He wiped his brow and his hands shook.

'We both understand the highly confidential nature of our encounter, I hope. Are you well connected with the Jewish community here in Copenhagen?'

The doctor nodded.

'There may well be a time in the coming months when I will need to contact them, to be of help. You should realise from my presence here today that I am to be trusted. If I need to see you, we can meet here; Jensen can arrange it. If you hear from him that he needs to see you because he has a strained knee, you will know it's me.'

The doctor nodded again, glancing from the diplomat to the card and back.

'And it may be best if you give me the card back.'

Hitler's birthday that Tuesday provided Ferdinand Rudolf von Buhler with the perfect cover. He was able to slip out to the consulate on the ground floor.

'I need some travel papers.'

'Where are you going, sir?' The clerk was trying to close the office early.

'Not for me. I need to send a new courier over to Sweden. Annoyingly, he doesn't return from the Reich until next Monday, and then he's supposed to travel the next day. If I give you his details, can you draw up the necessary papers?'

'We really need his identity documents, sir. How long would he be in Sweden for?'

'No more than twenty-four hours.'

'In that case, I suppose I can issue temporary papers. It's slightly irregular, but I'm sure it will be fine. Do you want me to book the transport too?'

'I would be most grateful. Book him onto Tuesday morning's ferry to Malmö, please. Charge it all to my budget. I wouldn't want you to get into trouble, so I don't mind if you book everything more informally.'

'No problem, sir. I'll have everything ready by Friday afternoon.'

Ferdinand Rudolf von Buhler collected the travel papers from the consulate on Friday afternoon and prepared to leave the embassy. It had been a long week, he told his secretary, and he seemed to be developing a cold, so he would be going home early.

Before that, though, there was an important telephone call to make. On Tuesday, after seeing Prince in the bicycle shop, he'd rung an acquaintance, a fellow diplomat with the thankless job – amongst other things – of being liaison officer at the Danish police headquarters on Polititorvet.

'Probably nothing, Hermann, but it may be something I need to refer to the Gestapo, and I thought I'd ask you first. Could you very discreetly find out what's happened to a Hanne Jakobsen; she's a police officer in Copenhagen?'

'Give me until the end of the week, Ferdinand. Call me back then.'

He called Hermann before leaving the embassy on Friday afternoon.

'I don't think you're going to need to refer the matter to the Gestapo after all, Ferdinand.'

'How come?'

'They arrested her back in January. As far as I can gather, she's being held somewhere back in the Reich.'

Ferdinand Rudolf von Buhler had told his housekeeper she could leave early on Friday as long as she was back on Sunday afternoon, which gave him two full days to himself. From the garden shed he removed a wooden box hidden under a pile of junk and brought it into his study. It was a small typewriter he'd brought with him from Germany after his last visit home. He'd found it in a second-hand shop, and apart from being compact, it had a smaller font size than normal, and tighter spacing.

From the back of a shelf high on his bookcase he removed a pad of very thin paper, so thin that each sheet had to be backed against regular paper. And then he began to type, carrying on well into the night and for much of the next day, starting again early on Sunday morning. By lunchtime, he'd finished, two overflowing ashtrays, an almost empty bottle of Cognac and a dozen empty coffee cups a testament to his concentration. He packed the typewriter back in the wooden box and returned it to the shed.

He took the sheets of normal paper he'd used as backing and consigned them to the fire, watching until the last fragments were reduced to ash.

Then he brought out the trilby he'd bought the previous week. By the light of his Anglepoise lamp, he carefully unpicked the thread of the lining. He'd already folded the typed sheets of flimsy paper lengthways, which reminded him of when he and his brother made paper aeroplanes: there were two dozen sheets, and he was able to insert them almost perfectly into the lining before sewing the seam back.

He held the hat up, admiring his work. Deciding it looked too new, he ran a clothes brush along the rear porch, and soon the trilby had a well-worn appearance.

He added some logs to the fire and watched as the flames took hold of them, the occasional spark shooting onto the carpet.

He'd come to terms some years ago with the side of his nature that was too willing to please, too amenable, too keen to help out, too reluctant to say no.

It accounted for where he was now. All his instincts had told him not to agree to join the diplomatic service in the first place. Whichever way he looked at it, it was still serving the Reich, something he'd sworn not to do. He should have gone to Switzerland while he had the chance. And the meeting with Gilbey in the weeks before the war started, something that at the time had seemed like a chance meeting but was obviously not: even then he should have said thank you very much but I'm really not your man – not sure I'm brave enough, to be honest.

But he also knew that had he not eventually agreed to help, he'd never have forgiven himself.

He returned to Jensen's bicycle shop on Monday at lunchtime. It was open, but Jensen was serving a customer, so he walked round the block before going back in.

'How is he?'

'He's much improved: very keen to leave.'

Prince was sitting in the small lounge in Jensen's rooms above the shop.

'You leave tomorrow morning for Sweden: here are your papers. The ferry sails from Copenhagen at nine in the morning and you'll be in Malmö before noon. There's a tram from the ferry terminal in Malmö to the central station. The Swedish trains are very good; they don't have to worry about bombs. You should arrive in Stockholm around six that evening. There are plenty of cheap hotels around the station – and I've put some Swedish currency in that envelope. My advice would be to head to the British Embassy the following morning. I'll give you the address in a moment. You'll need to memorise it.

'Don't go into the embassy, though, or even too close to it: the Nazis watch the place like hawks. Hang around nearby, observe people going in and out, and if you can approach someone in the street away from the embassy who looks like a British diplomat, then do that. I'm sure you know what to do. Oh, and this hat: wear it and make sure you keep it safe. When you get to London, please give it to Gilbey. It's most important.'

–

Prince took a few minutes to study the papers and take in what the German had told him. He couldn't believe that this time tomorrow he could be in Sweden. His nightmare might be coming to an end. There was one other matter, though.

'You promised to find out about Hanne – Hanne Jakobsen?'

'I was about to come to that, my friend, and it's not good news I'm afraid. She was arrested by the Gestapo in January and taken to Germany. I'm sorry, but I know no more than that. Do give Gilbey my warm regards.'

Prince spent the next few hours sitting in Jensen's lounge, too distressed to move.

She was arrested by the Gestapo in January.

He went over those words again and again, as if there might be some cause for hope hidden within them.

Taken to Germany.

Maybe she'd escaped, like he'd managed to do. She was so resourceful, her German was excellent… but as the light began to fade, he realised her situation was most probably hopeless. It was too much for him to even think about. The nightmare he'd hoped was coming to an end was destined to continue.

He had to force himself to put her out of his mind, at least for long enough to study his new identity. As he did so, he realised he was brushing tears from his eyes.

The thought of Hanne and whatever had been her fate was more than he could manage.

–

The ferry was exceptionally busy, and although security was tight, most of it seemed to be reserved for Danish or Swedish passengers. Prince's papers showed he was a German, a courier for the embassy, and so he had few problems. He caught the first tram to the station and within half an hour was on a train to Stockholm.

He slept little that night in the hotel by the station. It was a mixture of nerves, the excitement of travelling home and the anticipation of seeing Henry, but also the realisation that every step of his journey was taking him further from Hanne. He felt partly responsible for whatever terrible predicament she was in.

The following morning, he found a bench in a small square near enough to the British Embassy to be able to keep the main entrance in view. At eleven o'clock, he spotted a man coming out who looked just like a bank manager from any English high street. Taking his chance, Prince followed him, making sure at the same time that he wasn't being followed himself. Three blocks later, he intercepted the man as he was about to cross a main road.

'Excuse me, I work for the British government and I urgently need to see George Weston. I fear my life may be in danger.'

The man looked at him kindly, as if he'd encountered a lost child. Prince realised that tears were forming in his eyes. 'I've escaped from Germany…'

The man took him by the elbow and guided him towards a side street. 'You see that café over there? Wait inside and I'll go and get George. Don't worry, old chap, it'll be all right. I say, where are you from?'

'Lincoln, sir.'

'Nickname of the football team?'

'The Imps.'

'Colours?'

'Red and white striped shirts, sir, black shorts.'

'And the ground?'

'Sincil Bank.'

'Splendid: and I'll need a name to give George.'

'Just say Laertes, sir. Agent Laertes.'

–

'That's an awful lot to take in.' George Weston looked somewhat put upon, though not altogether unsympathetic. 'I knew something was up with Agent Osric, told London as much. No consolation being right, though. Still, well done you – getting in and out of Germany like that, and then over here. I imagine Gilbey will have lots to ask you. You'll stay at the embassy for the time being; much the safest option. I've got my work cut out. I need to file to London and then see what we can do about getting you home.'

Richard Prince travelled to London the following Monday on a British passport issued by the embassy in Stockholm. From Bromma airport he took a Swedish Intercontinental Airlines flight to Scone in Scotland, where Hendrie greeted him with a brisk handshake and a 'Well done... welcome home' before leading him across the tarmac to a waiting Halifax.

'Tom's got lots to ask you, Prince.'

'If you see him before I do, you may want to give him this.'

'The hat?'

'Apparently so.'

Chapter 23

'Come here, Hanne, I have something to tell you.'

She hadn't seen the Norwegian girl from her hut for a couple of weeks and was surprised to bump into her near the camp infirmary. When Hanne had arrived at Ravensbrück two months earlier, Marit had been a big help, showing her around and telling her who to befriend and, far more importantly, who to avoid. They'd been drawn together by a more or less common language. Marit, though, was a few years younger than Hanne and seemed to treat life – even life in a concentration camp – as one big adventure.

The fact that she'd disappeared two weeks ago was just one of those things that happened all the time in Ravensbrück: you'd meet someone, become friendly – even reliant on each other – and then they'd be gone. Some were moved to another camp, or elsewhere in the vast complex; others were taken to be murdered or to become the subject of medical experiments.

Marit appeared to have put on weight, and her skin didn't have the sallow pallor of the other inmates. Hanne could have sworn there was a trace of make-up around her eyes, along with a faint smear of red on her lips, and her hair looked as if it had been washed.

'Marit, you look almost well – what on earth has happened to you?'

'You won't believe it, Hanne, and if you do, I suspect you won't approve.' She giggled like a schoolgirl telling a friend about a boy who'd asked her out.

'Unless you've become a Nazi, I can't think of anything I could disapprove of.'

'I'm not so sure. I'm working in one of those houses by the SS barracks.' Marit looked down, embarrassed.

Hanne grabbed her by the forearm. 'You mean the brothel?'

'Not so loud, Hanne! I'm only telling you because I trust you. They told me it was a choice between working there and going to a labour camp in the east. And they promised me that if I work there for six months, they'll set me free – I'll be able to go home to Oslo!'

'And you believe them?'

Marit shrugged. 'Why not? Apparently a couple of French women were allowed back to France last month. Anyway, it's not like I've become a prostitute or anything. I don't get paid, so I can't be a prostitute!'

'You look well on it, Marit.'

'I have to admit, we get decent food, and when the SS men come in, we get to wear nice clothes and have a bath first. Some of the men aren't violent. One that I had last night was actually quite sweet: he showed me pictures of his daughters. You could join us, Hanne. I could put in a good word for you, and hopefully they wouldn't think you're too old. It's easier than working in those bloody fields.'

Hanne glanced down at her hand, which was bandaged after an accident with a spade that morning. She'd been working the fields for the last few weeks and it was back-breaking toil, dawn to dusk with barely a break.

She told Marit not to be so ridiculous and said she'd see her soon. But as she walked back to the field, she found herself wondering whether going to work with Marit would be so dreadful after all.

–

She wondered if she'd ever recover from the shock of that morning in Copenhagen at the end of January. She'd been at her desk in the Major Robbery Unit at Nørrebro when she became aware of the door being flung open and people marching towards her. She had no time to react, not even enough time to put the cap on her pen. They asked if she was Hanne Jakobsen, and when she said yes, she was hauled to her feet and more or less dragged outside and thrown into a car. A few minutes later, they were at the Gestapo headquarters on Kampmannsgade.

'Do you know a Peter Rasmussen?'

At least she'd had enough time to anticipate that question. She frowned, appearing to rack her brain, then shook her head. 'I'm terribly sorry, but it doesn't ring a bell. It's not exactly an uncommon name, is it? You'll have to help me…'

'You have to help us, not the other way round. Do you know a Peter Rasmussen?'

'In what context?'

'For fuck's sake!' A different man took over; a thickset man with a lisp of some sort. 'You either know him or you don't.'

'In that case, the answer is no, I don't know anyone of that name. Is he supposed to be someone I may have arrested – or worked with, maybe?'

Another man spoke, younger and quite presentable, his voice quieter and his approach very clear and calm. 'Back in November, you went to the registration and records department at Polititorvet and asked them to issue a *legitimationskort* for a Peter Rasmussen. You authorised it yourself; we have all the paperwork. This Peter Rasmussen, using the very same *legitimationskort*, travelled to Berlin in December in the company of a Danish businessman called Otto Knudsen. While in Berlin, Rasmussen and Knudsen were involved in acts of espionage against the Reich. It therefore follows that you know Peter Rasmussen and I'd appreciate your help' – his voice rose slightly – 'in telling us where he is.'

A wave of utter relief swept over her. Such a basic and naïve error to reveal that they didn't know where Peter was. 'I'm sorry, but I'm still struggling to recollect this man. What did you say the other gentleman was called?'

'Otto Knudsen.'

Agent Horatio.

'Maybe if you ask him?'

'Don't try and be clever. We were about to try that yesterday and then the bastard went and killed himself.'

She felt she did a reasonable job of not reacting one way or the other to the news of Horatio's death. She was sorry, of course, but she doubted he'd have coped too well with an interrogation. Perhaps it was for the best. But she knew they'd find something out sooner or later. She'd have to play for time.

I'd really like to help... I just cannot recall a Peter Rasmussen... I deal with dozens of people each month... My apartment? Of course, here's the key.

They'd find absolutely nothing in the apartment, but she realised they were unlikely to leave it at that. They'd ask her neighbours, and one of them was bound to mention her father's flat – the one opposite hers, the one where Peter lived. And even though she'd done her best to tidy that up after he'd left for Rostock, they'd ask more questions and it was hard to think they wouldn't eventually establish a link.

The interrogation went on for days, the Gestapo using their predictable tactics of allowing her an hour's sleep then waking her up and questioning her for a few hours, keeping the light on in her cell all the time, depriving her of food and drink, even some quite unpleasant roughing up, though they stopped short of what she'd describe as torture.

But it was bad enough, and there were moments when she felt she couldn't hold out much longer and thought that wouldn't be so bad, because she'd resisted for long enough and Agent Laertes ought to be safe.

Agent Laertes. Peter. Her Englishman. Safe.

In the end, they told her they didn't believe her: there was the irrefutable evidence that she'd requested the identity papers for the same Peter Rasmussen who'd travelled to Berlin, and neighbours said that a man matching his description had been seen going in and out of the block where her father's apartment was.

'Our orders,' said the man with the lisp, 'are to send you to Berlin. Our colleagues there are going to deal with you. You'll soon wish you'd been more forthcoming with us.' He sounded quite disappointed.

–

Two or three days later, she'd been flown to Berlin on a military aircraft. She knew little about the journey, as she was blind-folded and in handcuffs. The plane was cold and the noise almost unbearable. It seemed like an age while they waited for a van to collect them from the airport, followed by a long and uncomfortable drive into what she took to be the city.

The van drove into what felt like a basement garage, and she was led through a series of corridors and down some narrow steps into a room where the blindfold was finally removed.

It took a while for her eyes to become accustomed to the light, and when they did, she saw she was standing in front of four men behind a table, rather like the panel that had interviewed her for her last promotion.

'Welcome to Berlin.' The man who spoke looked dishev-elled, as if he'd slept in the clothes he was wearing – a feeling she was familiar with. When he spoke, his mouth opened wider than normal, revealing a set of yellow teeth. His name was Lange, he told her, Manfred Lange, and he was the officer in charge of finding Peter Rasmussen.

'Have you heard of Prinz Albrecht Strasse?'

She replied that she hadn't.

'Well that is where you are now. This is the headquarters of the Gestapo. And let me tell you,' he added, leaning forward and smiling broadly, 'that I am one of the most...' he paused, obviously thinking about which words to use, 'accomplished investigators here. I am personally responsible for breaking the spy ring that Peter Rasmussen was involved with.'

He stopped and looked at her carefully, hoping to discern some kind of reaction. She remained as impassive as possible. She was desperate for the toilet and was using that to focus her attention on. She wondered whether to smile or look defiant, but settled on what she hoped was a neutral expression.

'Does the name Albert Kampmann mean anything to you? He also went under the name Kurt? He was an *Oberst* in the Luftwaffe. Thanks to my officers,' he looked appreciatively at the men either side of him, 'he's now dead. He was one of your spy ring.'

Your spy ring. She shook her head.

'And Bruno Bergmann, perhaps… is that name familiar? He worked for Spandau Locomotive Engineering and was a contact for your Peter Rasmussen and an Otto Knudsen. Bergmann had his trial two days ago and was found guilty of espionage. He will be executed today, an event you will have the pleasure of witnessing.'

She said nothing.

'And you are aware that this Otto Knudsen took his own life before we had the opportunity to find out what he knew. He worked for Mortensen Machinery Parts in Copenhagen – does that help?'

She shook her head once more. It appeared the idiots had managed to kill most of the people involved, which was careless in the extreme.

'That leaves you and Peter Rasmussen. Rasmussen is missing, and we will find him, and because you are connected to him, you will help us. But we will begin that process tomorrow, after you have visited Herr Bergmann. That will give you a taste of what we have in mind for you in the unlikely event of you being unwilling to help.'

She was taken to a cell not unlike the one in Copenhagen. She was able to lie down for a while, use the bucket in the corner, and they even brought her a meal of sorts, which was surprisingly not as bad as the others she'd been given since her arrest. She wondered why they hadn't interrogated her further when she was undoubtedly at her most vulnerable.

She must have fallen asleep, because she was woken by the sound of her cell door being noisily unlocked. She was hand-cuffed and marched down a corridor and up a flight of stairs. Outside a pair of double doors was the smiling figure of the Gestapo officer she'd met earlier, the man who'd introduced himself as Manfred Lange.

'We are about to have the pleasure of witnessing the execution of Bruno Bergmann. Please be assured the same fate awaits you in the event of you not cooperating with us.'

They went into a long room crowded with people. She was pushed towards the front, where the man she took to be Bergmann was standing against a wall, supported by two guards. She suspected that even had she known him, she'd have had trouble recognising him. He looked terrified, his body emaciated, his face showing signs of several beatings and most of his teeth missing. His eyes darted around the room, anxious to spot anyone who might help him.

In front of him stood a man in a dark suit, reading out the death warrant in a high-pitched voice.

...and crimes against the German state... against the German people... guilty of espionage... sentenced to death... Signed Roland Freisler, President, People's Court.

The official stood back, and Hanne noticed that Lange was now at the front of the room. He stepped forward. 'Look around carefully, Bergmann: is there anyone here you recognise?'

The prisoner peered anxiously at the people gathered in the room. Hanne suspected he was having trouble focusing. 'My wife, is my wife here? She knows nothing! I tell you, she's a loyal German. I have wronged her and my children terribly. I beg of you to spare them. For me, I deserve my fate, I—'

'Shut up, Bergmann! We do not regard your wife as innocent and she will certainly never see your children again. I can offer you a quick end, or a more painful one. For the final time, tell me: where is Peter Rasmussen?'

Bergmann shook his head in an almost manic way. 'I tell you, I have no idea whatsoever. I was surprised when he turned up with Knudsen. I never liked him or trusted him. I beg of you…'

Lange nodded, and the two guards dragged a whimpering Bergmann to a platform in the corner of the room. His wrists and ankles were bound and a wire dangling from the ceiling was placed round his neck. As the noose was tightened, his face turned red and his eyes bulged. Another nod from Lange and the platform was pulled away. Hanne tried to avert her gaze, but she was thumped in the small of her back.

'Watch!'

She'd expected it to be quick, but it was anything but. She tried to focus her mind on something else but found it impossible. The sound of Bergmann gasping for breath and then choking went on for far longer than she could bear.

As she was led back to her cell, Manfred Lange told her it had taken Bergmann three minutes and twenty seconds to die. 'It usually takes longer!'

–

Gruppenführer von Helldorf tried not to look at the man from the Gestapo with too much obvious disdain.

'I see you've killed another witness, Lange.'

'He was found guilty by the People's Court. I am surprised you question the verdict.'

'And now you want our help again?'

'We have drawn a blank in our hunt for Peter Rasmussen. The woman Jakobsen is not proving helpful. We shall have to resort to our tried and trusted methods or put her before the People's Court.'

'Whatever you do, Lange, keep her alive, eh? She's the only link with Rasmussen you have left. We can carry on looking for him, but she's no use dead. Put her in a camp by all means, but don't go and kill her too, at least not until we find Rasmussen.'

–

The afternoon following her encounter with Marit, Hanne had a few unexpected moments to pause and gather her thoughts. She was in the field, digging away at the unforgiving soil, when two prisoners began fighting and the guards all rushed over. She supported her weight on the spade and looked around as she caught her breath.

It could be worse.

She was physically fit, at least more so than most of the prisoners here. And as hard as the work was, it was now the end of April and the summer was bound to be easier. She'd developed an ability to let her mind take her to places well away from the hell she was in. Being in the fresh air all day reduced her chances of catching a disease, and at least she wasn't as badly treated as the Russian or Polish women, who were being experimented on, or the Jewish women shipped to their deaths in the east.

The next morning, she had cause to regret her brief lapse into optimism. Everyone in her hut was being reassigned. They were to report immediately to the Siemens factory in the south of the camp, where they'd be assembling parts for armaments. The conditions were meant to be terrible there, the air full of noxious smells making it hard to breathe, the temperature freezing cold one minute, stifling hot the next.

She had no idea how long she'd be able to survive.

Chapter 24

England, May 1943

It was late afternoon on Tuesday.

Richard Prince had landed in Scotland the previous afternoon before being flown on immediately to an airbase apparently somewhere near London and driven to a nearby safe house at the end of a long and narrow lane. The house was surrounded by a thick wood on all sides, the wind catching the trees in a way that made them appear as though they were advancing on the house.

He had no idea where he was, and Hendrie said it was best it remained that way. A doctor was waiting for him, and after a thorough check-up, he announced that Prince was on the mend. 'Take three of these four times a day for five days,' he said, thrusting a large bottle of pills into his hand. 'Just check what it says on the label, I may have got the numbers mixed up. And take this one tonight: you'll sleep like a baby.'

He must have slept for twelve hours. After breakfast, Hendrie took him into the library and introduced him to a severe-looking woman, who was introduced as Prudence. Her task was to commit to paper everything Prince could recall about his mission. She was skilled at asking the right question at the right time, prompting him carefully to ensure his account didn't stray in terms of dates and that any questions Hendrie asked were strictly relevant. She wrote everything down in shorthand, rarely looking up at Prince and occasionally holding up a hand for him to pause while she turned a page.

After three hours, she announced they were done and said she'd type up her notes before passing on the report to Mr Gilbey.

'Prudence is terribly good,' Hendrie told Prince. 'By far the best we have at this type of thing. Have some lunch, but stay around here. She'll probably want to double-check some dates with you or iron out any discrepancies. Then the report goes to Gilbey, and once he's read it, all three of us can have a chat.'

'When will I be able to get away? I'm terribly keen to see my boy. It would be wonderful if I could be driven up overnight and be there when he wakes up.'

Hendrie had moved over to the shuttered window and seemed preoccupied with it. 'That's probably pushing it – best not to get ahead of ourselves, eh?'

'Could I at least telephone my sister-in-law?'

'One step at a time, Richard, one step at a time.'

He couldn't recall Hendrie calling him Richard before.

–

Now it was late afternoon, and Prince sensed something was up.

He couldn't put his finger on what that something was, but when he entered the room where Tom Gilbey was waiting, he felt like a spendthrift customer about to ask his bank manager for another loan. It was that kind of atmosphere.

'Welcome back, Richard.'

That was it for a while. Gilbey had been standing behind a desk. He hesitated before coming to shake Prince's hand and then sitting down. He lit a cigarette, moved a sheaf of documents from one side of the desk to the other and tapped his fountain pen on the desktop.

'May I sit down, sir?'

'Of course, sorry. I'm told you're on the mend, eh?'

Prince assured him he was, though he tired quite easily.

'You're going to need a decent rest, old chap.'

'Thank you, sir. I hope that when I get home—'

'Don't underestimate how much these missions can affect you. Life when you return home can be almost as tricky as when you were on the mission. I'm told the difference feels rather... abrupt.'

Gilbey walked over to where Prince was sitting, pulling up another chair so he could sit opposite him. He leaned over and patted him on the knee.

'Well done, though. I would say that all things considered, that was a successful mission.'

'All things considered? That sounds rather grudging, if you don't mind me saying, sir.'

'Pluses and minuses, Prince, as my old maths master used to say. We've lost Horatio and his contacts in Berlin, and it's an awful pity about Agent Osric. However, the intelligence you gathered from your trips into Germany was excellent, and you were able to get into Peenemünde, which was more than we could have hoped for.

'The most important aspect of your mission was to provide us with irrefutable evidence that the V-1 and V-2 rocket programmes exist and represent a threat to this country. Amongst other things, the report you brought back from Browning corroborated that too. As you know, there was something of a disagreement in London about how seriously we should take the threat of these rockets. That battle has now been won. We now just have to deal with the bloody things.'

'Was the bombing raid on Peenemünde a success?'

'Tell me what *you* think, Prince. You were there.'

'I was arrested the following day, sir, so I didn't get much chance to check out the whole site. My impression was that there was a fair amount of damage, but perhaps it wasn't as extensive as one would have hoped.'

'Spot on. The RAF intelligence branch have done a good deal of analysis on the post-bombing photo reconnaissance. I don't know if you're a boxing man, Prince, but their conclusion is that we landed a couple of heavy blows, and one or two may even have put the opponent down on the canvas and cut him up a bit, but we didn't manage to knock him out. To extend the pugilistic analogy, it looks like this one is going to go to points. From what they can gather, the RAF boys think that at best we may have set the work at Peenemünde back by two, perhaps three months, which is not to be underestimated: a delay like that could save an awful lot of lives, and who can predict the course of the war?'

For the first time in months, Prince felt a slight sense of relaxation. The tension that had wrapped itself around him since September seemed to be detaching itself from him. He gazed out of the window onto a perfect English scene: lush green meadows rolling towards a hedge, beyond which a herd of cows grazed, all facing in the same direction. In the distance was a church spire, pointing to a sky in which the clouds were hurrying away to reveal an early summer sun. The breeze carried the faint sound of children playing from somewhere far away.

'I may indeed have been more grudging than I intended to be, Prince, for which I apologise. The problem with this business is you can never take anything for granted. Winston says our biggest enemy is complacency, and he's right. These days I tend to regard victories as simply a matter of avoiding defeat: one barely has time to catch one's breath before moving on to the next mission. You did very well in terribly difficult circumstances, which I'm aware probably sounds like a serious underestimation of the danger you were in and the risks you took. You got in and out of Germany twice: I don't think any other British agent has managed that. You're good, Prince, very good… you'd certainly be one of the first names on the team sheet for the first eleven. This mission was an undoubted success.'

'Thank you, sir.'

'Which is a way of saying we'd like you to carry on with us. You're a first-class agent: you remember how in Matlock I described you as *cum laude*? Well, you've proved me right. You're wasted in the police, finding house burglars and the like.'

'I think I'll need a while to think about it, sir. I had rather assumed I'd be returning to my old job, and most of all I do wish to spend some time with my son.'

Gilbey moved back to the desk and straightened a file or two, then adjusted the Anglepoise lamp. 'Hang on a moment, Richard, will you. I'm just going to ask Hendrie to join us.'

Prince waited for more than a moment. It was a good ten minutes before Gilbey returned to the room, followed by Hendrie – both men hesitating in the doorway, insisting the other enter first.

As soon as they came in, Prince knew something was up: it was the feeling he'd had when he'd first seen Gilbey, and now it was even more acute. It could have been the tentative nature of their approach, the excessive time they took to sit down and arrange their chairs, the lengthy clearing of throats and other nervous gestures, or quite possibly the fact that neither of them appeared to have looked directly at him since entering the room.

They sat next to each other, opposite him, and another period of silence followed. Gilbey looked at Hendrie, clearly willing him to speak first, and then Hendrie at Gilbey, obviously thinking likewise. The atmosphere in the room was such that it seemed no extraneous noise and little light was permeating it. The temperature had dropped by a few degrees.

Prince broke the stalemate. 'Is something the matter, sir?'

Hendrie leaned forward, his arms resting on his thighs, his hands clasped together. When he spoke, his Scottish accent was more noticeable than ever before.

'I'm afraid, Richard, there's no easy way to put this, but we have some terrible news for you.'

Chapter 25

England, May–June 1943

What surprised him afterwards was how calmly he took the news.

Calm was possibly the wrong word: detached would be more accurate. It was as if he reacted as a police officer rather than as a father: concentrating on the facts, not jumping to hasty conclusions before he'd heard everything, his emotions under control – more or less. Which wasn't to say, of course, that he hadn't been utterly stunned. It was indeed truly dreadful news. Maybe his apparent detachment could be explained by shock. It took Gilbey and Hendrie a good quarter of an hour to stumble their way through something that could have been said in less than five minutes.

...no easy way to put this, but we have some terrible news for you...

I'm sorry to tell you, Henry is missing...

From a hospital... adopted, actually...

must not lose hope...

...our very best efforts...

Not leaving a stone unturned...

They were both visibly relieved when there was a knock at the door and Prince's Chief Constable entered.

Perhaps you two should go and have a good old chat... I'm sure we'll have this sorted in no time.

-

Where Gilbey and Hendrie had been awkward and embarrassed, the Chief Constable was supportive and sympathetic, almost fatherly in his manner. He took Prince into a room on the ground floor with French windows open to a terrace, framing an enormous rose bush, the gentle breeze sending an early scent of summer into the room.

'What have they told you, Richard?'

'That Henry has disappeared, sir. It was such a garbled account, I'm rather confused. They said you were on your way down and would explain everything to me.'

'Let me tell you what happened, and then I can explain what we're doing about it. Are you sure I can't get you a drink?'

Prince shook his head. The two men had settled in comfortable armchairs opposite each other. Behind the Chief Constable was a large oil painting of a Victorian family standing against a large fireplace that looked just like the one the picture was above.

'You'll appreciate some of the information I'm about to give you is incomplete: we've had to piece together what we can. Some dates, for instance, are guesswork. Our main source is your housekeeper, Janet. We do know that towards the middle of January, your sister-in-law Evelyn went to stay for a few days with a friend in London and took Henry with her. Your housekeeper had taken a week off to visit her sick mother in Scotland and we think Evelyn decided to go away at the same time. Does the name Marsden mean anything to you?'

Prince shook his head.

'Janet recalls Evelyn saying they were going to stay with a friend called Anne Marsden who lived in Lambeth in south London. We have established that your sister-in-law and an Anne Marsden were at secretarial school together. Anne Marsden lived in a road called Upper Marsh in Lambeth, very near Waterloo station, and on the night of Sunday the seventeenth of January, there was a Luftwaffe bombing raid and a number of bombs fell in that area. Quite a few houses on

Upper Marsh were hit and four were destroyed, including the Marsdens'.'

'The bodies of Anne Marsden and your sister-in-law were found, but Henry's body wasn't. Now I have to make an important point here, Richard: no one would have known that Evelyn and Henry were staying at the Marsdens' house. More to the point, the rescuers at the scene would not have known a little boy was there so wouldn't have been specifically looking for him. Furthermore, about an hour after the bombing, an air raid warden found a young boy wandering down Royal Street, which runs off Upper Marsh. The boy was very dazed and was taken by ambulance to St Christopher's hospital, which is nearby. The boy was concussed and confused and it transpired he'd also broken his wrist. He had no idea what his name was and said very little at all throughout his time at the hospital.

'Now I have to say Mr Gilbey has been terribly helpful: once we became aware of the situation, he was most generous in terms of helping us. Thanks to him, the Metropolitan Police allocated a couple of officers to make enquiries in the hospital. Between us, we've talked with everyone who came into contact with this boy. He certainly matches Henry's description: we obtained recent photographs from your house, and everyone we showed them to agrees that it's the same boy. We are as certain as we can be that it was Henry who was found in Royal Street that night and taken to St Christopher's hospital.'

'And he was in the hospital for how long?'

'Two weeks.'

'It took that long to establish who he was?'

'It was a week before Janet returned from Scotland – it was only then that anyone realised that Evelyn and Henry were missing. It took us a further ten days to discover where they'd been staying and what had happened. By the time we made enquiries at St Christopher's, I'm afraid Henry had been adopted just a few days previously.

'I'm not going to pretend it's not a dreadful, dreadful predicament, Richard. We've worked tirelessly to identify the couple who adopted him, but with no luck so far. We're giving this top priority, I can assure you. I've taken personal charge.'

'I simply do not understand how a couple can walk into a hospital and walk out with someone else's child – my child!'

'I tell you what, Richard. First thing tomorrow morning, you and I will visit the hospital.'

–

The matron was defensive and defiant, sitting with her back to the window in a small office overlooking the Thames, the Houses of Parliament neatly framed behind her. Her arms were folded tightly under an ample bosom and her head was tilted high, as if trying to pick up a particular smell.

'Nothing we did was wrong or improper. We followed our procedures.' Her accent was from somewhere in Ireland.

'What I don't understand is how this couple who adopted Henry left no trace?'

'I shall explain again how these matters work, Mr Prince. When children are orphaned as a result of hostilities and there are no family or close friends to take them in, they are discharged as patients and sent to a children's home, unless...' she paused to underline the importance of that 'unless', 'a suitable family is available to adopt them.'

The matron inhaled deeply. 'From time to time we are approached directly by couples looking for a child to adopt. A Thomas and Susan Brown with an address in Croydon in south London had contacted us in January I believe it was. In my opinion they were suitable for adopting a child. In the case of this boy, when he was ready to be discharged I contacted Mr and Mrs Brown. I hope you can accept that however regrettable the situation is, we acted in good faith. If it's any consolation, we have learned lessons from this.'

'I can assure you it's no consolation. And this couple,' said Prince, 'what were they like?'

'They seemed pleasant enough,' said the matron. 'They said they had no children. I'd use the word nondescript to describe them. They seemed to be in their forties.'

'And you have no address?'

'We had the address in Croydon.'

'Which turns out to be a boarding house.'

The matron smiled weakly. 'Which of course I wasn't to know at the time.'

Not a word was spoken as Richard Prince absorbed what he'd been told. His eyes filled with tears and he struggled to speak.

'Were they nice people?'

The matron leaned across the table and placed her hand on his, her tone less defensive.

'As I said, sir, they seemed nice enough; perhaps a bit formal, but then you must understand these are not easy situations – visiting a hospital, adopting a child at such short notice. I have no doubt he'll be very well cared for. I hope you find them soon, and obviously if there's anything we can do to help...'

—

'It's been what... a month now, Prince?'

'One month, sir – almost to the day, in fact.'

They were in Tom Gilbey's office in Broadway in central London. Gilbey was doing his best to appear sympathetic. 'And Hendrie tells me there are still no leads?'

'I'm afraid not, sir.'

'He assures me you've been most thorough.'

'I have, sir, but there are literally tens of thousands of people with the surname Brown in this country, probably over a hundred thousand. Henry could be anywhere. It's possible Brown was never their real name and they've moved to another part of the country; apparently there's something of a stigma about adoption and it's by no means uncommon for people to use different identities so people don't realise a child is adopted.

It's beginning to feel utterly hopeless, sir. Henry was adopted by these people in early February, which was what... four and a bit months ago? He's young. He may well have forgotten everything about his past. Would he even recognise me? After all, it's been over seven months since he last saw me. At that age...'

Gilbey walked round the room, pausing by Prince to pat him on the shoulder. 'What I said to you last month – about going on another mission. Something's cropped up and I know you'd be the ideal person for it...'

'While Henry is still missing? How could I possibly contemplate that?'

'You're the best man we have at the moment, and this mission requires our best man. I give you my word that I will make finding Henry a priority while you are away – I can pull strings few other people can. I promise you we put top people on this. The process may take time, but I'm sure we'll find him. You should only be away for a few weeks.'

'Really, sir?'

'Hopefully, yes.'

Prince got up and paced the room, started to speak, then paused. Gilbey said nothing, letting him make up his mind. But he was hopeful: he could see the signs. It was apparent he wanted to say no but couldn't bring himself to. When Gilbey had first entered this world, one of his seniors had taken him aside and told him the most important thing he needed to know about espionage was that it was an addiction. His experience since then had convinced him the man was right. All the best spies were addicts. They couldn't say no.

Prince continued to pace, then returned to his chair, looking annoyed with himself. 'Very well then, sir, but I want another month to look for Henry. At least then I can set in train various lines of enquiry and know I've done my best.'

'Very well. One month, but after that I'll need you.'

'There is one other thing, sir: Agent Osric, Hanne.'

'MI6 say they're convinced she's not being held in a conventional prison. They believe she's most likely being held in one of these places the Germans call concentration camps. George Weston is keeping an eye on things in Copenhagen, in as much as he can from Stockholm. He says no one has heard any more news about Hanne. His instinct is that if she was dead, somehow that information would have worked its way back to Denmark. It's probably a case of no news being good news.'

'Not if she's in a concentration camp, sir.'

A plane flew low overhead and both men looked nervously out of the window. It was warm in Gilbey's office and he removed his jacket and loosened his tie.

'One month, Richard. In my experience, this kind of search will yield results some way down the line: sow the seeds now and eventually someone will put two and two together and we'll find Henry. The new mission is vital for the war effort, that's all I can say. We'll need a month to prepare you. See you in July – and good luck.'

Chapter 26

Copenhagen, September 1943

At five to eight on the morning of Tuesday 28 September, Ferdinand Rudolf von Buhler opened the front door of his residence in Lyngby and exchanged Heil Hitler greetings with his driver.

He settled into the back of the Horch with a mounting degree of trepidation and lit his fifth cigarette of the day. Over the past fortnight there had been increasing tension at the embassy. It was unclear what the cause of this was: as the commercial attaché, he wasn't exactly a member of the inner circle, for which he was most grateful. He probably sat somewhere between the second and third circles, and as far as he was concerned, if there was a fourth circle he'd happily reside there.

In truth, the tension had been on the rise ever since the Danish government resigned at the end of August. Now the Germans were running Denmark themselves and there could no longer be the pretence that this wasn't a real occupation.

At first, he attributed the more recent atmosphere to the constant flow of bad news about the course of the war. It had become unrelenting, not least how the Red Army was pushing in from the east, but this tension had a different feel: it was something closer to home. Maybe it was politics – there was always plenty of that at the embassy – between the Nazi Party fanatics, the army, and the professional diplomats like himself. He had become aware of more frequent meetings behind closed doors, urgent conversations in corridors and the rumour mill starting to work overtime.

King Christian is going to be arrested… The Danish police are going to be disbanded… They want us to send twenty thousand Danes to the Reich as forced labour… make that fifty thousand… They're going to deal with the Jews, at last… Half of us are going to be sent to the Eastern Front…

Ferdinand Rudolf von Buhler was careful not to contribute to the rumours himself, though he did his best to make sure he heard them all. As crazy as they sounded, they were also perfectly feasible.

He knew that when the rumours firmed up, he'd have to tell the British. He'd avoided contact with them since helping that agent escape to Sweden in April. He'd not slept properly for weeks after that, and indeed had been so unnerved by the experience he'd even told his driver to change his route into work so as to avoid passing the pharmacy in Nørrebro where the appearance of a red medicine bottle would be a signal to make contact.

What you don't see you don't know.

But the heightened trepidation he felt that particular Tuesday morning was a result of an order issued to all the diplomatic staff the previous afternoon. They were to ensure they were at the embassy in good time for a meeting at nine o'clock the next morning. Any other engagements had to be cancelled. The meeting was to be addressed by none other than Werner Best.

Best was a fearsome character: a career Nazi who'd been a stalwart of the Reich Main Security Office in Berlin before being sent to Paris to run the occupation. The previous November he'd arrived in Copenhagen with the title of Plenipotentiary, which was as good as saying he was the ruler of Denmark.

The meeting took place in the ballroom of the embassy, its rococo architecture and enormous chandeliers lending an incongruously grand air to the occasion. The room was full, with everyone standing: not just the diplomats from the embassy and senior military figures, but also, as far as von Buhler could tell, all the important Germans involved in the occupation.

Best marched into the room, mounted a rostrum at the front and began speaking immediately. His Hessian accent and quiet voice meant people shuffled forward to catch what he was saying.

'Heil Hitler!'

The response was less clamorous than von Buhler expected it to be. People were nervous with anticipation.

'Last year – on the twentieth of January, to be precise – a conference was held in Berlin on the specific instructions of the Führer to discuss the Jewish question, which still plagues us. At the outset of the war, there were eleven million of them in Europe. Some of them are in territories we now control, others in countries we will soon conquer. Eleven million…'

Best paused to allow everyone in the room to absorb that shocking statistic: so many of them.

'I am pleased to say that a detailed and effective solution was agreed upon. It was decided that the Jewish populations in every country we control will be deported to the east, where six camps have been established to dispose of them. This map here – turn to the next sheet, please – shows the camps: they're all in the General Government zone in what was Poland: Auschwitz-Birkenau, Treblinka, Bełżec, Chełmno, Sobibor and Majdanek. The transportation and extermination programme has been proceeding with great efficiency. Last year alone we dealt with two million seven hundred thousand Jews. Taking into account those we have also dealt with…' he smiled appreciatively as laughter filled the room, 'since the start of the war, we have managed to reduce the Jewish population by some four million.'

A loud murmur of approval.

'So far this year we have already dealt with a further three hundred thousand Jews. But the Führer is unhappy that the progress is not quick enough. And specifically, he wants to know why the Jews here in Denmark are still at liberty. I have been in Berlin on a number of occasions recently. I have endeavoured to explain that the particular situation pertaining in this country means we need to be careful about upsetting the delicate nature of the occupation. I have pointed out that the last thing we want is trouble here in Denmark, and I fear if we dealt with the Jews here in the same way as in France or Poland, for example, we could have a serious problem that would mean a distraction for our armed forces.

'Notwithstanding this, the patience of Eichmann and others in Berlin has worn thin. On my last visit to Berlin I was instructed to deal with the Jewish question in Denmark once and for all. In recent weeks, some of you will have been aware of the work we have been doing to identify the Jews here and discover where they live. This work is now complete: we have identified somewhere in the region of eight and a half thousand. The arrests and deportations will start next week: I expect that by the middle of October, Denmark will be free of Jews.

'For this to happen, I require the cooperation of everyone here. From now on, this is the priority of each and every one of you. All your normal duties should be postponed until the Jews have been dealt with. All leave is cancelled and you should expect to work over the weekend. Heil Hitler!'

–

Ferdinand Rudolf von Buhler waited until the following day before making his move. The simplest course of action would be to do nothing, avoid making contact with the British and keep his involvement with the arrest and deportation of the Jews to a minimum.

But he knew he couldn't possibly do that: his conscience would not allow him to be a bystander.

That morning he managed to slip out of the embassy and hurry to Jensen's bicycle shop in the narrow alley off Pilestræde.

In his haste he forgot to check whether there were any other customers there, but fortunately Jensen was on his own.

'Hadn't you better come into the workshop?'

'Not now, I need to be quick. Dr Oppenheim, the man I met in April...'

'What about him?'

'I must speak to him urgently, later today if possible. Get a message to him and say you have a strained knee and need to see him as soon as possible. He'll know what you mean.'

Jensen clearly sensed from von Buhler's manner quite how urgent this was. 'I'll call him now. Go over there and pretend to be looking at bikes: the one with the tan saddle is just in.'

Von Buhler heard him make a brief call.

'He can be here at five o'clock. Take this key and let yourself in at the back.'

It was an effort to get away from the embassy at that time. Von Buhler had been given the task of working on the transport of the arrested Jews to Poland: there seemed to be some problem he couldn't quite understand about trains.

But such was the chaos at the embassy that he'd managed to photograph a number of documents, including one with the names and addresses of all the Jews in Copenhagen. He'd slipped the film into his pocket and made his way back to Pilestræde. He understood full well that if he was caught, he'd signed his own death warrant.

Dr Julius Oppenheim appeared to have aged considerably in the few months since they last met. He, von Buhler and Jensen huddled around a cluttered table in the middle of the workshop. The German diplomat carefully explained everything; by the time he had finished, Oppenheim was shaking. He took the film and put it in his inside jacket pocket. Was Herr von Buhler absolutely certain about all of this?

Yes.

Jensen placed an arm round the German's shoulders, his voice quiet and determined. 'I'll make sure the resistance also knows right away.'

Copenhagen at the end of September 1943, where the lives of thousands and the fate of millions hung by a thread becoming more frayed by the day.

Ravensbrück concentration camp at the end of September 1943, where Hanne Jakobsen was about to enter her ninth month in captivity, her existence now even more perilous.

And a thousand miles to the south at the end of September 1943, where Richard Prince was a few weeks into his new mission and in another world, one quite unlike anything he'd experienced before, though no less menacing.

But his heart was elsewhere, torn between his son and the woman he loved.

Author's Note

Prince of Spies is a work of fiction, so any similarities between characters and circumstances in the book and real people should be regarded as purely coincidental.

That said, it is based on actual events and places in Europe during the Second World War. Some characters featured or referred to in the book did exist, Winston Churchill being an obvious example. Likewise, Air Marshal Harris was the actual head of RAF Bomber Command during the war.

Other less well-known examples include SS Obersturmbannführer Max Pauly (Chapter 20), who was the commandant of Neuengamme concentration camp and was executed as a war criminal in 1946. Just over 40,000 people were murdered at Neuengamme during the war.

Gruppenführer von Helldorf (Chapter 17) was the head of the police in Berlin during the relevant part of the story. He was executed by the Nazis in 1944 for his part in the bomb plot against Hitler.

Colonel General Friedrich Paulus (Chapter 19) was the commander of the German 6th Army, which suffered such a devastating defeat at Stalingrad. Hitler did indeed promote him to field marshal in a bid to prevent him surrendering, but Paulus did surrender and lived in East Germany until his death in 1957. The victory of the Red Army at Stalingrad in February 1943 was a key turning point of the Second World War.

Werner Best (Chapter 26) was the German Plenipotentiary (effectively the ruler) in Denmark from November 1942 until the country was liberated in May 1945. He was convicted as a war criminal but spared the death penalty. Best claimed he'd been involved in informing the Danish resistance about the planned deportation of the country's Jewish population.

This deportation is referred to in the last chapter and is based very closely on real events. The Danish Jewish community and the resistance were tipped off about the planned deportations, and as a result, more than eight thousand Danish Jews and non-Jewish relations were smuggled across the Øresund to neutral Sweden. This was one of the very few examples of an occupied country resisting the maltreatment of its Jewish population.

Readers may possibly consider Agent Browning to be an unlikely figure working against his own government. In fact, there was a diplomat at the German Embassy in Copenhagen – Georg Ferdinand Duckwitz – who tipped off the Danish resistance about the planned deportations. There is no doubt that by 1943, Duckwitz was anti-Nazi, and he became a leading West German diplomat after the war.

The conference regarding the fate of Europe's Jews (Chapter 26) is the Wannsee conference, which set in motion the Final Solution. The figures used in this context are accurate: some 2,700,000 Jews were murdered in 1942, mostly at the six Nazi death camps in Poland.

Like Agent Horatio (Otto Knudsen), there was a Danish businessman, Aage Carl Holger Andreasen, who picked up information about the V-1s and V-2s while travelling in Germany. He contacted the British, and after some doubt about his motives, he became a British agent.

Ravensbrück (Chapter 23) was a concentration camp almost exclusively for female prisoners, approximately 40,000 of whom were murdered there.

The murder of the Jewish children described in Chapter 19 is fictional, though it is based on thousands of war crimes of a similar nature. In July 1946, forty-two Jews who'd returned to Kielce from Nazi camps were murdered by local Poles in a now notorious pogrom.

Lord Swalcliffe (Chapter 9 onwards) is loosely based on Frederick Lindemann, Viscount Cherwell. He was Churchill's scientific adviser and a vocal opponent of the view that the V-1 and V-2 rockets presented a real threat.

The V-1 and V-2 were of course two of the secret weapons the Nazis hoped would win the war for them. Some nine thousand V-1s and a thousand V-2s were used against the British mainland, with around 10,000 people believed killed as a result.

There was a major RAF raid not dissimilar to the one described in Chapter 18 on Peenemünde. The actual raid took place in August 1943.

The towns and cities referred to in the book are all actual places, with the exception of Peascombe St Mary (and Peascombe St Thomas) near Mablethorpe. Where named, places such as hotels, railway stations and airports are real. St Christopher's hospital is an exception to this.

Deutsche Lufthansa did continue to fly passenger aircraft between Copenhagen and Berlin (and via Oslo) during the war. The hotel that Horatio and Prince stayed at in Berlin, the Excelsior on Askanischer Platz, was one of the largest in Berlin before it was destroyed in an Allied air raid in April 1945.

The engineering company Feuchtwanger and Wolff is fictional, but many similar Jewish-owned businesses were stolen from their owners.

The Grimsby trawler fleet made an enormous contribution to the war effort, including as minesweepers, serving on the convoys and on clandestine missions as described in Chapter 4. Nearly 300 trawler men and 30 trawlers from the port were lost in the war.

Adoptions in the UK were less well regulated before the 1960s, so the informal nature of Henry's rushed adoption (Chapter 25) would have been feasible in 1943.

I'd like to express my sincere thanks and appreciation to the many people who've helped bring about the publication of this book. As ever, to my agent Gordon Wise at Curtis Brown and his colleague Niall Harman. I'm delighted to now be published by Canelo and my thanks there go to Michael Bhaskar, Kit Nevile, Sophie Eminson and all the team. To Jane Selley for her very skilful copyedit and to the many people who helped me with aspects of the book and answered seemingly odd questions as I was writing it. And finally to my family – and especially my wife Sonia – for their encouragement, understanding and love.

Alex Gerlis
London
December 2019